PRINCIPLES OF

AND FLOW

PRODUCTION

1954

INCLUDING

"Some Notes on British Methods
of Continuous Production"

1925

55th Anniversary
Special Reprint Edition
January 2009

Frank George Woollard

Frank G. Woollard
M.B.E. M.I.Mech.E. M.I.Prod.E. M.S.A.E.

PRINCIPLES
OF
MASS AND FLOW
PRODUCTION

55th Anniversary
Special Reprint Edition

INCLUDING

"Some Notes on British Methods of Continuous Production"
1925

**With Commentary and Analysis
by Bob Emiliani, Ph.D.**

This 55th Anniversary Special Reprint Edition is
dedicated to Frank George Woollard (1883-1957).

Gone but not forgotten.
May he receive the recognition that he truly deserves.

ACKNOWLEDGEMENTS

I would like to thank the following people for their help in creating this 55th Anniversary Special Reprint Edition of Frank G. Woollard's book: Regeen Runes Najar of the Philosophical Library, Inc.; Peter Williams, Academic Director, Professional Engineering Publishing, London, U.K.; Dean Michael West and Colleen Bass of Aston Business School, Birmingham, U.K.; John Blunsden, publisher of Motor Racing Publications; Jonathan Wood; Malcom McKay of the Bullnose Morris Club; Chas J. Moody; Robin Barraclough; Professor Nick Tiratsoo, London School of Economics; Bob Bristow; Chris Tucker, and Professor Richard Brown of the University of Rhode Island.

A very special thanks to Peter J. Seymour, formerly of Morris Commercial Cars Ltd. and of the British Motor Corporation, for his enthusiastic support and many valuable connections to other experts on Morris Motors Ltd. Peter's thoughtful and detailed reviews of Emiliani's contribution to this Special Reprint Edition were invaluable.

CONTENTS

By Bob Emiliani, Ph.D.

By Frank G. Woollard, M.B.E.

Preface to the Reprint Edition

I am proud to present to you a remarkable book that has been, until now, long forgotten. It was written by a man whose contribution to progressive manufacturing management practices is comparable to the legendary Taiichi Ohno (1912-1990), the principal architect of Toyota Motor Corporation's production system. Without a doubt, anyone interested in Lean management, the evolution of flow production, or the history of industrial management and automation will want to read this very important book.

This 55th Anniversary Special Reprint Edition of *Principles of Mass and Flow Production* [1, 2], revives the brilliant work of a practical engineer named Frank George Woollard (1883-1957), M.B.E. M.I.Mech.E. M.I.Prod.E. M.S.A.E. [3]. Woollard sought to apply a modified form of the production methods pioneered by Henry Ford [4], coupled with inspiration from late 1800s continuous production methods used in the "soft" process industries (e.g. textiles, soap, chemicals), in which the materials being processed are soft and flow easily (versus hard metal components), to the British automobile industry. In addition to his successful application of flow production in the first decades of the 1900s, he was the first to develop and implement mechanical materials handling equipment known as automatic transfer machinery.

A paper written in 1922 by Herbert Taylor [5], chief engineer at the French-owned Hotchkiss et Cie engine plant on Gosford Street in Coventry, U.K., which would later become the Engines Branch of Morris Motors Ltd.†, was the inspiration for Woollard *et al.* to create hand transfer machines for engine block production. That soon led to the design, fabrication, and use of automatic transfer machines for gearbox and flywheel manufacturing; a collaboration between Woollard, Taylor, Leonard Lord (future chairman of British Motor Corporation Ltd.), and the machine tool builders James Archdale & Company, Ltd. and Wm. Asquith, Ltd.

While at Morris Engines Ltd. in Coventry, which supplied engines to both Morris Motors Ltd. and Morris Commercial Cars Ltd. [6], Woollard successfully achieved high-volume flow production between 1923 and 1925, supported by innovative automatic transfer machinery. He did this more than 20 years before Toyota embarked on its post-World War II efforts to do the same – also starting in an engine machine shop [7, 8]. Woollard and his staff developed their flow production system without ever visiting Ford Motor Company as most others had done. The flow production system and associated automatic transfer machinery were an entirely British effort borne of British ingenuity, the result of focused efforts by a dedicated general manager and an automobile company owner who was an enthusiastic supporter of new production methods and a financier of new machine technologies.

Woollard realized that Ford's production system was the result of unique circumstances; a very large market and robust sales that permitted an incredible level of vertically integrated production activities. Ford's approach to large-scale production could not be replicated by other companies due to practical considerations such as limited capital, smaller markets, and diverse consumer needs [9]. Morris Motors was no exception, nor was Toyota. Instead, both sought to go beyond large-scale mass production by adapting Ford's production system to achieve flow production without extensive vertical integration and within the context of their respective domestic markets – much lower volumes than Ford and more diverse customer needs.

Woollard's 1954 book, as well as in his seminal 1925 paper titled "Some Notes on British Methods of Continuous Production" [10], which can be found in the Appendix, demonstrates deep practical knowledge of the limitations of batch-and-queue production and the differences between Ford's production methods and the new flow production. The focus of Woollard's writing is on achieving flow in processes upstream of final automobile assembly. These upstream processes include subcomponent assembly and parts manufacturing, as well as parts purchased from outside suppliers, to support flow in final assembly. Woollard's application of flow production in a modern high-volume industrial setting means that timelines for discoveries and attributions of key accomplishments must be revised [11].

The post-1950s British automotive industry is most frequently associated with decline, reorganization, and bankruptcy. However, there was a time, a golden era, where its prospects were bright and its innovations in industrial management practice and manufacturing technology were unparalleled. Unfortunately, innovations in production methods and machinery are not sufficient to ensure long-term survival, as was the case with Morris Motors which eventually ceased to exist [12, 13]. Companies – their managers and employees – must excel at many other business processes including responding to the voice of the customer with new designs, short cycle-time product development, distribution, sales and marketing, and aftermarket support. That is why the current-day quest for "operational excellence," with its narrow focus on operations, greatly misleads its adherents.

The significance of Woollard's work is his association with the introduction of a basic flow production line to assemble steel railroad coach bodies in 1904, his introduction of a more advanced flow production in automobile parts manufacture c. 1917, and his pioneering introduction of high-volume flow production coupled with development and use of innovative automatic transfer machinery for automobile engine manufacturing beginning in 1923.

Conversations by academics and management practitioners on the origins of Lean management center almost exclusively upon Ford Motor Company in the 1910s and 1920s and Toyota Motor Corporation in the 1950s through the 1970s. There is no mention of the British automaker Morris Motors Ltd., the pioneering work of Frank G. Woollard in the mid-1920s, his important book *Principles of Mass and Flow Production*, or their possible influence on Toyota Motor Corporation in its formative years. Woollard's work has been forgotten, overlooked, or ignored. That now has to change.

As you shall see, Mr. Woollard deserves widespread recognition within the industrial management academic and management practitioner communities for his groundbreaking work, and especially within the Lean management community. While reading this book, you will wonder how so many people could have missed Woollard's important work for so many years.

I hope readers will appreciate Frank G. Woollard's remarkable work in flow production and his prescient innovations in industrial automation. Mr. Woollard deserves a prominent place in the history of industrial management, production engineering, and automation, and his work is clearly congruent with today's Lean management principles and practices.

Woollard understood the idea and practice of continuous improvement in a flow environment, saying that the need for modifications to the flow line "should cause no anxiety, but rather should be a matter for rejoicing... the virtue of flow production lies in the fact that it brings all inconsistencies into the light of day and so provides the opportunity for correcting them," and "[the] high visibility conferred on the company's activities by flow production will lead to unceasing and continuous improvement" [14].

In addition, Woollard's long-standing recognition that flow production will not work if it is used by management in a zero-sum manner is particularly insightful and distinctive. He understood the importance of what we now call the "Respect for People" principle in Lean management [15], and appears to have been a skillful practitioner [16].

Woollard's work is of great importance because it significantly expands our understanding of progressive management practices in the British motor industry in the mid- to late-1920s, and also informs us of new contributions that likely helped shape today's practice of Lean management. I truly hope you enjoy this book; I think you will be simply amazed at what you read.

Bob Emiliani
December 2008
Wethersfield, Conn.

†Note on Morris Motors: Few people today are familiar with the pre-1950 British automobile industry, and with Morris Motors Ltd. in particular. William Morris initially bought engines and gearboxes from U.S. manufacturers. After being copied in the U.K. these components powered many of the vehicles made by Morris Motors during the 1920s and 1930s, and contributed to the company becoming Britain's leading motor vehicle manufacturer. Not only was Morris Motors the first British automobile manufacture to make one million vehicles, it also became the owner of the well known maker of sports cars, M.G., the carburetter manufacturer S.U., and Wolseley, itself a pioneer in motor vehicles. Morris Motors' history, with respect to design and manufacturing practices is fascinating, while its founder, businessman and philanthropist William Morris – Lord Nuffield, appointed several capable and gifted engineers who were at the forefront of production technology. In addition, there were many other brilliant men and colorful characters that made the British automobile industry come alive. It is a topic well worth studying; those that do will gain greater appreciation of industrial history and the world-wide nature of the automobile business. A selected bibliography of books and articles about Morris Motors Ltd. appears after the list of publications by Frank. G. Woollard (p. E-43).

Notes

[1] F.G. Woollard, *Principles of Mass and Flow Production*, Iliffe & Sons, Ltd., London, U.K., 1954. Note: The publisher's name, Iliffe, is pronounced phonetically as "eye-liff."

[2] Woollard's book was published for distribution in the U.S. one year later by Philosophical Library, New York, NY. The exact bibliographic information is: F.G. Woollard, *Principles of Mass and Flow Production*, Philosophical Library Inc., New York, NY, 1955

[3] The letters that follow Frank G. Woollard's name stand for: M.B.E., Member of the British Empire (an award given by the Monarch for services to the country; Woollard's M.B.E. was recommended to the Monarch by Winston Churchill); M.I.Mech.E., Member of The Institution of Mechanical Engineers; M.I.Prod.E., Member of The Institution of Production Engineers; and M.S.A.E., Member of the Society of Automotive Engineers (U.S.A.).

[4] Frank Woollard was well-read in American production methods. He was very familiar with U.S. technical publications and machine tools; see Woollard (1925), p. 419. He likely read Henry Ford's 1922 book, *My Life and Work*, U.S. magazine and newspaper articles and technical papers published in automotive engineering journals prior to 1922, as well as later works by Henry Ford and others.

[5] H.E. Taylor, "Factory Planning" in *Proceedings of the Institution of Production Engineers*, The Institution of Production Engineers, Proceedings of the Session 1922-1923, Volume II, London, U.K., pp. 243-253 and 254-257

[6] P. Seymour, *Morris Light Vans: 1924-1934*, P&B Publishing, East Sussex, U.K., 1999

[7] *Toyota: A History of the First 50 Years*, Toyota Motor Corporation, Toyota City, Japan, 1988, pp. 141-142

[8] T. Ohno, *Toyota Production System*, Productivity Press, Portland, OR, 1988, pp. 9-10, 13

[9] S. Tolliday, "The Diffusion and Transformation of Fordism: Britain and Japan Compared" in *Between Imitation and Innovation*, R. Boyer, E. Charron, U. Jürgens, S. Tolliday, editors, Oxford University Press, New York, NY, 1998, pp. 57-95

[10] F.G. Woollard, "Some Notes on British Methods of Continuous Production," *Proceedings of The Institution of Automobile Engineers*, The Institution of Automobile Engineers, London, U.K., Proceedings of the Session 1924-1925, Volume XIX, pp. 419-474, 885-890, and Plates XVI to XXXII (Figures 1-26). Woollard first presented this paper to 92 members of the Institute (and visitors) on Tuesday, 3 February 1925, at the Broadgate Café in Coventry, U.K. starting at about 7:30 pm. Woollard also presented this paper to members of the Institute in other U.K. locations: at the Royal Society of Arts in London on 10 February, 1925 (114 members and visitors present); at the Engineering and Scientific Club in Wolverhampton on 11 February 1925 (23 members and visitors present); at the Chamber of Commerce in Birmingham on 16 February 1925 (83 members and visitors present); and at the Royal Technical College in Glasgow, Scotland on 16 March, 1925, (310 members and visitors present).

[11] See the timeline of the development of Toyota Motor Corporation's production system in the front and rear endpapers of Taiichi Ohno's book *Toyota Production System*, Productivity Press, Portland, OR, 1988. Also, notice the timeline of developments in *My Life and Work*, H. Ford with S. Crowther, Garden City Publishing Co., Inc., Garden City, NY, 1922.

[12] Morris Motors Ltd. merged with Austin Motor Company, Ltd. in 1952, resulting in the formation of British Motor Corporation Ltd., reducing the number of major U.K. automobile producers from six to five (BMC, Ford, Rootes, Standard, and Vauxhall). See

G. Maxcy and A. Silbertson, *The Motor Industry*, George Allen & Unwin Ltd., London, U.K., 1959, pp. 19-20 and 229.

[13] K. Williams, C. Haslam, S. Johal, and J. Williams, *Cars: Analysis*, *History*, *Cases*, Berghahn Books Ltd., Oxford, U.K., 1994, pp. 134-165

[14] Woollard (1954), pp. 87 and 105. See also, pp. 50-52, 57, and 91

[15] "The Toyota Way 2001," Toyota Motor Corporation, internal document, Toyota City, Japan, April 2001

[16] Seymour, p. 38

Foreword to the Reprint Edition

It is very important for executives to grasp the actual market conditions their company faces because it determines prices, allowable costs, and sales growth. The production method selected must be congruent with allowable costs and will determine, in part, whether or not management can advance the company from a start-up to an enduring business. Long-term commitment by management to a production system must inevitably lead to decades of individual and organizational capability-building specific to that system. Operating capabilities that have developed over long spans of time are extremely difficult to change or unlearn. Thus, a large price will eventually have to be paid for decisions made decades earlier if the initial choice of production method, or subsequent changes to it, proves to be wrong.

The choice most commonly made by senior managers in the early stages of a company's existence, regardless of market conditions, is to commit to batch-and-queue production, also known as lot production. This expensive, unresponsive production system will become a company's Achilles' heel when competition intensifies. The far less common choice is flow production – single- or mixed-model flow production – which is less costly and much more responsive to changes in market conditions. Comprehending flow production, either by seeing it with one's own eyes when visiting an automaker, reading about it, or by thinking for one's self, can help a company start out as a low-cost producer, or later convert to one. This will help ensure survival in tough economic times and avoidance of severe financial distress sometime in the future.

The accomplishments of William Morris (1877-1963) [1], Chairman of Morris Motors Ltd. (est. 1919), and of Frank G. Woollard, general manager of Morris Engines Ltd., in the 1920s are an important early example of how turn-of-the-century automobile production methods were selected by senior managers and adapted to fit within the context of different market conditions. This helped lead to Morris Motors' success, which was truly remarkable for the time: "From the 1920s to the 1950s, the British motor industry developed the most successful alternative productive model to that of 'Fordist' American mass production" [2]. Morris Motors converted to flow production in 1923 to reduce costs, cut prices, and increase output in response to greater customer demand. Their flow production system was unique and would have been extremely valuable to a start-up company seeking to enter the automobile business with limited resources.

What follows is an examination of the possible influence of Morris Motors on Toyota's development of their production system in the late 1930s, and perhaps into the late 1940s and early 1950s. The focus is on Kiichiro Toyoda

(1894-1952), the founder of Toyota Motor Corporation, and his decision to switch from batch-and-queue production used in automobile manufacturing in 1935 and 1936, to flow production in 1937 [3]. The fundamental question that will be examined is this: Did Morris Motors' success as a medium-sized automaker and Woollard's flow production method influence Kiichiro Toyoda and his nascent Toyota Motor Corporation?

From Looms to Automobiles
Kiichiro Toyoda was the driving force behind Toyoda Automatic Loom Works, Ltd. entry into the automobile business and would later become the president of Toyota Motor Corporation [4]. The timeline for the founding of Toyota Motor Corporation Ltd. is as follows [5]: Kiichiro's father Sakichi established Toyoda Spinning & Weaving Co., Ltd, in January 1918. Kiichiro Toyoda graduated from Tokyo Imperial University in July 1920 with a degree in mechanical engineering. Sakichi Toyoda established Toyoda Automatic Loom Works, Ltd. in November 1926, with Kiichiro appointed as managing director responsible for all activities from loom design through manufacturing [6].

Kiichiro Toyoda became interested in entering the automobile business in the late 1920s but did not disclose this to anyone until late 1930 or in 1931 [7]. In the fall of 1929 through the spring of 1930, Toyoda visited U.S. and U.K. automakers, parts suppliers, and machine tool makers [8] to study their production methods and identify equipment that would be necessary to manufacture automobile parts. He would have been particularly interested in seeing final assembly and engine manufacturing. Kiichiro Toyoda received formal approval from the board of directors of Toyoda Automatic Loom Works, Ltd. to conduct automobile research and development activities in the fall of 1933. These activities continued into the spring of 1935, and production of the first vehicles began in the summer of 1935. Toyoda Automatic Looms Works Ltd. produced approximately 3500 vehicles prior to the incorporation of Toyota Motor Corporation Ltd. in August 1937 [9].

It is well known that Kiichiro Toyoda was greatly influenced by Henry Ford [10]. However, Ford Motor Company's market conditions in the United States in the 1910s and 1920s, and, as a result, its highly vertically integrated, single-model, large-scale flow production system, were dramatically different than the market conditions in 1920s Japan [11]. Ford's production system would have been much less useful for a fledgling automobile company like Toyota to model themselves after [11, 12]. The characteristics of the British automotive market in the 1920s were a much closer match to the Japanese market conditions that Toyoda Automatic Loom Works, Ltd. faced in the mid-1930s and what Toyota Motor Corporation faced post-1945: much smaller and with greater product diversity.

The British automobile market and Woollard's flow production method, inclusive of automation, would have been a far better example for Toyota executives to study and learn from. Also, we know from Kiichiro Toyoda's biography [13] and Taiichi Ohno's book, *Toyota Production System* [14], that the principal modifications made to Ford's system are almost identical to those made by William Morris and Woollard over 20 years earlier: equipment arranged in process sequence, standardized work, quick set-ups, visual controls, on-time delivery of materials, level selling, production leveling, one person operating two or more machines, mechanization, and extensive use of outside suppliers (vertical disintegration).

However, Woollard's work is not mentioned in the published writings of any retired Toyota senior executive which suggests that they were not familiar with him or Morris Motors Ltd. Retired Toyota executives frequently make reference to Henry Ford and their adoption and modification of the "American mass production system" [15]. It is possible that the characterization "American mass production system" could have included the automobile production methods Kiichiro Toyoda saw first-hand in visits to British automakers and parts suppliers in the fall of 1929 [16], which where also broadly based on the American mass production system.

While Toyota executives do not mention specific British automakers or Woollard's work explicitly, it does not mean they had no influence. The flow production system in use at Morris Engines Ltd. c. 1930 could have easily been overlooked or misunderstood by Kiichiro Toyoda. He was a mechanical engineer whose career to that point in time was focused on textile machinery research, design, and new product development. Toyoda had only a few years of loom manufacturing experience, from November 1926 to September 1929, and it was at a high level as an operations manager [6]. Automatic looms were produced at a rate of about 4,000 per year in the late 1920s using conventional batch-and-queue production methods [17]. Therefore, Kiichiro Toyoda could have grouped the British flow production method in with the characterization of "American mass production system." As a result, British flow production may have lost its identity.

Kiichiro Toyoda was eager to learn from the leading British automaker of the late 1920s, Morris Motors Ltd., and why it was successful, including their production methods – just as he was eager to learn from the leading American automakers. He would have been motivated to learn from both sources because they had so much to teach him. We should not forget that:

1) Toyota managers have, since the company's inception, excelled at information gathering, sorting the useful information from the useless, documenting information, and taking action to apply new information

in practical ways [18].

2) Generally, senior managers like to search for relevant examples from businesses similar to their own from which they can learn; typically, examples that *closely* match their own circumstances, and then base their course of action on that information. This activity is well-documented in Toyota history [16, 19]. Also, overseas trips were expensive, months-long journeys, in which one would certainly seek to visit all the leading companies and return home with an abundance of useful information.

3) Leading U.K. automotive books, journals, and conference proceedings would have been extraordinarily pertinent to Toyota's efforts to become a viable automaker and must have been highly sought-after information. These print resources featured the work of engineers from leading British automakers, Morris and Austin, as well as the U.S. auto company's subsidiaries operating in Europe: Ford U.K. and Vauxhall (owned by General Motors).

4) Toyota managers have long placed great emphasis on actual practice, not theory, and Woollard's successful, innovative work was rooted in practice. It is work that they would have been very interested in and likely would have admired.

From Batch to Flow
In 1933 Kiichiro Toyoda said that Toyoda Automatic Loom Works, Ltd. would "base our method of production on the American mass production system," and that "it will not be an exact imitation but will reflect the particular conditions in Japan" [15]. Perhaps Kiichiro Toyoda saw flow production in his visits to British automakers in late 1929, but instead committed to the "American mass production system" because it was similar to how looms were manufactured. That is what he and his managers were most familiar with and it would be easier for the fledgling automobile company to implement. Maybe Kiichiro Toyoda could not yet see how to make flow work in his circumstances. In general, factory visits convey limited information about the production system, and there may have been a delay of several years until he realized the significance of what he saw. For most people, the logic and practice of flow takes some time to comprehend. In 1935 and 1936, Toyota Automatic Loom Works, Ltd. produced a total of 1162 vehicles [9] using a "lot production system" [20].

Kiichiro Toyoda soon recognized that the Japanese market could not support expensive lot (batch) production, driven by high inventory costs and long throughput times. In early 1937 he "decided to introduce a flow-production system at the new plant at Koromo" to reduce costs [21], and wrote a 10-centimeter thick (over 750 page) training manual explaining the new flow production system – a document which no longer exists [13]. The seven-year period from his late 1929 visit to American and British automobile plants to the 1937 decision to introduce flow production indicates that he spent quite some time thinking about flow production, how to do it, and when to introduce it. Did his knowledge of flow production and its cost reduction potential in *low-volume* manufacturing come from Ford or from Morris Motors? Or, did Kiichiro Toyoda come to it by himself?

The late 1930s and early 1940s were a wartime period for Japan; war with China and then the U.S. In wartime, there is an urgent need to increase production of trucks to move supply and personnel and airplanes for combat and to support supply operations. There must have been a great imperative from within the automobile and aircraft industries and by the Japanese government in the 1930s to search the world for improved methods of production. One would obviously turn to the leading industrialized nations at the time, the United States, Great Britain, and Germany, for the best ideas on what to do.

The challenge would be to identify the latest production methods that yield high throughput and productivity, and then copy, adapt, and modify these methods to existing equipment, knowledge, capabilities, and circumstances [22]. For the leading Japanese airplane makers, that production method would be a form of flow production [23]. The same would be true for Toyota, leading to the possibility, likely remote, that flow production came to Kiichiro Toyoda from Japanese aircraft company managers who may have been influenced by both American and British automakers [24]. After all, they share a common interest: low cost, high productivity production methods, and the best place for both to look would have been the world's leading automakers – which at that time would have been Morris in the U.K. and Ford in the U.S.

Despite Toyota senior management's long-standing pacifism in World War II, they would soon be forced by the Japanese government to increase output. While vehicle production was increased 300 percent [9], wartime caused extensive raw material shortages and supply disruptions from subcontractors and forced Toyota to abandon efforts to realize their Just-in-Time system and revert to batch-and-queue production [25]. Flow production would be revived post-World War II by Taiichi Ohno [26].

The British Influence
Based on the preceding discussion, the following scenario seems possible: Kiichiro Toyoda may have been familiar with Morris Motors Ltd. and Woollard's flow production method at Morris Engines Ltd., but characterized it as the "American mass production system," and that Toyota's transition to

flow production in 1937 was aided by knowledge he obtained in his trip to study British automakers, as well as written accounts of Woollard's flow production system [27]. This raises some interesting questions:

- Was Kiichiro Toyoda familiar with Frank Woollard's 1925 paper, "Some Notes on British Methods of Continuous Production?" If so, did it influence him?

- Was Taiichi Ohno familiar with Woollard's 1925 paper or his 1954 book? If so, did they influence him?

- Did Kiichiro Toyoda develop vertically disintegrated flow production independently, or was it an adaptation of Ford's vertically integrated mass production system? Or was he influenced by Morris Motors, who showed you could be a leading automaker by purchasing many components and sub-assemblies from outside suppliers?

- Would flow production become the obvious path for both William Morris and Kiichiro Toyoda to take because there were significant differences in their respective domestic markets compared to Ford in the United States [28]? Was this apparent to Toyoda independent of Woollard's work?

- In addition, what sparked Toyota management's interest in automatic transfer machines in the 1951-1954 time period, leading to their use in production starting in 1956 [29]? Was it the publication of Woollard's nine-part series of articles on flow production in 1952-1953 or his 1954 book? Or, was it visits taken by Toyota managers to Ford Motor Company, perhaps to its Cleveland engine plant c. 1951 [30], where they would have seen automatic transfer machines in operation [31]? Was it visits to British automakers who had put into use new, more advanced automatic transfer machine technology in the late 1940s and 1950s [32]? Did automatic transfer machine technology come to Toyota from Japanese aircraft manufacturers several years after World War II [33], or was it simply the result of Toyota's need to cut costs and improve productivity by eliminating waste [34]?

Answers to these questions will further clarify the timing of the many important contributions made by William Morris, Frank Woollard, Kiichiro Toyota, and Taiichi Ohno made to modern industrial management, flow production, and production equipment engineering [35].

The published record is clear; there is no doubt that Kiichiro Toyoda [9], and later Taiichi Ohno, learned much from Henry Ford [11, 12, 36], and not just automobile production. Henry Ford's overall philosophy of business could have had a very large impact as well. However, is it possible that some of Kiichiro Toyoda's ideas were inspired by Morris, e.g. vertical disintegration [37], and by Woollard, e.g. the cost reduction potential of flow in low-volume production (compared to Ford) [38]? Or, did Kiichiro Toyoda come upon these ideas independently? The latter explanation is plausible because people faced with similar problems in the same (or different) industries, in lands near or far, can come up with similar solutions independent of one another.

While Henry Ford's books *My Life and Work* and *Today and Tomorrow* [39] contain few details of flow production at the Highland Park, Michigan, plant, perhaps they were sufficient to teach Kiichiro Toyoda, and later Ohno, enough of the broad outlines of flow production for them to create their own unique flow production system. Both men could have gained additional details from a 1915 series of magazine articles featuring Ford's production methods or from a 1936 book titled *Ford Production Methods* [40]. Also, note that Kiichiro Toyoda did not see flow production in his visit to Ford in early 1930, likely at the new River Rouge plant (Ford Model A production period), because it converted to batch-and-queue mass production c. 1927. He would have seen final assembly lines both in the U.S. and U.K., which likely inspired his views on the importance of synchronization and Just-In-Time [13]. Hence, the choice made by Toyoda to use the "American mass production system," adapted to Japanese market conditions.

It is important to recognize that in fall 1929 Kiichiro Toyoda visited U.S. automakers first in the Detroit region (Ford and General Motors) and then British automakers in the Birmingham region (likely Morris and Austin) [8], and he certainly would have wanted to see two key manufacturing processes: engine manufacturing and final assembly. U.S. automobile production methods would have made the first impression on Toyoda, though production would have been on a scale that he likely could not have related to based on his experience with loom manufacturing. He would likely have viewed Ford's facilities as expansive and very impractical or unrealistic for 1930s Japan. Toyoda Automatic Loom Works' circumstances more closely matched a mid-sized auto manufacturer like Morris rather than a giant-sized auto manufacturer like Ford; the latter being an enormous stretch, while the former would be more easily within his company's grasp. However, Ford's production facilities would have made a much greater impression on Kiichiro Toyoda than Morris' production facilities despite their noteworthy flow production method and market success.

There is a substantial body of evidence that British automakers, in general, and Morris' flow production system, in particular, may not have been relevant to Kiichiro Toyoda in the beginning years of his automobile business, c.

1933-1940 [41]. Perhaps he thought British methods were deficient in some specific way, that they were not materially different than those pioneered by American automakers, or that their smaller scale indicated a lower level of accomplishment. Therefore, he may have viewed British automakers' production systems as interesting and helpful, but Ford's global prominence and impressive operations made it the better example to emulate.

Still, it seems likely that Toyoda, and later Ohno, may have known of Morris and Woollard's work because it was so relevant to their own work and not at all difficult to find. They might have implemented some of what they learned from them because Morris Motors' experience in the 1920s was so obviously a much closer match to Toyota's domestic market and the competitive challenges it faced against the subsidiaries of U.S.-based auto companies operating in Japan – Ford and General Motors.

In addition, Toyota's early efforts in automobile parts design were based on reverse engineering – copying – U.S. automakers' designs [42]. It is logical, intelligent, and practical that an entrepreneurial start-up with limited financial and technical resources would initially make extensive use of copying, particularly automobile parts and body design [43] – and automobile production systems as well, of which they had no understanding. This explains the need to study U.K. and U.S. automobile manufacturer's production systems. Toyota's flow production system post-1937 may have thus been an adaptation of both Morris' and Ford's production systems, with the latter receiving greater emphasis.

This analysis does not diminish Kiichiro Toyoda or Toyota Motor Corporation in any way. Their accomplishments are enormous and impressive. Rather, it is recognition of the very nature of innovation in which breakthroughs are typically achieved by building upon the work of earlier pioneers; in this case, perhaps William Morris and Frank Woollard, along with the very influential Henry Ford and Charles Sorensen. As in any innovative process, people such as Kiichiro Toyoda and Taiichi Ohno [44] make numerous small adjustments and adaptations to past ideas and practices and develop many major new ideas and practices (e.g. kanban) to make the system they wish to create function much better.

Even if Morris Motors and Woollard had zero influence on Kiichiro Toyoda, which seems unlikely, their accomplishments are very impressive nonetheless. Morris Motors Ltd. was the largest automaker in the U.K. and its facilities were among the best in Europe. The Morris Engines Ltd. factory was a model for British industry, decades ahead of competitors, and was open to visitors [45].

The next section will briefly review Frank G. Woollard's 1925 paper "Some Notes on British Methods of Continuous Production," as well as his 1954 book *Principles of Mass and Flow Production* [46], to better understand his distinctive contributions to flow production and automation – which were made possible by the support of the Chairman of Morris Motors Ltd., William R. Morris.

Notes

[1] The official biography of William R. Morris was produced by: P. Andrews and E. Brunner, *The Life of Lord Nuffield: A Study in Enterprise and Benevolence*, Basil Blackwell, Oxford, U.K., 1955. Many other biographies were produced including: R. Overy, *William Morris, Viscount Nuffield*, Europa Publications Limited, London, U.K., 1976

[2] S. Tolliday, "The Diffusion and Transformation of Fordism: Britain and Japan Compared" in *Between Imitation and Innovation*, R. Boyer, E. Charron, U. Jürgens, S. Tolliday, editors, Oxford University Press, New York NY, 1998, p. 83

[3] E. Toyoda, *Toyota: Fifty Years in Motion*, Kondasha International, New York, NY, 1987, pp. 57-58

[4] *Toyota: A History of the First 50 Years*, Toyota Motor Corporation, Toyota City, Japan, 1988, pp. 38-77

[5] Toyota. p. 490

[6] K. Wada and T. Yui, *Courage and Change: The Life of Kiichiro Toyoda*, Toyota Motor Corporation, Toyota City, Japan, 2002, pp. 113-154

[7] Wada and Yui, pp. 168 and 200-202

[8] Toyota, pp. 39 and 41, Wada and Yui, pp. 168-169 and 187-190. The major U.S. and U.K. automobile producers and auto parts makers were concentrated in two convenient, easy-to-visit regions. Kiichiro Toyoda would have been in the Detroit-Dearborn area to visit General Motors Corporation and Ford Motor Company, and in the Coventry-Birmingham (Midlands) area to visit Morris Motors Ltd. (commercial vans and trucks) and Austin Motor Company, Ltd. Kiichiro Toyoda would have had to travel south to Oxford to view Morris's passenger car assembly operations.

[9] Toyota, p. 461

[10] Toyota, p. 42

[11] Tolliday (1998), pp. 72-73

[12] T. Ohno, *Toyota Production System*, Productivity Press, Portland, OR, 1988, p. 91

[13] Wada and Yui, pp. 279-280, 287-292, 296

[14] Ohno, pp. xiii-xv and 1-74. See the timeline of the development of Toyota Motor Corporation's production system in the front and rear endpapers of Taiichi Ohno's book *Toyota Production System*, Productivity Press, Portland, OR, 1988.

[15] Toyota, p. 45

[16] Toyota, pp. 39 and 41. Unofficial biographies of the Toyota Motor Corporation and the Toyoda family also confirm Kiichiro Toyoda's visits to American and British automakers and parts suppliers between fall 1929 and spring of 1930. See Y. Togo and W. Wartman, *Against All Odds*, St. Martins's Press, New York, NY, 1993, p. 37 and S. Kimoto, *Quest for the Dawn*, The Dougherty Company, Milwaukee, WI, 1991, p. 38

[17] Wada and Yui, pp. 197n and 203-204

[18] S. Hino, *Inside the Mind of Toyota*, Productivity Press, New York, NY, 2006, Chapter 1

[19] Toyota, pp. 39-41 and 112-113 and Toyoda, pp. 106-110

[20] Toyoda, p. 57

[21] Toyoda, pp. 53 and 57-58

[22] K. Wada and T. Shiba, "The Evolution of the 'Japanese Production System:' Indigenous Influences and American Impact" in *Americanization and its Limits*, J. Zeitlin and G. Herrigel, editors, Oxford University Press, Oxford, U.K., pp. 316-339

[23] Wada and Shiba, pp. 323-329

[24] Wada and Shiba, p. 232

[25] Toyoda, pp. 58, 63 and Toyota, pp. 59, 73-77

[26] Ohno, pp. 3 and 9-11 and Toyota, p. 142

[27] F.G. Woollard, "Some Notes on British Methods of Continuous Production," *Proceedings of The Institution of Automobile Engineers*, The Institution of Automobile Engineers, London, U.K., Proceedings of the Session 1924-1925, Volume XIX, pp. 419-474, 885-890, and Plates XVI to XXXII (Figures 1-26); F.G. Woollard, "Some Notes on British Methods of Continuous Production," excerpt published in *Automobile Engineer*, The Institution of Automobile Engineers, London, U.K., Vol. 15, March 1925, pp. 85-93; F.G. Woollard, "Some Notes on British Methods of Continuous Production," excerpt published in *Automotive Industries*, Class Journal Co., New York, NY, Vol. 52, 28 May 1925, p. 940

[28] Senior managers of Ford's U.K. operations had great difficulty transferring Ford's U.S. production system to the U.K. in the 1920s due to significant differences between these two markets. See S. Tolliday, "Management and Labor in Britain 1896-1939," in *Between Fordism and Flexibility*, S. Tolliday and J. Zeitlin, editors, Berg Publishers Inc., New York, NY, 1992, pp. 29-56.

[29] Toyota, p. 141 and M. Cusumano, *The Japanese Automobile Industry*, The Council on East Asian Studies, Harvard University, Harvard University Press, 1985, p. 95

[30] Eiji Toyoda, for example, visited Ford's factories in the U.S. in the summer and fall of 1950, followed by Soichi Saito who also visited U.S. automobile companies for a few months after Toyoda. See Toyoda, pp. 106-111. Both were managing directors of Toyota at that time (July 1950). See Toyoda, p. 110. Eiji Toyoda and Soichi Saito formulated Toyota's five year production equipment modernization plan upon their return from the United States, in February 1951, which appears to have included the future use of automatic transfer machines. See Toyoda, pp. 112-114.

[31] D. Hounshell, "Ford Automates: Technology and Organization in Theory and Practice," *Business and Economic History*, Vol. 24, No. 1, Fall 1995, pp. 59-71

[32] J. Zeitlin, "Reconciling Automation and Flexibility?: Technology and Production in the Postwar British Motor Vehicle Industry," *Enterprise & Society*, Volume 1, Issue 1, March 2000, pp. 9-62

[33] E. Daito, "Automation and the Organization of Production in the Japanese Automobile Industry: Nissan and Toyota in the 1950s," *Enterprise & Society*, Vol. 1, Issue 1, March 2000, pp. 139-178. At least one aircraft company with experience in automatic transfer machines during World War II, Mitsubishi Heavy Industries, was located in Toyota's home town of Nagoya, Japan.

[34] Tolliday (1998), pp. 77-80

[35] Woollard's work has not been recognized by the Lean community. See for example: S. Shingo, *Study of 'Toyota' Production System from Industrial Engineering Viewpoint*, Japan Management Association, Tokyo, Japan, November 1981, distributed by Productivity Press, Inc., Cambridge, MA; Y. Monden, *Toyota Production System: Practical Approach to Production Management*, Industrial Engineering and Management Press, Norcross, GA, 1983; R. Schonberger, *World Class Manufacturing*, The Free Press, New York, NY, 1986; K. Suzaki, *The New Manufacturing Challenge*, The Free Press, New York, NY, 1987; J. Womack, D. Jones, and D. Roos, *Lean Thinking*, Simon & Schuster, New York, NY, 1996; Y. Monden, *Toyota Production System: An Integrated Approach to Just-In-Time*, 3rd Edition, Engineering & Management Press, Norcross, GA, 1998; A. Kawahara, *The Origin of Competitive Strength*, Springer-Verlag, New York, NY, 1998; T. Fujimoto, *The Evolution of a Manufacturing System at Toyota*, Oxford University Press, New York, NY, 1999; W. Tsutsui, *Manufacturing Ideology: Scientific Management in Twentieth-Century Japan*, Princeton University Press, Princeton, NJ, 1998; James P. Womack, "A Century of Lean Thinking,"

presentation given at the 10th Annual Lean Manufacturing Conference, University of Michigan, Ann Arbor, Mich., 11 May 2004, http://www.lean.org/Community/Resources/PresentationLibrary.cfm; J. Liker, *The Toyota Way*, McGraw-Hill, New York, NY, 2004; H. Hirano and M. Furuya, *JIT is Flow: Practice and Principles of Lean Manufacturing*, PCS Press Inc., Vancouver, WA, 2006; "Lean Timeline," Lean Enterprise Institute, Cambridge, MA, http://www.lean.org/WhatsLean/Timeline.cfm, accessed 3 October 2008

[36] What was the purpose of Ohno's extensive citation and lengthy adulation of Henry Ford and Charles Sorensen in his book *Toyota Production System*? He appears to be honoring the acknowledged greats, Ford and Sorensen, which is the logical thing to do and would certainly satisfy other people's expectations for humble attribution. Ohno's admiration for Henry Ford and Charles Sorensen is probably sincere, but this also could have been a misdirection by Ohno to throw off the competition. Perhaps Ford's books offered a sufficient quantity of insights and lessons relevant to Ohno's work that there was no need to cite other sources of influence.

[37] Toyota, p. 76

[38] Woollard (1925), p. 420

[39] H. Ford with S. Crowther, *My Life and Work*, Garden City Publishing Co., Inc., Garden City, NY, 1922; H. Ford with S. Crowther, *Today and Tomorrow*, Doubleday, Page & Company, Garden City, NY, 1926

[40] H. Arnold and F. Faurote, *Ford Methods and the Ford Shops*, The Engineering Magazine Co., New York, NY, 1919. The series of articles was originally published in *The Engineering Magazine* in 1915. H. Barclay, *Ford Production Methods*, Harper & Brothers Publishers, New York, NY, 1936

[41] Please keep in mind that while the "dots" seem to connect nicely on paper, there is no guarantee that they did so in reality.

[42] K. Wada and T. Yui, pp. 239 and 247. See also: M. Cusumano, *The Japanese Automobile Industry*, The Council on East Asian Studies, Harvard University, Harvard University Press, 1985, pp. 58, 62, 64-67, 70

[43] The first production passenger car, the Toyoda Model AA sedan (1936), had a body design that is very similar in appearance to the 1935 model year Morris Eight Series II 4-door (introduced in September 1934). Toyota says that the AA's body design was based on the 1934 DeSoto (Chrysler) Airflow 4-door passenger car (see *Toyota Automobile Museum*, Toyota Motor Corporation, Toyota City, Japan, 1989, pp. 19-21). Perhaps it was a combination of the two body styles.

[44] It is interesting to note that there is very little discussion of machinery in Taiichi Ohno's book *Toyota Production System* (Productivity Press, Portland, OR, 1988). The lack of discussion of machinery used by Toyota in support of automobile manufacturing is conspicuous by its absence. It is unusual because Toyota Motor Corporation has long been a major shareholder in Toyoda Machine Works, Ltd. (est. 1941), a maker of machine tools that supplied Toyota with many different types of innovative machines. In comparison, Woollard's book contains extensive discussion of machinery in modern (1920-1950s) manufacturing industry, and its future importance in manufacturing. But he was also careful to note their limitations and emphasized that management is much more important than machines.

[45] P. Seymour, *Morris Light Vans: 1924-1934*, P&B Publishing, East Sussex, U.K., 1999, p. 38

[46] F.G. Woollard, *Principles of Mass and Flow Production*, Iliffe & Sons, Ltd., London, U.K., 1954

Introduction to the Reprint Edition

The focus of *Principles of Mass and Flow Production* is on achieving flow in processes upstream of final automobile assembly. Flow must be also achieved in subcomponent assembly and parts manufacturing, and even into raw material production, to support flow in single-model or mixed-model final assembly. According to Woollard: "flow production starts with the sales department and extends throughout the whole organization" (p. 104). With respect to internal operations: "flow production commenced with the assembly line and then spread to the machine shops, being applied first to the larger, heavier components and then to the smaller parts" (p. 77), and "The golden rule [of flow production] is to commence with the assembly lines and work back" (p. 104), including to outside parts suppliers.

Flow production at Morris was reduced to fully-functioning practice starting in a production automobile engine machine shop, principally because it was the bottleneck, and was spread from there, just as Taiichi Ohno did [1]. Woollard was not an owner of an automobile company, but instead was a manager in charge of manufacturing, just as Ohno was. Woollard conceptualized and implemented flow production with strong support from the top executive, William R. Morris (ennobled as Lord Nuffield in 1934 and 1st Viscount Nuffield in 1938), just as Ohno had. And both Woollard and Ohno viewed their accomplishments with strong nationalistic pride. These parallels are striking, and do not end there.

We will begin with a brief overview of Woollard's 1925 paper, "Some Notes on British Methods of Continuous Production" [2], followed by his 1954 book *Principles of Mass and Flow Production* [3]. In both of these works you will easily recognize many of his flow production principles and practices as part of today's Lean principles and practices, though some, as expected, were in nascent form.

Overview of "Some Notes on British Methods of Continuous Production"
Woollard's 1925 paper, "Some Notes on British Methods of Continuous Production," appears in the Appendix. This must be our starting point, and I recommend you read it first. One of Woollard's distinctive contributions was to prove that achieving flow in small volume production (compared to Ford in the U.S.) resulted in costs that were almost as low as that which could be achieved by large-scale mass production. Thus, medium-sized companies producing tens of thousands of automobiles could compete against foreign companies that produced automobiles in much larger volumes. Kiichiro Toyoda had this same insight in 1937, 12 years after Woollard reduced it to practice [4].

"Some Notes on British Methods of Continuous Production" explains how Woollard achieved flow production at Morris Engines Ltd. between mid-1923 and early-1925. Woollard points out that while the discussion is limited to engine manufacturing, "for the sake of illustration" (p. 419), the same method applies to "the motor car as a whole" (p. 420).

In the second paragraph, Woollard notes that economic reasons "demand the practice of continuous production" (p. 419), and that with continuous flow, "a relatively small factory may meet the greater overseas plants on fairly level terms" (p. 420). He characterized continuous production as "no new thing," but "comparatively new to the engineering [durable goods] industry, and it presents many novel problems" (p. 420).

Woollard had the insight to say: "The ideal of continuous flow must be present from the design and raw material stages up to and even beyond the sales stage" (p. 420). In other words, achieving flow in production activities alone is not enough; management and workers must connect all processes, beginning to end, to achieve flow throughout the business. This is an aspect of Lean that most senior managers have yet to understand, mistakenly thinking that achieving flow in operations is sufficient.

While much of the paper discusses details of the operation of the new automatic transfer machinery, Woollard is careful to point out that that automatic transfer machines, a "British development" (p. 441), "are only incidental to the whole organization of the factory," and that "it must not be imagined that I suggest special machines as the essential method of attacking the continuous production problem" (p. 462). He also says that "given a similar problem [economical manufacturing in large quantities], it can be handled as well in this country as overseas, and… the development will be on similar lines" (p. 419). Toyota's experiences years later surely validates this statement.

Woollard notes that machine shops originally started out as engineering shops in which it was sensible and convenient to group together similar types of machine tools. This led to the idea that foremen should manage groups of machine tools – an idea that "persisted even when engineering shops were placed on a repetitive basis" (p. 425) and materials required extensive transport. It was not obvious that moving from one-off jobs to repetitive manufacturing should lead to re-arrangement of machines. Woollard's remedy was: "machines were arranged for the work to flow naturally from stage to stage" (p. 425). This "in line" (p. 425) arrangement of machines, instead of individual shops containing groups of like machines, is better suited to smaller production volumes. These changes resulted in a 400 percent increase in weekly output of automobile engines, from 300 to 1200 engines per week – about 55,000 vehicles in 1925 [5]. In comparison, Toyota would not produce more than 55,000 vehicles in a single year until 1957 [6], while Ford, achieved an output of greater than 55,000 automobiles in 1911 [7].

In order to achieve flow, Woollard notes the importance of how "standardized product" leads to "standardized materials, standardized operations, standardized production methods and even standardized [tolerance] limits" (p. 421). He also discusses the importance of regularity, where: "Regularity, then, is the key-note of continuous production; regularity in sales as to quantity and type; regularity in material as to quantity, quality, and time; regularity in processing, workmanship, and inspection" (pp. 422-423). Regularity in sales and regularity in processing is what the Lean community today calls level selling and production leveling in the factory.

With regard to material deliveries, Woollard says that they "must be delivered to time so that there shall be no shortage or glut" (p. 422). The phrase "delivered to time" obviously has similar, if not the same, meaning as "Just-In-Time," by which Kiichiro Toyoda meant: "Just make what is needed in time, but don't make too much" [8]. Woollard used a supermarket-type system to store engine blocks and limit inventory to a four-day supply (p. 428), just as Toyota did more than two decades later [9].

The cycle time for machining in the automatic transfer machinery is four minutes (p. 429). It is not clear how this figure was arrived at, but it was likely a response to robust U.K. automobile sales, which doubled between 1923 and 1925 [10]. He says later in the Discussion part of the paper that "Four minutes is the standard time-cycle to-day, but it may be altered as required" (p. 463). This seems to imply its use as a takt time.

Woollard recognized that "if there is trouble… [it] is highly visible to the management, and consequently is more quickly remedied than sporadic trouble" (p. 434). He goes on to say that the mechanized movement of the automatic transfer machinery "is a metronome which beats out time for the whole of the works… If used wisely, it sets a pace which in itself it helps to maintain: it discovers weak spots in the organization, and shows up inequalities in method which, once visible, good management can quickly remedy" (p. 441). In other words, automatic transfer machines serve as a visual control. Woollard also described the use of visual controls in automobile engine testing.

There were both human and machine interventions to identify problems and stop the work to eliminate production of defective parts. In contrast to today's operator-performed inspections, Woollard thought that: "Inspection between operations is of little or no value… while the value of the group inspection at the end of the line is very great" (p. 434). The human that would intervene was "the inspector, who is stationed at the end of the line… is empowered to stop the whole line if a fault is discovered in the work-piece" (p. 437). Thus, the line-stop that the Lean community was so familiar with was in operation in Woollard's factory, though not the responsibility of the operator. In a fly-wheel automatic transfer machine, "All the heads are mechanically inter-locked to stop the machine as a whole if any parts fail to function" (p. 438), indicating an early example of jidoka (autonomation) [11].

In this paper, Woollard succinctly summarizes the impact of continuous pro-duction on the workers as "men will take quite kindly to new machines and methods if they once realise that they will be dealt with equitably" (p. 424). He goes into much more detail on the human impact and benefits to workers and other stakeholders in his book *Principles of Mass and Flow Production*.

Finally, at the end of the paper, Woollard thanks William Morris, Chairman of the Morris group companies "for the opportunity of putting these 'Continuous Production' theories into practice" (p. 442). Taiichi Ohno sim-ilarly thanked Kiichiro Toyoda and especially Eiji Toyoda for supporting his work [12].

The Discussion pages at the end of Woollard's paper are fascinating because they reveal people's reactions to the "unusual machines and new methods and organisation, all of which are British developments" (p. 419). Discussion topics include: the effect of increased inventory turns on working capital and company financial condition; differences between U.S. and U.K. automobile markets; manufacturing throughput; model change-over time; work stop-pages and visual management; impact of flow production on workers; argu-ments over the terms "mass production," "continuous production," "progres-sive manufacture," and "flow production;" skepticism on whether flow pro-duction can be applied to entire automobiles; the inflexibility of elaborate machines; timely delivery of materials; bottlenecks; worker pay; how to han-dle long cycle-time processes such as heat treating (called the "curtain effect" in Lean); triple sourcing supply and buying parts locally; and, finally, sharing Morris' flow production system with other people via Woollard's conference paper and plant tours – which Kiichiro Toyoda would have benefited from on his trip to the U.K. in late 1929. Similarly, Toyota has shared its production system with others for decades. Sharing is a quintessentially non-zero-sum, Lean thing to do.

The 1925 paper, written when Woollard was 42 years old, is remarkable in many different ways. Foremost among them is Woollard's effort to clear the ground of past British manufacturing practices – expensive and unresponsive batch-and-queue processing – and to create a new foundation for flow pro-duction upon which to build and further improve. His use of automatic trans-fer machines to facilitate flow production of gearbox and flywheel manufacturing is truly visionary for the time, especially his recognition of the information that such machinery provides in terms of visual management. At the same time, he notes that such equipment is not necessary to achieve continuous production. What appears to be undeveloped at this point is the idea of a pull system based upon market demand, as was the case with Henry Ford's production system at Highland Park [13].

The next section is a brief overview of selected passages from Woollard's book, *Principles of Mass and Flow Production*. It is not my intent to re-state what Woollard has written, as you can surely read that for yourself, but to highlight some key points that will be of interest to Lean management practitioners and academics.

Overview of *Principles of Mass and Flow Production*
Principles of Mass and Flow Production was published when Woollard was 71 years old. The book came about as a result of a six-part course he taught as a lecturer in 1951 for senior engineering executives in the Department of Industrial Administration at the College of Technology in Birmingham, U.K. (now known as Aston Business School, Aston University). This and other opportunities to lecture on flow production led Woollard to write a nine-part series of articles in the journal *Mechanical Handling* (U.K.) in 1952 and 1953, and this, in turn, led to an expanded presentation of his work in book form published in 1954.

Woollard dedicated the book to (p. 5):

ALL WHO SEEK TO LIFT THE
CURSE OF ADAM FROM
THE SHOULDERS OF MANKIND

What Woollard meant is to lift the curse that God placed on Adam to labor. Woollard viewed flow production as the means to work more efficiently and effectively, thus lifting the curse of hard labor so that mankind can enjoy the fruits of life.

The Foreword was written by Sir Leonard Lord (1896-1967), the then chairman of British Motor Corporation Ltd., which was formed in 1952 by a merger of Austin Motor Company, Ltd. and Morris Motors Ltd., a position he held until 1961 [14]. In 1922 he worked at the French-owned Hotchkiss et Cie plant in Coventry as assistant chief engineer. One year later William Morris acquired Hotchkiss which became Morris Engines Ltd., with Woollard appointed as general manager. Woollard assigned Lord responsibility for the design and purchase of machine tools, and was thus deeply involved in the development of manual and automatic transfer machinery. In 1933 Lord became a managing director of Morris Motors Ltd. Having known Woollard for many years, he says: "…I know that he regards the waste of 'the unforgiving minute' with something akin to horror" (p. 11).

Woollard's Preface notes that "flow production is closely associated with mechanical handling" (p. 13) of materials, specifically though the use of automatic transfer machines. All other companies in the global automotive industry would come to agree with Woollard's view more than two decades later. The Lean community often thinks in terms of simple right-sized equipment, but the reality is that this is not always the case. It depends upon the job that needs to be performed, productively and at low cost. At times, elaborate, but flexible, machinery can be essential to improving the work itself, workflows, quality, and increasing economic prosperity.

Woollard says that the intention of his book is to be "a reliable guide for those who contemplate these new methods of production for which we must adopt – adapted to our own needs – if we are to meet world competition" (p. 13). He also notes that he has warned his associates "against that dangerous hobby of falling in love with mechanism for its own sake" (p. 14). To do so would, among other things, ignore workers, an outcome which Woollard sought to guard against.

Chapter 1 presents a brief history of flow production, and begins with the following paragraph (p. 15):

> "Flow production, where it is applicable, can be a major factor in
> increasing production since the results accruing from the adoption
> of this comparatively new system are little short of astounding.
> Indeed, it is scarcely too much to claim that this new technique is,
> in itself, another complete turn in the industrial revolution."

Having experienced a 400 percent increase in output in automobile engines 1924, Woollard knows well what he speaks of. However, he is not simply concerned with the application of flow production on a large scale. He goes on to say: "small-scale production can frequently benefit to a surprising degree by a study of the principles of flow production" (p. 15).

Chapter 2 describes the range of application of flow production, particularly on smaller scales. Woollard gives a detailed example of the flow production method applied to the small-scale manufacture of railway coaches at a carriage shop in Eastleigh, where he had worked in the early 1900s. Woollard notes that (p. 42):

> "The managers of concerns that have only short runs of work are

usually under the impression that flow production can hold no interest for them and that batch production is the only method suited to their needs… Progressive firms are finding there are many useful lessons to be learned from flow production techniques which can be applied to small outputs and that when this is done a very near approach will be made towards achieving flow production costs."

He goes on to say (p. 42):

"Then by studying the machine equipment, the fixtures, jigs, tools and gauges can be modified to reduce the change-over time to a minimum. The other advantages are that there is less work in progress, giving not only a smaller inventory but a quicker throughput, especially as there is no need to wait for batches to finish before passing to the next operation. Since inspection will be in line with machines, faulty work will be found almost immediately and the necessary adjustments made."

In this passage and the ones that follow, Woollard clearly outlines what today we would characterize as basic elements of Lean applied to production activities – set-up reduction, arranging machines in operation sequence, standardization, job simplification, visual management, flexible layout, inexpensive material conveyance devices – and the resulting benefits. Note that in his 1925 paper, Woollard advocated end-of-line inspection, while now he advocates in-line inspection. This illustrates the evolution in thinking and practice associated with Woollard's work over the years, as one would expect. Finally, he notes that machine utilization rate is not a desirable metric in flow production, training time is reduced, worker morale is improved, and the work becomes self-paced.

Chapter 3 begins Woollard's explanation of his "18 basic principles for flow production." First, however, he distinguishes between mass production and flow production. Mass production is (p. 48):

"…the method of making vast quantities of similar articles – simple or complicated – by a series of individual acts which are not necessarily connected with each other."

Whereas flow production is (p. 48):

"…the passage of the part from operation to operation in a direct and uninterrupted sequence."

He then says, in apposite metaphor (p.48):

> "The ideal arrangement for flow production should resemble a watershed; the river being the main assembly track, fed by tributaries in the shape of sub-assembly lines which, in turn, would be supplied by streams representing the machine lines fed by brooks typifying the material conveyors. Each part should flow continuously forward. There should be few bends, no eddies, no dams, no storms, no freezing should impede the inevitable flow to estuarine waters – the dealers – and ultimately to the sea – the customers."

Before presenting his 18 "Basic Principles" of flow production, Woollard reminds us of the objectives of flow production (p. 50):

> "In general, the aim is to produce goods more economically and more quickly with less stress or strain on the producers than that which is inherent in the older methods."

He sets up the principles by stating (p. 52):

> "When setting up a flow production plant, there are certain basic principles that must be obeyed. They are all simple and virtually axiomatic… In the list on page 51 [Figure 1] the principles of both mass and flow production are stated, but items 6, 7, 8, 9, 10, 12, 13, and 17 apply more particularly to flow production."

Woollard's "Basic Principles" of flow production is shown in Figure 1:

Figure 1

THE BASIC PRINCIPLES

(1) *(a)* Mass production demands mass consumption.

    (b) Flow production requires continuity of demand.

(2) The products of the system must be specialized.

(3) The products of the system must be standardized.

(4) The products of the system must be simplified in general and in detail.

(5) All material supplies must conform to specification.

(6) All supplies must be delivered to strict timetable.

(7) The machines must be continually fed with sound material.

(8) Processing must be progressive and continuous.

(9) A time cycle must be set and maintained.

(10) Operations must be based on motion study and time study.

(11) Accuracy of work must be strictly maintained.

(12) Long-term planning, based on precise knowledge, is essential.

(13) Maintenance must be by anticipation—never by default.

(14) Every mechanical aid must be adopted for man and machine.

(15) Every activity must be studied for the economic application of power.

(16) Information on costs must be promptly available.

(17) Machines should be designed to suit the task they perform.

(18) The system of production must benefit everyone—consumers, workers and owners.

Note that Woollard used the word "obeyed" when referring to the application of the principles in striving to achieve flow production. This means they must be followed; that they are not optional. Too many mangers throughout the history of progressive management have subjectively judged this or that to be optional, only to find out later that it was actually very important and its absence unfortunately contributed to their failure. Cherry-picking principles, processes, and tools are always the death of efforts to reform management thinking and workplace practices. Remember, Woollard is not dispensing theoretical advice; his principles are rooted in practice, in the real world – the business world, in which Morris Motors Ltd. once thrived.

The remainder of the book, Chapters 4 though 16, presents a detailed discussion of the 18 basic principles. For the sake of brevity, I will not review each one, but say only that the eight principles that especially apply to flow production – 6, 7, 8, 9, 10, 12, 13, and 17 – are easily recognizable to people with knowledge of Lean management. It is, of course, worth reading Woollard's descriptions of each principle to comprehend his views of the technical aspects of flow production. His descriptions are detailed and practical, and must be read and re-read in order to comprehend them fully. While Woollard's book focuses mainly on production aspects, he does note that: "Naturally, flow production concerns [businesses] apply the flow technique to the office as well as to the factory" (p. 134).

It should be noted that Woollard did not explicitly calculate a takt time, or rate of customer demand to pace production. Instead, a cycle time, principle 9, was calculated based on current and expected demand by the sales department, and then the workday in production was shortened or lengthened based on actual demand (see pp. 87-88). In numerous locations throughout the book, Woollard emphasizes the importance of maintaining the cycle time.

We must focus for a moment on Woollard's pioneering work in automation because it would become common practice in the automobile industry some 25 years later. Chapter 14 describes Principle 17, "Machines should be designed to suit the task they perform," and includes a detailed discussion of automatic transfer machines. Woollard's overarching concern was that management's drive to reduce labor costs would lead to indiscriminate application of automatic machines. Again, he emphasizes that "automatic machinery is not an essential of flow production." (p. 151). He says that "while flow production is a marriage of mechanism and management, the accent is emphatically on *management*" (p. 151, italics original). Woollard means that managements' practices are more important that the machinery used to facilitate flow production. If the business is managed poorly, then there is nothing that machines and automation can do to help overcome that fundamental shortfall.

Woollard did not focus solely on the technical aspects of flow production. He was very concerned about human aspects as well [15, 16, 17]. Part of what drove his concern is workers' normal, negative reaction to automation, in general, and automatic transfer machines in particular. He did not want the technology to be used by managers to eliminate workers. The redundancy problem, Woollard said, is "rather one of redeployment [of workers] than of unemployment" (p. 179). Pitting machine against worker, rather than with worker, will always cause strife and should therefore be avoided. It is better to grow the business and make use of workers who have been displaced by machines.

The disinterest in human relations normally displayed by technocratic managers focused only on improving labor productivity suggests that we must emphasize the human aspect of business, as Woollard did, to help prevent executives from making critical errors. Principle 18 states: "The system of production must benefit everyone – consumers, workers and owners." It says: "*must* benefit" for a reason; if it does not benefit these stakeholders, then you can not expect to succeed with flow production – or with mass production. He is saying that management must operate the production system, and the business at large, in a non-zero-sum fashion. Something that is good for the owners but is not good for customers or workers is bad; something that is good for customers but is not good for owners and workers is also bad because it undercuts the interests of two key stakeholders that customers need. Woollard is not offering this to managers as an optional principle.

Unfortunately, this is the principle which dooms most Lean transformation efforts. Managers typically focus on the technocratic aspects of Lean management, on flow production itself, and miss important, required elements that must also be practiced in order to be successful. In other words, their accent is emphatically on machines, tools, and techniques of flow production instead of management. Most managers, therefore, get it backwards. To correct this, managers must pay great attention to the human aspects, what is known as the "Respect for People" principle in Lean management [18], where "People" includes the following key stakeholders: employees, suppliers, customers, investors, and communities.

Rudimentary cause-and-effect analysis tells us that marginalizing the interests of one key stakeholder over another will cause problems. Lean people do not deny that reality, but most other people do. The marginalized party will work against the other parties in any way possible to restore justice. If management operates the system in a zero-sum fashion, in which one party gains at the expense of another, then flow production is not possible; there will be many bends, eddies, dams, storms, and freezings that impede flow. We all know this from our own experiences working in zero-sum managed organizations, yet we accept it as normal. It is not normal, and it should cause us to question our personal commitment to improvement and to other human beings.

In the post-modern application of Lean management, the "Respect for People" principle serves as an inviolate rule so people do not blindly pursue zero-sum thinking in the name local optimization; to achieve a company or a shareholder objective, for example, at someone else's expense. The uniqueness of Lean management, and flow production, if we wish to practice it correctly, is the non-zero-sum nature of the management system. That is the crucial factor that most people fail to recognize. That is why Woollard made non-zero-sum a "basic principle."

The "Respect for People" principle is required [19]; it is not an option that senior managers can cherry-pick and discard from the system. Yet that is what managers typically do, and then a few years later they wonder why so little progress has been made. They will blame people for the lack of progress and, by doing so, again fail to practice the "Respect for People" principle.

Woollard expands on the importance of principle 18, "The system of production must benefit everyone – consumers, workers and owners," in Chapter 16. Please pay attention to these wise words (p. 180):

> "Unless the eighteenth principle is satisfied the [flow production] system cannot reach full stature and, if it does not, the equipment and appurtenances necessary for flow production will not be utilized to the full. They might even, in some instances, become an embarrassment. This principle of 'benefit for all' is not based on altruistic ideals – much as these are to be admired – but upon the hard facts of business efficiency."

At the end of Chapter 16, Woollard offers a warning and a challenge to management (p. 187):

> "...like all tools of management, it [flow production] can be misused... [it] could be the instrument of a slave driving tyranny, whereas properly employed it will promote discipline in an equitable and gentle, if irresistible, manner, making the daily task lighter for us all."

This concludes the overview of Woollard's landmark 1954 book *Principles of Mass and Flow Production*. I hope you will read his book carefully to gain a sense of his great contributions to flow production and automation, and also in the context of the evolution and current-day practice of Lean management.

The Margate Conference Paper

I would like to mention the last paper that Woollard personally presented at a conference before he died in late 1957: "Machines in the Service of Man." This paper was given at The Institution of Production Engineers' conference held at Margate (seaside, east of London) on 16-19 June, 1955 [16]. Figure 2 shows Mr. Frank G. Woollard and Miss Woollard at the Mayor's dinner reception at the Margate Conference [20].

Figure 2

Source: The Institution of Engineering and Technology,
London, U.K. Used with permission.

The paper contains a wide-ranging discussion of the nature of automation, the advantages of automation, the social effects of automation, and the impact of automation on consumers. At the end of the paper he says (p. 206):

> "We must always remember that men were not made for
> machines, but that machines were made for man… the motto
> must be… 'Machines in the Service of Man'."

That, no doubt, would include today's computer hardware and software. Corporate enterprise software systems are an unfortunate example of humans serving machines. For humans to serve machines is to doom the human race.

In closing, it is unfortunate that Frank Woollard's work has received so little attention. This may have been because most of Woollard's papers were published in journals whose focus was mechanical materials handling and automation, resulting in a more narrow audience than his impressive work in production engineering and manufacturing management deserves.

Woollard correctly believed that automatic transfer machines were the logical extension of manual transfer devices, and that they would further enable and improve continuous flow if applied judiciously. Automation and materials handling became a topic of great interest in the British, American, and Japanese motor vehicle industries in the late 1940s and 1950s. Woollard's pioneering work in flow production and automation, it seems, should have been noticed by the people who have been credited with creating Lean management.

At least we can now say that Mr. Woollard's work has risen from obscurity and entered into a bright new day. Though "Some Notes on British Methods of Continuous Production" and *Principles of Mass and Flow Production* were written decades ago, they contain many important insights into the development and evolution of what we today call "Lean management." Now, when we think of the origins of Lean management, the conversation should include Ford Motor Company, Henry Ford and Charles Sorensen; Morris Motors Ltd., William Morris (Lord Nuffield) and Frank Woollard; Toyota Motor Corporation, Kiichiro Toyoda and Taiichi Ohno.

Frank G. Woollard was a pioneer and should be given due recognition for his penetrating insights and numerous real-world accomplishments. He was the first person to successfully adapt Ford's production system to local market conditions outside of the United States. Not even Ford could do that [21]. Frank G. Woollard stands with Taiichi Ohno of Toyota Motor Corporation as one of the greats.

Notes

[1] *Toyota: A History of the First 50 Years*, Toyota Motor Corporation, Toyota City, Japan, 1988, p. 142

[2] F.G. Woollard, "Some Notes on British Methods of Continuous Production," *Proceedings of The Institution of Automobile Engineers*, The Institution of Automobile Engineers, London, U.K., Proceedings of the Session 1924-1925, Volume XIX, pp. 419-474, 885-890, and Plates XVI to XXXII (Figures 1-26)

[3] F.G. Woollard, *Principles of Mass and Flow Production*, Iliffe & Sons, Ltd., London, U.K., 1954

[4] E. Toyoda, *Toyota: Fifty Years in Motion*, Kondasha International, New York NY, 1987, pp. 53 and 57-58

[5] R. Overy, *William Morris, Viscount Nuffield*, Europa Publications Limited, London, U.K., 1976, p. 128

[6] Toyota, p. 461

[7] H. Ford with S. Crowther, *My Life and Work*, Garden City Publishing Co., Inc., Garden City, NY, 1922, p. 145

[8] Toyoda, p. 58

[9] T. Ohno, *Toyota Production System*, Productivity Press, Portland, OR, 1988, p. 25-27

[10] G. Maxcy and A. Silbertson, *The Motor Industry*, George Allen & Unwin Ltd., London, U.K., 1959, p. 223

[11] Ohno, pp. 6-7

[12] Ohno, p. 119 and T. Ohno and S. Mito, *Just-In-Time for Today and Tomorrow*, Productivity Press, Cambridge, MA, 1988, p. 75

[13] Ford, (1922), pp. 12, 71-72, 166-167 and H. Ford with S. Crowther, *Moving Forward*, Doubleday, Doran & Company, Garden City, NY, 1930, pp. 2-3, 7, 12, 20-21, 28, 64

[14] J. Wood, *MG from A to Z*, Motor Racing Publications Ltd., Croydon, U.K., 1998, pp. 99-101

[15] Woollard (1925), pp. 424, 451, 464, 889

[16] F.G. Woollard, "Machines in the Service of Man," *The Automatic Factory: What Does it Mean?*, Report of the Conference Held at Margate 16th to 19th June, The Report of the Margate Conference of The Institution of Production Engineers, E.&F.N. Spon, Ltd., London, U.K., 1955, pp. 198-206

[17] In a letter to William Morris' auditor, R.W. Thornton, dated 21 May 1931 ("Balance Sheet and Accounts for the Year Ended 31st December 1930"), Woollard discusses Morris Motors' labor policy, and in doing so displays his high regard for workers. He says in paragraph (d): "...there is a marked and deplorable tendency for many Concerns to cut their production costs by the employment of female and juvenile labor to the exclusion of the natural bread winner. This has not been, and I hope never will be, the policy of Morris Motors Limited." Source: Robin Barraclough by way of Peter Seymour, Library of Nuffield College, University of Oxford, Oxford, U.K., File No. N5/1/1-10. Used with permission.

[18] "The Toyota Way 2001," Toyota Motor Corporation, internal document, Toyota City, Japan, April 2001

[19] To learn more about the "Respect for People" principle, see: B. Emiliani, with D. Stec, L. Grasso, and J. Stodder, *Better Thinking, Better Results: Case Study and Analysis of an Enterprise-Wide Lean Transformation*, second edition, The CLBM, LLC, Wethersfield, Conn., 2007; B. Emiliani, *Practical Lean Leadership: A Strategic Leadership Guide for Executives*, The CLBM, LLC, Wethersfield, Conn., 2008; B. Emiliani, *REAL LEAN: Understanding the Lean Management System*, Volume One, The CLBM, LLC, Wethersfield,

Conn., 2007; B. Emiliani, *REAL LEAN: Critical Issues and Opportunities in Lean Management*, Volume Two, The CLBM, LLC, Wethersfield, Conn., 2007; B. Emiliani, *REAL LEAN: The Keys to Sustaining Lean Management*, Volume Three, The CLBM, LLC, Wethersfield, Conn., 2008; B. Emiliani, *REAL LEAN: Learning the Craft of Lean Management*, Volume Four, The CLBM, LLC, Wethersfield, Conn., 2008

[20] Woollard (1955), p. 209

[21] Senior managers of Ford's U.K. operations had great difficulty transferring Ford's U.S. production system to the U.K. in the 1920s due to significant differences between these two markets. See S. Tolliday, "Management and Labor in Britain 1896-1939," in *Between Fordism and Flexibility*, S. Tolliday and J. Zeitlin, editors, Berg Publishers Inc., New York, NY, 1992, pp. 29-56.

Frank George Woollard, circa 1947

Source: Professional Engineering Publishing, London, U.K. Used with permission.

1883   Frank George Woollard born in London on 22 September, son of George and Emily Woollard.

c. 1893   Educated at City of London School.

c. 1900   Educated at Goldsmiths and Birkbeck Colleges at the University of London.

c. 1900   Engineering apprentice at London & South Western Railway in Eastleigh, working on rail cars. Participated in the design and development of the Clarkson steam omnibus, a steam-powered city bus.

1904   London & South Western Railway introduces flow production line to assemble steel railroad coach bodies. Gains first experience with a basic form of flow production.

1905   Worked in the design office at Weigel Motors Ltd., London.

1910   Chief designer at E.G. Wrigley and Company, Ltd., Birmingham, a maker of axles and steering assemblies for various automobile companies.

1912   Woollard meets William Morris regarding the supply of components to W.R.M. Motors Ltd., the forerunner of Morris Motors Ltd., and designs parts for his automobiles.

1914   Production engineer. Experiments with improving machine shop layout through 1918.

1915   Becomes a member of The Institution of Automobile Engineers, London.

c. 1917   Engineering manager and chief designer, and later assistant managing director at E.G. Wrigley and Company, Ltd., Birmingham. Re-organizes production from batch to flow to meet increase in orders.

1923   William Morris buys engine plant of Hotchkiss et Cie., Gosford Street, Coventry, which then became Morris Engines Ltd (later Morris Motors Ltd., Engines Branch). Morris recognized Woollard's ideas and capabilities and named him as general manager. Woollard re-organizes engine production from batch to flow.

1924   Implements flow production using manual transfer between machining operations and hand clamping with Herbert Taylor and Leonard Lord.

    Woollard, Taylor, and Lord design the first automatic transfer machines with engineers from machine tool builders James Archdale & Company, Ltd., Birmingham, (gearboxes) and Wm. Asquith, Ltd., Halifax, (flywheels).

1925   Equipment reliability problems force a return to manual transfer and hand clamping.

1926   Becomes a Director of Morris Motors Ltd.

1931   Leaves Morris Motors Ltd., Engines Branch, due to personal disagreements.

1932   Becomes managing director of Rudge-Whitworth Ltd., Coventry, a motorcycle manufacturer.

1936   Joins Birmingham Aluminum Castings, Ltd., Birmingham, and Midland Motor Cylinder Co. Ltd., Smethwick, as director.

1945   President of The Institution of Automobile Engineers, London (1945-1947).

1947   Led the merger between The Institution of Automobile Engineers and The Institution of Mechanical Engineers, London.

Chairman of the Automobile Division of The Institute of Mechanical Engineers, London.

1951   Lecturer on the principles of mass and flow production at the University of Birmingham and at the College of Technology, Department of Industrial Administration, Birmingham U.K. (now Aston Business School, Aston University).

1953   Woollard retires. Consultant to British industry on flow production and automation.

1955   Steps down from his Directorships at Birmingham Aluminum Castings, Ltd., Birmingham, and Midland Motor Cylinder Co. Ltd.

1957   Frank George Woollard dies on Sunday, 22 December, at the age of 74. Recognized as one of the fathers of the British motor industry. Predeceased by his wife, Woollard is survived by his daughter Joan, an artist. Interned in a churchyard cemetery in Warwickshire County, south of Coventry.

Geographical Reference

Birmingham-Coventry Region

London

Sources for Summary Biography

- P. Andrews and E. Brunner, *The Life of Lord Nuffield: A Study in Enterprise and Benevolence*, Basil Blackwell, Oxford, U.K., 1955
- G. Georgano, *The Beaulieu Encyclopedia of the Automobile*, Taylor & Francis, Oxford, U.K., 2000, p. 1072
- W. Lewchuk, "Frank G. Woollard" in *Dictionary of Business Biography*, D. Jeremy and C. Shaw, editors, Volume 5, pp. 888-891, Butterworths, London, U.K., 1986
- R. Overy, *William Morris, Viscount Nuffield*, Europa Publications Limited, London, U.K., 1976
- P. Seymour, personal communications, October 2008
- J. Wood, *MG from A to Z*, Motor Racing Publications Ltd., Croydon, U.K., 1998, pp. 184-185
- F.G. Woollard, *Principles of Mass and Flow Production*, Iliffe & Sons, Ltd., London, U.K., 1954, p. 11
- F.G. Woollard, "Machines in the Service of Man," *The Automatic Factory: What Does it Mean?*, Report of the Conference Held at Margate 16th to 19th June, The Report of the Margate Conference of The Institution of Production Engineers, E.&F.N. Spon, Ltd., London, U.K., 1955, pp. 198-206
- "Mr. F.G. Woollard," obituary in The Times, London, U.K., 28 December 1957
- "Obituary: Frank G. Woollard, M.B.E.," *The Journal of The Institution of Production Engineers*, The Institution of Production Engineers, London, U.K., Vol. 33, No. 3, March 1958, pp. 204-205

Publications by Frank G. Woollard

Unlike most other early pioneers of new production methods whose books and papers were ghostwritten, Frank Woollard wrote his own works and published extensively throughout his career. The papers and books listed below are thought to comprise a full accounting of Woollard's writings.

"Some Notes on British Methods of Continuous Production," *Proceedings of The Institution of Automobile Engineers*, The Institution of Automobile Engineers, London, U.K., Proceedings of the Session 1924-1925, Volume XIX, pp. 419-474, 885-890, and Plates XVI to XXXII (Figures 1-26)

"Novel Machine Tests Engines at Morris Plant in England," *Automotive Industries*, Class Journal Co., New York, NY, Vol. 52, 19 February 1925, pp. 308-310

"Some Notes on British Methods of Continuous Production," excerpt published in *Automobile Engineer*, The Institution of Automobile Engineers, London, U.K., Vol. 15, March 1925, pp. 85-93

"Some Notes on British Methods of Continuous Production," excerpt published in *Automotive Industries*, Class Journal Co., New York, NY, Vol. 52, 28 May 1925, p. 940

"Automobile Plant Depreciation and Replacement Problems," *Proceedings of The Institution of Automobile Engineers*, The Institution of Automobile Engineers, London, U.K., Volume 25, 1931, pp. 250-276

"Address by the President [of The Institution of Automobile Engineers]: The Automobile and the Community – A Study in Action and Reaction," *Proceedings of The Institution of Automobile Engineers*, The Institution of Automobile Engineers, London, U.K., Volume 40, October 1945, pp. 1-20 and 255-256

"Prologue by the President [of The Institution of Automobile Engineers]," *Quadragenary Celebrations, 1906-1946*, The Institution of Automobile Engineers, London, U.K., July 5th, 1946, pp. 230-231

"Continuous Production Techniques," *The Times Review of Industry*, London, U.K., August 1948

"Flow-Line Production," paper presented before British Association at Birmingham, 4 September 1950. Abridged version published in *Engineering*, London, U.K., 3 November and 24 November 1950

"The Basic Principles of Mass and Flow Production: First Instalment," *Mechanical Handling*, London, U.K., Vol. 39, No. 4, April 1952, pp. 150-154

"The Basic Principles of Mass and Flow Production: Second Instalment," *Mechanical Handling*, London, U.K., Vol. 39, No. 5, May 1952, pp. 207-215

"The Basic Principles of Mass and Flow Production: Third Instalment," *Mechanical Handling*, London, U.K., Vol. 39, No. 6, June 1952, pp. 277-283

"The Basic Principles of Mass and Flow Production: Fourth Instalment," *Mechanical Handling*, London, U.K., Vol. 39, No. 7, July 1952, pp. 363-369

"The Basic Principles of Mass and Flow Production: Fifth Instalment," *Mechanical Handling*, London, U.K., Vol. 39, No. 8, August 1952, pp. 398-403

"The Basic Principles of Mass and Flow Production: Sixth Instalment," *Mechanical Handling*, London, U.K., Vol. 39, No. 10, October 1952, pp. 478-483

"The Basic Principles of Mass and Flow Production: Seventh Instalment," *Mechanical Handling*, London, U.K., Vol. 40, No. 1, January 1953, pp. 33-39

"The Basic Principles of Mass and Flow Production: Eighth Instalment," *Mechanical Handling*, London, U.K., Vol. 40, No. 2, February 1953, pp. 67-62

"The Basic Principles of Mass and Flow Production: Final Instalment," *Mechanical Handling*, London, U.K., Vol. 40, No. 3, March 1953, pp. 125-133

"The Advent of Automatic Transfer Machines and Mechanisms," *The Institution of Production Engineers Journal*, The Institution of Production Engineers, London, U.K., Vol. 32, No. 1, January 1953, pp. 18-36

"The Advent of Automatic Transfer Machines and Mechanisms," paper presented before Second Scottish Conference of the British Institute of Management, Gleneagles, Scotland, U.K., 10-12 April 1953

Principles of Mass and Flow Production, Iliffe & Sons, Ltd., London, U.K., 1954

Flow Production and Automation: Eighteen Axioms, Industrial Administration Group, College of Technology Birmingham (now Aston Business School, Aston University, Birmingham), U.K., 1954, with Foreword by Professor David Bramley, Department of Industrial Administration, College of Technology (22 pp)

Principles of Mass and Flow Production, Philosophical Library Inc., New York, NY, 1955

"Automatic Transfer Production," *The Institution of Production Engineers Journal*, The Institution of Production Engineers, London, U.K., Vol. 34, February 1955, pp. 85-101

What Automation Means, British Productivity Council Bulletin Supplement, London, U.K., June 1955 (12 pp)

"What Automation Means," *Personnel Management & Industrial Equipment* (U.K.), September 1955, pp. 144-152

"Machines in the Service of Man," *The Automatic Factory: What Does it Mean?*, Report of the Conference Held at Margate 16th to 19th June, The Report of the Margate Conference of The Institution of Production Engineers, E.&F.N. Spon, Ltd., London, U.K., 1955, pp. 198-206

"Sir Leonard Lord," *The Motor*, 6 July 1955

"Machines in the Service of Man," *The Institution of Production Engineers Journal*, The Institution of Production Engineers, London, U.K., Vol. 34, September 1955, pp. 555-562

"Mechanical Handling – Prospects and Problems," *Mechanical Handling*, London, U.K., Vol. 43, No. 7, 1956, pp. 421-428

"Automation in Engineering Production" in *Automation in Theory and Practice*, E.M. Hugh-Jones (editor), Basil Blackwell, Oxford, U.K., 1956, pp. 29-47

Important papers describing Morris Motors Ltd. production facilities:

H.E. Taylor, "Factory Planning" in *Proceedings of the Institution of Production Engineers*, The Institution of Production Engineers, Proceedings of the Session 1922-1923, Volume II, London, U.K., pp. 243-253 and 254-257. Herbert Taylor was chief engineer at the French-owned Hotchkiss et Cie plant on Gosford Street in Coventry, which would later become the Engines Branch of Morris Motors Ltd. Taylor became a member of Woollard's staff when he was named director and general manager of the Engines Branch in 1923. This paper was the inspiration for Woollard *et al.* to create hand transfer machines for engine block production at Morris Engines Ltd., soon thereafter leading to the design, fabrication, and use of automatic transfer machines for gearboxes and flywheels, in collaboration with Taylor, Leonard

Lord, and the machine tool builders James Archdale & Company, Ltd. and Wm. Asquith, Ltd. Taylor's paper contains many practices from the 1920-1922 time-frame that we would describe today as Lean production. For more information on Herbert Taylor, see W. Lewchuck, *American Technology and the British Vehicle Industry*, Cambridge University Press, New York, NY, 1987, pp. 167-170.

Anonymous, "Specialized Production: An Outline of Morris Methods in the New Assembly Plant," *The Automobile Engineer*, London, U.K., October 1934, pp. 359-365. This paper describes the layout and operation of Morris Motors Ltd. recently completed Cowley assembly plant. Among the new features are "different types of work handling equipment in addition to novel methods of mechanical handling" (p. 361). The September 1926 and June 1929 issues of *The Automobile Engineer* describe the previous plant layout and operation.

Selected Bibliography of Morris Motors Ltd.

Few people today are familiar with the pre-1950 British automobile industry, and with Morris Motors in particular. Morris Motors became Britain's leading motor manufacturer and the first to produce one million vehicles. Its history with respect to design and manufacturing practices is fascinating, while the life of its founder, the businessman and philanthropist William Morris - Lord Nuffield, is equally fascinating. Morris appointed several capable and gifted engineers who were at the forefront of production technology and he encouraged them to innovate. The history of Morris Motors and the life of Lord Nuffield are worthy of extensive study.

"William R. Morris," SYSTEM: The Magazine of Business, Vol. XLV, No. 2, February 1924, pp. 73-76

"William R. Morris," SYSTEM: The Magazine of Business, Vol. XLV, No. 3, March 1924, pp. 148-150 and 200

At Cowley, Morris Oxford Press, February 1929

F.G. Woollard, Principles of Mass and Flow Production, Iliffe & Sons, Ltd., London, U.K., 1954

P. Andrews and E. Brunner, The Life of Lord Nuffield: A Study in Enterprise and Benevolence, Basil Blackwell, Oxford, U.K., 1955

G. Maxcy and A. Silbertson, The Motor Industry, George Allen & Unwin Ltd., London, U.K., 1959

R. Jackson, The Nuffield Story, Frederick Muller Ltd., London, U.K., 1964

R. Overy, William Morris, Viscount Nuffield, Europa Publications Limited, London, U.K., 1976

L. Jarman and R. Barraclough, The Bullnose and Flatnose Morris, David & Charles Publishers, U.K., 1976

Morris Cars: The First Thirty-Five Years, Morris Register, 1978

P. Skilleter, Morris Minor: The World's Supreme Small Car, Osprey Publishing, U.K., 1982

H. Edwards, The Morris Motor Car: 1913-1983, Mooreland Publishing Co., Ltd., Derbyshire, U.K., 1983

G. Lanning, C. Peaker, C. Webb, and R. White, *Making Cars: A History of Car-Making at Cowley by the People Who Make the Cars*, Routledge & Kegan Paul. London, U.K., 1985

W. Lewchuck, *American Technology and the British Vehicle Industry*, Cambridge University press, New York, NY, 1987

J. Wood, *Wheels of Misfortune*, Sidgwick & Jackson, London, U.K., 1988

M.Adeney, *Nuffield: A Biography*, Robert Hale Ltd., London, U.K., 1993

F. Minns, *Wealth Well Given: The Enterprise and Benevolence of Lord Nuffield*, Alan Sutton Publishing Ltd., London, U.K., 1994

K. Williams, C. Haslam, S. Johal, and J. Williams, *Cars: Analysis, History, Cases*, Berghahn Books Ltd., Oxford, U.K., 1994, Chapter 8

J. Wood, *The Motor Industry of Great Britain Centenary Book*, The Society of Motor Manufacturers and Traders, London, U.K., 1996

J. Wood, *MG from A to Z*, Motor Racing Publications, Ltd., Croydon, U.K., 1998

C. Newbiggin, S. Shatford, and T. Williams, *The Changing Faces of Cowley Works (Book 1)*, Robert Boyd Publications, Oxfordshire, U.K., 1998

P. Seymour, *Morris Light Vans: 1924-1934*, P&B Publishing, East Sussex, U.K., 1999

J. Wood, *The Bullnose Morris*, Shire Publications, U.K., 2001

G. Bardsley and S. Laing, *Making Cars at Cowley*, The History Press, Gloucestershire, U.K., 2006

FRANK G. WOOLLARD

M.B.E. M.I.Mech.E. M.I.Prod.E. M.S.A.E.

PRINCIPLES

OF

MASS AND FLOW

PRODUCTION

Published for "MECHANICAL HANDLING"

PRINCIPLES OF MASS
AND FLOW
PRODUCTION

The assembly plant at the Austin Motor Co. Ltd., Longbridge, Birmingham.
A car body is being delivered to the A30 (Austin Seven) assembly line

PRINCIPLES OF MASS

AND FLOW

PRODUCTION

BY

FRANK G. WOOLLARD, M.B.E.

Past President, Institution of Automobile Engineers
Member, Institution of Mechanical Engineers
Member, Institution of Production Engineers
Member, Society of Automotive Engineers, U.S.A.
Member, Institute of Industrial Administration
Founder Member, British Institute of Management
Hon. Member, Motor Industry Research Association
Hon. Associate, College of Technology, Birmingham

WITH 102 ILLUSTRATIONS

LONDON · ILIFFE & SONS, LTD.
NEW YORK · PHILOSOPHICAL LIBRARY

First Published 1954

Published for "Mechanical Handling" by Iliffe & Sons, Ltd., Dorset House, Stamford Street, London, S.E.1.

Published, 1955, by Philosophical Library, Inc., 15, East 40th Street, New York 16, N.Y.

Printed in England by James Cond, Ltd., Birmingham and bound by Nevett Ltd., London, N.W.9.

BKS 2388

*DEDICATED TO ALL WHO SEEK TO
LIFT THE CURSE OF ADAM FROM
THE SHOULDERS OF MANKIND*

ACKNOWLEDGMENTS

I wish to express my grateful thanks to all those who have helped me by providing photographs and information. In the majority of examples the acknowledgment is either implicit or expressed in the text or caption, but there are instances where this could not be done and these appear below.

If, by inadvertence, anyone has been omitted, I sincerely apologise, for without the kind and generous help of my many friends this wide variety of examples could not have been collected.

The Rt. Hon. The Lord Nuffield for his encouragement during the years 1923-1931.

Sir A. Rowland Smith and the Ford Motor Company Ltd.

The late Mr. James E. Maclaren (B.S.A. Tools Ltd.).

Mr. F. E. Moskovics, Industrial Consultant to A. O. Smith Corporation.

Mr. John Sargrove (Sargrove Electronics Ltd.).

Mr. W. E. Ballard (Metallisation Limited).

Mr. Eric Milner (Benton and Stone Ltd.).

The Constructive Department of H.M. Dockyard, Portsmouth.

British Railways.

The Institution of Locomotive Engineers.

Imperial Smelting Corporation Ltd.

And, in particular, Sir Leonard Lord and Mr. Geo. W. Harriman of the Austin Motor Company Limited.

I would also like to thank the technical press for their assistance. In particular:

The Machinist for the photographs of "Ford Automation".

The Machinery Publishing Co. Ltd., for the photographs of the Cross Toolometer.

Automobile Engineer for photographs of British automatic transfer machines.

Also for permission to quote from papers that I presented to the Institution of Production Engineers and the British Institute of Management.

CONTENTS

*A

FOREWORD

By SIR LEONARD LORD, K.B.E.

Chairman, British Motor Corporation Ltd.

I AM GLAD to have the opportunity of recommending this book to all those who are seeking economical means for increasing production, and also to students of engineering economics, for it is a practical exposition of the laws which lie behind modern manufacturing.

Frank Woollard was somewhat of a pioneer in flow production, since he was experimenting with machine shop layout immediately after the end of the 1914-18 War, so that when he joined the Engines Branch of Morris Motors in 1923 he had a clear idea of what was required for the economic handling of large amounts of material through the machining and assembling processes.

He tells us that flow production is a "marriage of management and mechanism with management as the dominant partner" and he stresses the fact that great capital is not essential in order to start on the road to flow production, in fact anyone can do it provided they have a continuous demand for a more or less standard product.

Perhaps then the greatest value of this book lies in the fact that it shows quite clearly that flow production can be applied to small as well as to large quantities; thus it offers encouragement to the little firms to adopt the flow system wherever this is possible . . . and it is possible far more often than is generally believed.

A great concern like the British Motor Corporation is dependent for its supplies on a number of lesser firms and this applies throughout the whole structure of industry. If, by adopting flow methods, those lesser concerns could reach the efficiency of the larger companies, then I believe that Britain would be able to meet any challenge.

Perhaps I might add that, as a young man, I was associated with Frank Woollard in his early endeavours, and I know that he regards the waste of "the unforgiving minute" with something akin to horror. He believes that industry should provide the good life and that leisure should be the reward of efficiency during working hours. You will find this philosophy in this book, which I recommend for your serious attention.

AUTHOR'S PREFACE

THE WRITING of this book started with an address to the graduates of the Birmingham Branch of the Institution of Mechanical Engineers. I had chosen for my theme "The Fundamental Basis of Mass and Flow Production", a subject in which I had had considerable first-hand experience and on which I had contemplated "going into print". As I was leaving the lecture theatre Mr. David Bramley, head of the Department of Industrial Administration of the Birmingham College of Technology, remarked that it was obviously impossible to cover so important a subject in one evening and invited me to the College to deliver a six-lecture discussion course for senior engineering executives.

Meanwhile I had also been invited, on the recommendation of Professor T. U. Matthew, of the Department of Production Engineering in the University of Birmingham, to present a paper on "Flow-line Production" to the British Association. Other invitations quickly followed and the reception was such that I decided to publish my lectures in the form of articles and, for this purpose, was given hospitality in the pages of *Mechanical Handling*. This was a very suitable vehicle, since flow production is closely associated with mechanical handling.

The present volume embodies the subject matter of these lectures with considerable additions to both text and illustrations. It is hoped that it will form a reliable guide for those who contemplate these new methods of production, which we must adopt—adapted to our own needs—if we are to meet world competition.

With regard to such new tools as automatic transfer machines, which are, of course, an extension of the flow production system, I would point out that, after an interim of twenty years or so, they have become recognized as a new force in the production of mass-consumed articles and are being employed in the U.S.A., France, Germany and the U.S.S.R.—the latter has laid down a number of plants—as well as in our own country: in other words, they are in use where there exists a mass-consumption public.

The value of these new machines and methods for the production of domestic appliances (perhaps the widest market of all) is undoubted; thus they will come to the aid of the housewife and so help to make life much more bearable in a world which is almost without domestic help.

Much of the matter in these pages relates to automaticity, and there-fore I must assure my readers that I am not a technologist with a mechanistic "bee in my bonnet". On the contrary, I have always warned my associates against that dangerous hobby of falling in love with mechanism for its own sake. Nevertheless I have a profound belief in the flow production system as a means of raising the standard of material prosperity. In my opinion, provided that the human relations aspect is properly safeguarded, flow production methods can become a most powerful factor in easing the labour and promoting the well-being of mankind.

Birmingham, 1954.   F. G. W.

CHAPTER ONE

HISTORY OF FLOW PRODUCTION

F LOW PRODUCTION, where it is applicable, can be a major factor in increasing production since the results accruing from the adoption of this comparatively new system are little short of astounding. Indeed, it is scarcely too much to claim that this new technique is, in itself, another complete turn in the industrial revolution.

It is certainly a branch of technology which is worthy of the most careful study, for it will be found that it can be applied over a much wider field than is generally recognized. This depends on an appreciation of the range and scope of the system and it will be the author's endeavour to elucidate and illustrate the basic principles on which flow production is founded. The principles must be axiomatic—they must stand out as self-evident truths. Therefore the sub-division is closely graded, so much so that in some instances it may appear that a slightly broader statement would embrace two or even more of the principles.

In practice, however, it was found that in order to define precisely the laws governing the situation it was essential to adopt a somewhat meticulous method. The principles are illustrated by practical examples, but these, owing to the rapidity with which the art of flow production is developing, may be quickly superseded. This fact is of little importance for the principles remain—no matter how the examples may be outmoded. The object of quoting examples is to impress the principles on the memory rather than to give the latest information on this wide-ranging, rapidly changing art.

The majority of the examples are drawn from the automobile industry, for it must be conceded that this particular industry has been foremost in the development of flow production techniques. The methods are, of course, applicable to all the repetitive engineering and mechanical trades.

It is a mistake to think that flow production can only be applied to vast outputs. While it is true that it is in quantity output that the most spectacular successes are achieved, small-scale production can frequently benefit to a surprising degree by a study of the principles of flow production. Moreover, it is unnecessary to turn over a whole establishment to flow production. It is quite possible to apply these principles to a part of a factory and even to set up flow lines for similar components of different sizes and sometimes of different shapes.

Most of the examples will be from highly organized factories: even so, in some instances the precept and the example will be idealized. This idealization is essential in order to avoid explanations—so many "ifs" and "buts"—that tend to obscure the main issue. Probably none of the plants, from which the illustrations are derived, is perfect in all particulars: but since the examples are, of necessity, simplified, they may appear more perfect than they are in actual fact, but, again, this is not so much a "documentary" as a survey of ideas that can be put into practice. They will be just as perfect as those employing them are perfect or imperfect.

Most of, if not all, the principles tend to be mandatory in tone. That is the way of principles, but it is by no means suggested that, in practice, flow production is carried on without divergence from these principles. To do so would be absurd; but if the reader is tempted to criticize what may seem to him a perfectionist attitude, let him remember that each departure from the ideal is an index of inadequacy—a measure of the lack of efficiency—in the carrying-out of the task. The great advantage gained by the adoption of flow production lies in the fact that it focuses the light on these deviations from principle and thus definitely assists in raising the efficiency ratio nearer to the impossible goal of parity—that 100 per cent that we shall never attain.

The term "mass production" became current in England towards the end of the First World War. It is an adopted Americanism which came to stay and is still common coin in everyday speech, although engineers of to-day usually associate the phrase with flow production, which is a later development of mass production. Incidentally, there are a number of adjectival expressions used to describe this later method, such as flow-line production, straight-line production, continuous production and line production. Flow production is probably the most expressive and will be adopted throughout this volume. Mass production and flow production are by no means synonymous terms. Mass production, it is true, leads to flow production when demanded by the nature of the product, but it can also be achieved by independent and unrelated operations. On the other hand, flow production necessitates a highly integrated system of processing. This is not a mere quibble, it will be found that "flow" is the operative word throughout all the processes to be described.

Mass production in a simple form has probably been practised over the centuries, for instance in the manufacture of the arms of war, but the classic example is the process of pulley-block making planned by Sir Marc Isambard Brunel (1769-1849). Ships' blocks—having regard to the times—can legitimately be described as fairly complicated articles which, for efficient production, demanded specially contrived machinery. Such machinery was devised, built by Henry Maudslay of London, and set up at Portsmouth Dockyard in the first decade of the nineteenth century. This was definitely mass production in the modern

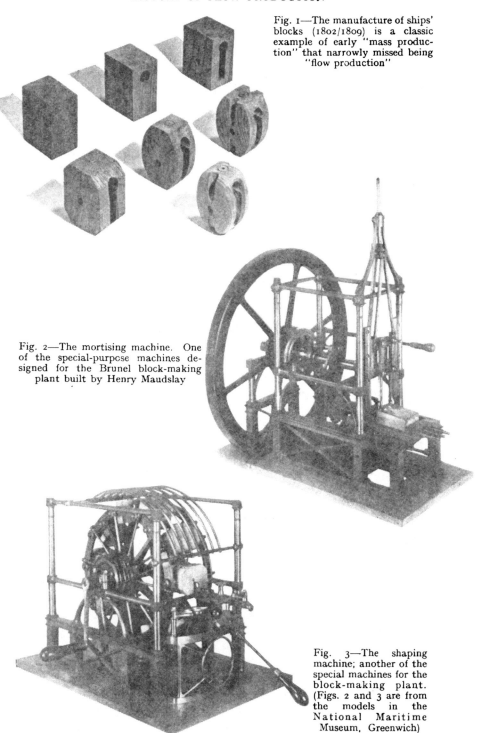

Fig. 1—The manufacture of ships' blocks (1802/1809) is a classic example of early "mass production" that narrowly missed being "flow production"

Fig. 2—The mortising machine. One of the special-purpose machines designed for the Brunel block-making plant built by Henry Maudslay

Fig. 3—The shaping machine; another of the special machines for the block-making plant. (Figs. 2 and 3 are from the models in the National Maritime Museum, Greenwich)

meaning of the term, and, but for an accident, it would have been the first example of flow production.

The block components comprised (a) the elmwood body, (b) the *lignum vitae* sheaves (pulleys), (c) the iron pin, (d) the brass coak or bush and (e) the rivets. For the bodies, elm trees were reduced to logs of the required section. These were passed to a circular saw which cut the logs into rectangular blocks, thus providing the stock for the specialized machines. The sawing machinery, incidentally, was designed by General Samuel Bentham.* The first Brunel operation, done on a "boring engine", was the drilling of two holes, one for the sheave pin, the other for the initial hole for the mortising machine which, as a second operation, cut the slot or slots to house the sheaves. The bodies then went to the cornering saw which, by removing the corners, gave a rough shape to the piece which was passed to the shaping machine for the fourth operation. The shaping machine carrying 12 blocks at a time produced the outline which is characteristic of this component. The last operation was performed on a scoring machine which cut the grooves for the rope strop. (Figs. 1-3.)

The machinery for the sheaves consisted of a combined rounding and drilling machine for turning slabs of *lignum vitae* into pulley blanks by the use of a trepanning tool for the outside and a drill for the centre. These blanks were transferred to the coaking engine which made trefoil shaped recesses for the reception of the coak flange. The coaks, i.e. bushings, were pressed into place and, in the larger sizes, were riveted through the flanges after which the hole in the coak was broached to provide a smooth bearing for the pin. The next operation was performed on a lathe which faced the sheaves and at the same time formed the rope groove.

There were three sets of machines: small, medium and large. The small set made 3 in. to 7 in. blocks. The medium group made the 8 in. and 9 in. series, while the large machines made the 10 in. to 13 in. sizes and also any specials that might be required. The machines were arranged in sets and not in batteries, but the grouping followed no set pattern. It just fell into line with the plan of the buildings and the arrangement of the overhead shafting. The factory did not, in any case, encourage flow production, for it was no more than a roofed-in roadway between two older sheds.

In this early example—it was conceived in 1802 and was working in full production in 1809—can be found all the main elements of mass production and, but for the fact that the plant was housed in a makeshift building, it might easily have been the first example of flow production. Incidentally, the demand for large quantities of blocks arose from the Napoleonic wars, and the shortage of these components was a major

* Brother of Jeremy Bentham, the philosopher.

cause of delay in refitting ships for service. The installation of the block machinery reduced the number of men required to make the bodies from 50 to four and for the sheaves from 60 to six (many blocks had multiple sheaves). "So that", said Richard Beamish, who was Brunel's biographer, "ten men, by the aid of machinery, can accomplish with uniformity, celerity and ease, what formerly required the uncertain labour of *One Hundred and Ten.*"

This block-making episode illustrates very clearly the difference between mass production and flow production. Brunel's scheme could readily have been arranged on the flow principle because the product was specialized, the components were simple in nature and were standardized by necessity. Moreover the machines were designed to suit the task they had to perform. All that was lacking was the progressive and continuous processing and, of course, the conveyance between the machines.*

No particular accuracy was called for in the making of ships' blocks but, as the engineering art developed, accuracy became a prime essential and this crystallized the tendency towards dividing works into shops according to trades. There were turning shops, milling departments, drilling and shaping sections and so forth. New gauging methods made view rooms for inspection a necessity. The foremen became specialists in various branches of machining and the inspectors became specialists in viewing certain operations. Flow production has completely changed such methods, but there are still many products that are best served by specialized shops and individual view rooms; with them we are not concerned.

Flow production technique, as we know it to-day, originated on the automobile assembly lines. Here the natural sequence of first operations consisted of attaching the springs to the frame and mounting this combination on the axles. Then the wheels were fitted so that the chassis became mobile and could be transferred, by short stages, down the assembly line. At each station various components would be added to the chassis until it reached the end of the line as a complete vehicle which could be driven away under its own power. This, of course, did not happen all at once; it was a matter of evolution. In fact, a considerable time elapsed since the first conception, when a bare chassis with a soap-box body emerged for test, and the time when a car complete with

---

* Two American examples of early quantity production may be of interest. (1) In 1798 Eli Whitney obtained a contract from the U.S. Govt. for 10,000 muskets— 4,000 to be delivered in the first year and the balance in the year following. Actually it took eight years to complete the contract; but Whitney achieved interchangeability. (2) In 1807 a Connecticut clock maker, Eli Terry, converted an old mill for the manufacture of wooden clocks. He made 4,000 in three years. Fifty years later American clocks were being made at the rate of 400,000 per annum. Incidentally, the Portsmouth block-making plant had, by 1809, achieved an annual output of 130,000 blocks and dead-eyes.

body and all fittings could be driven off the assembly line to the despatch department. Meanwhile the mechanized assembly track had arrived— a prodigious and portentous forward step.

Originally the assembly track consisted of a simple chain or slat conveyor mounted at a suitable height for easy working. The components were brought to the track on trolleys and sack trucks. Frequently there were sub-stores alongside the track. In due course overhead conveyors were substituted for the wheeled transport and since these could be used as "stores in transit" the sub-stores disappeared except for the very small details such as bolts, nuts, screws, washers, plugs and the like, which must be handled in boxes.

Overhead conveyors offer three great advantages: they are out of the way; they serve to carry stock and stores in transit—from which the component is not drawn until the exact moment that it is required; and they deliver the units precisely where wanted. In addition they handle, with equal ease, such large components as complete bodies and front ends, such awkwardly shaped pieces as wings and bonnets and such heavy units as engines and gearboxes or front and rear axles.

The assembly line can be regarded as an epitome of flow production methods since in it most of the essentials appear in their simplest form. The engine and gearbox assembly lines at the Austin Motor Company form excellent examples of the system.

The assembly of engines at the Longbridge Works commences with a marshalling yard—a stores for receiving and issuing engine parts. This stores normally carries, when full, stock sufficient to supply the assembly tracks for two days. This is a buffer stock designed to take care of breakdowns and hold-ups. The stock is carefully watched and warning is given to the supplying departments—the machine shops, the body department and the purchase department for "bought-in" components —of any likely shortages. This goes far to ensure that the assembly lines will not have to shut down for lack of material. (Fig. 4.)

The staff in the marshalling yard are responsible for sending out matched sets of parts to the assembly line proper. The material is handled on slat conveyors running between the stores bins. Four of these conveyors feed the assembly shop, two for the smaller car, one for the medium car and one for the large car and truck engines. The cylinder block and head are the main components; these are drawn from the roller tracks on which they are stored and placed on the slat conveyor together with two baskets, one of which is loaded with internal parts made in the factory and which, preferably, should be given a final rinse in the washing plant before they are assembled in the engine. The other basket contains electrical equipment, carburettors and other parts for which rinsing is neither desired nor required. The pistons are placed over the cylinder block studs. They are graded for tolerance and the sizes marked on the top of the piston and on the block adjacent to the cylinder bore. Connecting rods are weighed and kept in sets of the same weight. The baskets do not contain such parts as studs, bolts, nuts, washers and cotterpins; these are kept in pans attached to the framework of the assembly conveyor and are refilled between shifts. As the cylinder block with its attendant baskets progresses through the marshalling area the various items are added until a complete set of parts is available for assembly. At the end of the marshalling yard there is a screened area which houses the rinsing machines through which the "washable" tray passes, the "non-washable" being by-passed on a track outside the rinser to meet the other tray at the discharge end of the machine.

The marshalling yard is the key to the situation, since it sets the pace for the whole of the engine factory. It is, in fact, the factory metronome —an automatic progress chaser, a balancing mechanism and a reservoir with a small but effective "head".

The assembly line is a continuation of the marshalling-yard slat conveyor, men being stationed on either side to perform their tasks— which is assembling, not fitting. There is no scraping-in of bearings; these are accurately produced to exact size. There is no grinding-in of valves; that has been done on the machining line. There are small adjustment and sub-assembly jobs to be done and these are accomplished on mandrel presses and sensitive drilling machines or in fixtures which the operator can reach by a "right-about" turn. Crankshafts are installed with the cylinder block standing on its head. Pistons, with connecting rods, are inserted from the top; but with the block lying on its side. Stage by stage the engine moves toward completion, each operation taking a cycle time which varies from just over 2 minutes for the smallest engine to 4 minutes for the largest. (Fig. 5.)

At the end of the assembly track the engine is lifted by a King electric hoist and taken on a mono-rail to the "running-in machine". This machine, designed by Austin engineers, consists of a large turntable on which several engines are mounted with their crankshafts coupled to an electric motor which turns the engines at 1,200 r.p.m., during which time they are flushed through with oil at 80 lb. pressure and a temperature of 165 deg. F. This running ensures that everything is free; it also polishes the mating parts, flushes out any small particles of metal or dust that may have eluded previous washings and rinsings, and makes sure that the oil circulation is functioning perfectly. During the test a stroboscopic lamp is connected to the contact breaker for a check on the ignition timing. The turntable revolves once in 20 minutes, by which time the engine arrives at the loading station for transference to a short track where oil pumps, oil strainers, sumps and rocker covers are added. They are then spray-painted and transported to the chassis erecting shop, collecting gearbox unit on the way. (Fig. 6.)

Flow production originated in the assembly shops. Here, at the Austin motor works, are some of the most modern assembly plants (Figs. 4-10)

Fig. 4—The Austin engine assembly line begins in a "marshalling yard" where all the components are placed on a slat conveyor which feeds the assembly line

Fig. 5—After passing through a final rinse, to remove any accumulated dust, the marshalled components pass to the assembly line proper. The assemblers turn about to perform minor operations, using small machines or hand fixtures

The assembly of the gearbox carries the continuous operation a stage further. Here again there is a marshalling area in which a similar procedure is followed, except that in this case there is a single tray for the components which, while being filled, is supported on a carrier suspended on runners attached to the bins. The trays, when filled, are loaded on to the lower portion of the gear-case fixtures which are fastened at intervals to a slat conveyor. Alternating with the gear-cases are sub-assembly fixtures for the mainshaft bearing housing. This is assembled on the track, the necessary arbor presses being above the track but within easy reach of the operator. As the gearboxes reach the end of the line, a flexible power drive is coupled to the primary shaft and an oil pipe is coupled to the filler plug. Thus the gears, while revolving, are flushed with oil to wash away any grit or metal particles. (Figs. 7-10.)

It is important to note that this assembly line carries the continuous process to a logical conclusion, since every operation is carried out on the line without the necessity for turning away from the work in hand. The sub-assemblies, the main assembly, running, testing for correct change-speed-lever movement and the oil flush-through are all continuous operations. The Austin Company have now carried this logical method into their final assembly of cars and trucks. This is a definite forward step and a real contribution to the art of flow production; it will be described at length in a later chapter.

Fig. 6—At the end of the assembly line, the engines are transferred to the Austin-designed running-in machine. There is no need for a "hot test" on an engine that is properly built

23

Fig. 7—The Austin gearbox "marshalling yard".
The component trays are carried on a trolley frame
mounted on the storage bins

Fig. 8—The beginning of the Austin gearbox assembly line. The boxes are
mounted on fixtures attached to a slat conveyor. In the foreground is a fixture
for assembling the primary shaft

After the system of mechanically moving the chassis from station to
station became an accomplished fact, plant managers saw that a
similar system might be applied to the machining of the larger component parts. The first move was made when the layout of the
machines was arranged to follow the sequence of operations on the
components. The author well remembers setting up five machines in
line for an axle casing—the five machines being manned by two
operators. He asked his co-directors to look at the new arrangement

Fig. 9—On the Austin gearbox assembly line tools for the minor operations are mounted over the track so that fitters need not turn round from their work. These presses are for assembling ball bearings on shafts

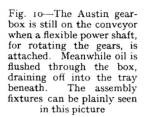

Fig. 10—The Austin gearbox is still on the conveyor when a flexible power shaft, for rotating the gears, is attached. Meanwhile oil is flushed through the box, draining off into the tray beneath. The assembly fixtures can be plainly seen in this picture

and after a few moments all three exclaimed with something like horror in their voices: "But what a waste of machines!" Then the trump card was produced: "In the original layout these five machines had five operators who produced no more than the present two!" After that incident several more machining lines were developed and then, of course, the balancing of operations was pursued to a logical conclusion. This incident is mentioned as no doubt it is an experience common to many who experiment with flow production.

So, tentatively at first and with boldness later, the milling machines, planers, boring mills, lathes and drilling machines and what-you-will were placed in line and departmental grouping became a thing of the past for most mass production shops. The piles of work, however, still remained by the machines as in earlier days until they were linked by slides and conveyors.

Before the Second World War the general pattern of shop layout in advanced factories was on lines such as these. Now a further stage has been reached, which was foreshadowed by experiments made in England during 1923-25.

It should, perhaps, be explained that the author's first acquaintance with large-scale repetitive machining of components for units that were in continuous demand came with his appointment as General Manager of Morris Engines (Coventry) Ltd. (later known as the Engines Branch of Morris Motors Ltd.). He had, earlier, been speculating on the possibility of utilizing a common bed or frame to carry a group of machine heads that could execute a series of operations. There were obvious advantages to be gained if this could be done. This was mentioned to Mr. Herbert Taylor (then chief engineer of Morris Engines) who referred to a paper he had given some months earlier to the Institution of Production Engineers under the modest title of "Factory Planning". From this conversation a hand transfer machine, for the production of cylinder blocks, was born. This ambitious undertaking was described at length in a paper by the author entitled "Some Notes on British Methods of Continuous Production".

In this paper a group machine for the production of complete cylinder blocks was described at length. Briefly, this piece of plant was 181 ft. long, it weighed 300 tons and employed 81 electric motors with an aggregate of 267 h.p. The machine had a common frame of box section built up of cast-iron segments to which, on both sides, a continuous knee or table was attached. The workpiece was moved on this table from fixture to fixture and the operations were performed by motor-driven heads which were attached to the main frame. There were, in all, 53 action stations, including some hand-fitting, inspection and two washing operations—this latter to rid the cylinder block of accumulated swarf and dust. The time occupied by the passage of the block from raw casting to finished article was 224 minutes. The actual time cycle was 4 minutes and, where longer operations had to be accommodated, the stations were duplicated—the longest operation being just under 8 minutes. The machine was hand-fed in as much as the blocks were moved (skidded) from station to station by hand and the fixtures were manually clamped. The self-acting machine heads were controlled by push-button switches. This group machine delivered a finished cylinder block every 4 minutes. The block was completely finished: that is to say, it was not only fully machined but it also had the bearing housings and shells fitted, all the studs driven and certain bushes pressed into place. This sub-assembly which occurred between the machining operations was necessary owing to the design of the cylinder block, which was unusual since the bearing housings were loose pieces like plummer blocks. (Figs. 11-14.)

This example is interesting in as much as it carried the flow principle several steps on the way to a logical conclusion. The machine was eminently successful. The capital cost was considerably less than a

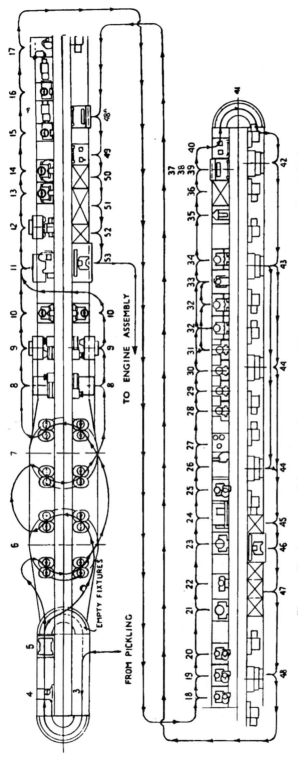

Fig. 11—The forerunner of the automatic transfer machine was a hand transfer machine built for Morris Motors in 1923. It produced a completely-machined cylinder block ready for assembly

27

Fig. 12—A view of the Morris hand transfer machine from station No. 35—the "water test". The machine was 181 ft. long, weighed 300 tons and had 53 action stations manned by 21 men

Fig. 13—Core drilling the camshaft bores in the cylinder block on the Morris hand transfer machine

28

Fig. 14—Drilling the locating holes in the cylinder block arms on the Morris hand transfer machine

group of normal machine tools would have been. It substantially reduced the machining costs while providing the operators with equal or even higher remuneration. It survived well beyond the normal period of obsolescence, in fact it outlived the engine for which it was made. A section of it was still at work in 1949, that is 25 years after it was first commissioned.

Two further group machines were built at a somewhat later date, one for machining gearbox castings and the other for flywheels. These were provided with automatic transfer and clamping mechanism to reduce manual operation to a minimum. The gearbox machine was designed to produce completely machined gearboxes, ready for the assembly line, within the same time cycle as the cylinder block machine.

The castings were loaded at one end into a series of fixtures. These travelled step by step under a complete series of operating heads, which in some cases carried jigs to control the accuracy of the cutting tools. At the end of the machine the boxes were unloaded and the fixtures returned on a gravity roller track to the loading station, the boxes in the meantime being passed to another series of fixtures on the off-side of the machine, where they were subjected to a further series of cutting operations. In due course they arrived at a point opposite the original loading station whence they were transferred to a conveyor which took them to the assembly line. All operations on this machine were controlled by a single camshaft, which set the cutting heads into motion and regulated the transfer of the fixtures from station to station, where they were locked in position by means of pneumatic clamping devices. The fixtures were moved to their stations by compressed-air operation. (Fig. 15.)

The third group machine was made for the production of complete flywheels from a 57 lb. mild-steel stamping, finishing at 43 lb. Here again the workpiece was automatically transferred through a series of operating heads, both the heads and the transfer mechanism being controlled by a master camshaft. The power busbars, the lighting cables, compressed-air lines, cutting oil service and the swarf conveyor were all contained within the machine frame. (Fig. 16.)

It would appear that these were the first automatic transfer machines, antedating those recently made in America and in this country by some 20 years. Unfortunately, in the state of the art at the time, they proved in practice to be over-complicated. They were, therefore, divided into individual machine units and the automatic system was abandoned, to be revived 20 years later.

With the end of the Second World War and the changeover to peacetime production, the U.S.A. made a very considerable contribution to flow production in the shape of both automatic cycle machines and automatic transfer machines, which had the same objective as the earlier British machines—the automatic handling of the workpiece through all operations. Only two examples have been chosen here to illustrate the historical trend of this flow production development, the first being the Transfer-matic rear-axle machine made by The Cross Co., of Detroit. In this group machine, the axle casings are loaded in fixtures which automatically advance from one set of machine heads to the next immediately the operation is finished. The fixtures are located and clamped by hydraulic mechanism. This group machine bores, turns and faces two housings at both ends of the axle simultaneously and one operator, only, machines 150 axle casings per hour. This is an increase of better than six times that of previous methods. The machine group can be altered by addition or subtraction because the transfer mechanism is independent and the locating and clamping devices are units applied to each individual operating station. Maintenance is greatly simplified since it consists of replacing the self-contained units and repairing the same at leisure. This "unitization"— a horrid but expressive word—goes far: it is, for instance, claimed that the hydraulic valves can be removed and replaced without disconnecting any piping. A centralized coolant system is used, and chip disposal is part of the automatic set-up. It is stated, and it can well be believed, that the capital investment for this group machine is lower than for the plant required to produce the same effect by normal methods. This is but one of many automatic transfer machines that are in use in the U.S.A. today. It serves to illustrate, most effectively, the inspiration given by due regard to flow production methods. (Fig. 17.)

After some delay, due largely to the very difficult post-war conditions, British automobile manufacturers are adopting automatic transfer machines. The larger producers either have machines building for them or have schemes in preparation. Vauxhall Motors Ltd. were the first in the field with a flow production line for machining the Bedford

Fig. 15—The first automatic transfer machine to be built. It was for machining gearboxes for the Morris car, and was delivered by James Archdale & Co., Ltd., in 1924

Fig. 16—A second automatic transfer machine for the production of flywheels from steel forgings was built by Wm. Asquith, Ltd., and delivered to Morris Engines late in 1924

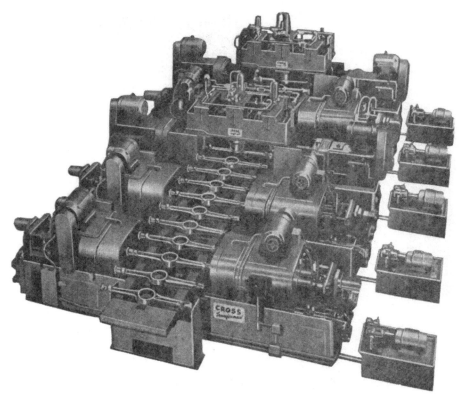

Fig. 17—A present-day automatic transfer machine. The Cross Transfer-matic for machining the outer ends of rear axle cases. Production 6½ times that of normal plant (U.S.A.)

truck cylinder head in which there are two four-station automatic transfer machines. The operating heads, of which there are five on one line and four on the other, are all multi-heads of the drilling type. One machine deals with the spot-facing of the valve guide holes and the drilling, counter-boring and tapping of the spark plug holes; the other with the core drilling and semi-finishing of the valve pockets and valve seats. It will be noted that these machines deal only with a section of the complete series of operations for which other special machines have been built. There has been no attempt to machine this complicated component outright on automatic transfer machines. From this one deduces that the first of these modern machines were tentative essays, and that machines to carry out a greater number of operations may be expected in due time. (Fig. 18.)

Nevertheless some important steps have been taken. Firstly, the transfer mechanism has been reduced to utmost simplicity. Secondly, all important controls are mechanical—the electrical functions, apart from switching, being limited to warnings. Thirdly, the components "go bare"—that is, without being loaded into fixtures.

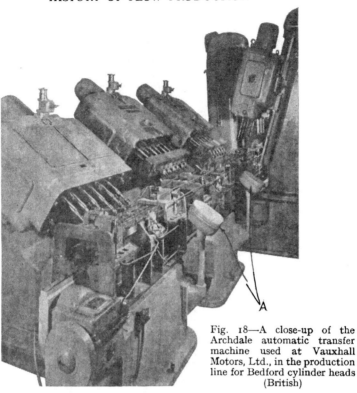

Fig. 18—A close-up of the Archdale automatic transfer machine used at Vauxhall Motors, Ltd., in the production line for Bedford cylinder heads (British)

Other modern-type machines go to make up the cylinder head line, such as specialized milling, drilling and fine boring machines; these are all connected by roller track to make a complete flow-line layout. Even when certain machines had not been delivered, the production time had been reduced by approximately one-third. True, an extra tool setter is required, but nine machinists were released for other service and the productivity, it is stated, shows an increase of some 70 per cent. This is due partly to the special machinery employed, partly to careful process planning, and partly to the design of the tooling equipment. The result was achieved by close co-operation between the Vauxhall engineers and the machine tool builders. The automatic transfer machines were built by James Archdale & Co. Ltd. of Birmingham and Worcester, who also built the gearbox machine previously mentioned. That early experience has borne fruit in the present design, for they have overcome the difficulties peculiar to this class of machinery. They can now claim complete dependability of transfer and clamping mechanisms, satisfactory swarf clearance from slides and precision in register and alignment.

This brings the history of the automatic transfer machine up to date. Development is still proceeding, and there is no doubt that this is one of the landmarks in machine tool evolution.

B

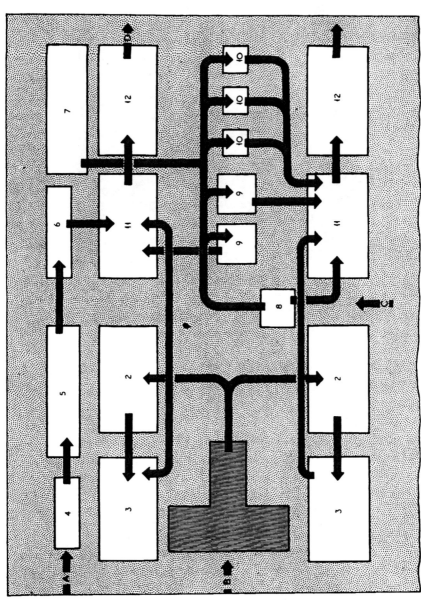

KEY

1. Spot welder for joining roof panels
2. Roof jigs
3. Roof racks
4. Spot welders for details on quarters
5. Mobile quarter jigs
6. Stacking ground for quarters
7. Spot welder for details on coach end, motor end and quarter jigs
8. Motor end assembly and welding jigs
9. Coach end jigs
10. Motor end quarter jigs
11. Main assembly jigs
12. Fitting and welding bays (Then to finishing production line)

A. Input of details for quarter jigs
B. Input of panels for roof jigs
C. Input of details for motor end jigs
D. Output of finished steel coach shell

Fig. 19—Plan of the assembly shop for the production of steel coaching stock (British Railways)

CHAPTER TWO

RANGE OF APPLICATIONS

B EFORE COMMENCING an analysis of the principles underlying the flow production system, there are certain other broad issues that can usefully be discussed since these will assist the understanding of the more detailed considerations. As indicated in the introductory remarks, it must not be thought that flow methods apply only to large-quantity production. The system can often be used, with great advantage, where the circumstances at first sight would appear to be prohibitive.

An excellent example of the flow-line method applied to the small-scale production of outsize units has been developed in the coach building shops at Eastleigh on the Southern Region of British Railways. *

The construction of the steel bodies was a new undertaking and the staff had a clear field for developing their ideas by devising sub-units which would be convenient to handle and allow rapid and economical production of coaches. Close co-operation between the technical and works staff during the construction of full-size experimental models resulted in the present form of the units and in the scheming of jigs best suited for line production.

Eastleigh carriage works, which were built some 50 years ago, did not allow for an entirely straight line run of building. In fact, two shops had to be adapted for the bodies; one for the production of the steel shell mounted on the under-carriage—making it mobile—and the other for the internal fitting and finishing operations. Fig. 19 indicates the layout of the erecting shop, which was originally planned for an output of four coaches per week. It was, however, found necessary to increase the amount to six per week for a period, so further operational stages became essential and this accounts for the fact that the flow of work is not entirely progressive. This, however, has had no adverse effect.

The perspective view of the body shell, shown in Fig. 20, indicates the method of construction. The main units of the shell are the roof, the side quarters and the coach ends, which may be motor or trailer ends. The body panels forming the shell in this class of stock are of steel. The floors are of cross-boarded soft wood and the partitions, in the

---

* This description is based on a paper entitled "Southern Railway All-steel Suburban Electric Stock", delivered before the Institution of Locomotive Engineers by L. Lynes and C. A. Shepherd.

35

compartment type of coaches, are of three-quarter block board or imported plywood.

Commencing with the roof assembly: the roof panels are sheared to size, punched and flanged in the sheet metal shop, whence they are passed to the erecting shop by the input route—marked B in Fig. 19—where they are joined longitudinally by spot-welding. The completed panels are then placed on a travelling bench where the lamp and ventilator bushes are fitted; this bench being also a conveyor to feed the panels to the roof jigs. Two jigs are used for assembling and joining the roof units. These have been designed so that the position of the roof-carlines can be arranged to suit the varying length of the compartments.

The assembly commences with the location of the carlines followed by the upper cant rail angles and the centre longitudinal member. Then the whole framework is welded together. The cant rail in these coaches is not placed, as is usual, at the door head, but higher, in order to provide for the attachment of the side quarters to the roof units. Incidentally, this position of the cant rail provides stronger body sides and simplifies the construction of the roof jig. The cant rails are drilled when in the roof jig, and all the frame work is painted before the roof panels are cramped into position for plug-welding; the transverse panel joints are welded and the longitudinal exposed edge of the panel is joint sealed by an arc-welding run. (Figs. 21-23.)

After panelling, the roofs are lifted by electric hoists and traversed by overhead runways to the racks (No. 3 in Fig. 19) for the conduit and light fixtures to be fitted and wired.

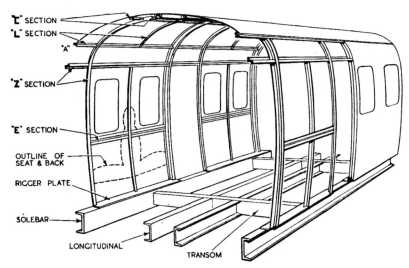

Fig. 20—Diagrammatic view of a steel coach built by the Southern Region of British Railways on the flow production system

Fig. 21—The first opera-
tion on a steel coach
assembly is to weld the
roof plates

Fig. 22—A jig is used for
the assembly of all the
roof members and the
welded roof plates

Fig. 23—Lifting the 60-ft.
roof from the roof building
jig

Fig. 24—The side quarters of the coach are assembled in this jig

The details for the side quarter assemblies are fed to the shop by the input route marked A when they flow, through stages 4 and 5 for various welding operations, to point 6, the painting and stacking ground. Location 7 is devoted to the welding of details of the coach and motor compartment ends. These latter are carried over to positions 8, 9 and 10 which deal with the motor end assembly, also the welding of the motor ends and motor end quarters, the input of the necessary details for the motor end jigs having meanwhile arrived by input route C. This slight complication is explained by the fact that there is much more work on the motor ends than on the ends of the trailer coaches, so that, while the main erecting jig for the motor coaches—No. 11 (upper) on the plan—draws on the locations 8-9-10 for the necessary components, the erecting jig, No. 11 (lower), which deals solely with the trailer-type coaches, can be fed with coach ends from locations 8 and 9 only. (Fig. 24.)

The main assembly commences with the erection of a coach end in the erecting jig (in the case of the motor coach it is the whole cab). An electrically-driven conveyor then brings a prepared roof from the roof rack, site 3, placing it in the jig where it is positioned and cramped to transverse struts which are located at each doorway opening. Then the side quarters are bolted to the roof, i.e. to the cant rail. Holes in the angles of both members govern the position at the top, whilst hinged locating arms on the jig sides engage service holes in the rigger plates provided at the bottom of the quarters. This method of building ensures that the sides of the quarters are kept square and that the correct width of doorway is maintained. Finally, the other end unit of the body is placed in position and both ends are arc-welded whilst the roof angles and the quarter top angles are cold riveted to unite in forming the upper cant rail. This latter operation is carried out by

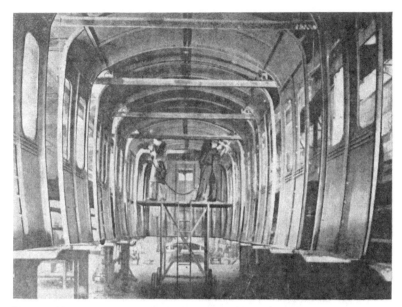

Fig. 25—Showing the assembly of the coach ends, quarters and roof in a jig which permits the introduction of the underframe mounted on its wheels. Note the movable staging for the coach builders

Fig. 26—General view of the body finishing shop. The platform is at the same height as the floor of the coach so that workmen have no steps or climbing. The coaches move to the next station every $7\frac{1}{2}$ hours

coach-makers working on a hand-propelled movable telescopic staging. (Fig. 25.)

While the fixing cramps are still in position, the underframe is moved into position and jacked up and the rigger plates are tack-welded to the underframe solebars. The cramps are then removed and the

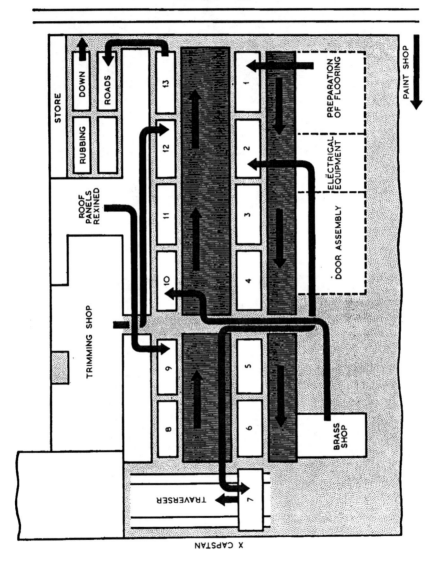

Fig. 27—This diagram shows the movement of the railway coaches through the body finishing shop. A key to the various operations is given in the text.

vehicle is transferred to site 12 for the final welding and fitting operations, including the attachment of the underframe trussing gear. This done, the coach is taken by traverser to the body finishing shop.

The plan of the finishing shop shows two roads at right-angles to the main works traverser, one inwards and one outwards, there being a short traverse for transferring the coaches from the "in" to the "out" road. On these roads the coaches pass through 13 operating stations. Between the roads there is a staging at platform height, wide enough to allow for the storage of sufficient components for one day's use and to accommodate a number of lightly constructed benches for the convenience of the fitters. Roof staging is also provided, at the first two stations, to enable painting to be done concurrently with operations inside the coach. (Figs. 26-27.)

Plug points are provided for portable tools and lighting plug switches come opposite each compartment doorway; general lighting is also furnished by 500-watt "Sie-Ray" lamps. The coaches are moved from station to station sites by means of power-operated capstans, in accordance with the output desired; for instance, coaches will be moved every $7\frac{1}{3}$ hours for six-per week production. The detail components are arranged on both sides of the dual coach roads for convenient assembly, which involves the following operations:

(1) Lay floors, fix switch boxes, paint outside roof and ends first coat.
(2) Wire switch boxes, fix cab equipment, paint roofs second coat, paint ends inside.
(3) Hang doors, fill plastic in joints of floor and panel recess, paint roofs and quarters inside second coat, paint ends inside third coat.
(4) Fix lower-half partitions and seat angles. Apply leather cloth on pillars, paint roof and quarters inside third coat.
(5) Fixed curved quarter lights, size partitions, paint body outside first coat.
(6) Fit door checks, striking plates, etc.
(7) Pipe and wire for electric heating and lighting.
(8) Apply leather cloth to partitions, fit roof packings and seat brackets, stop second coat filling outside.
(9) Hang ceilings and elbow pressings, paint roof outside third coat, stop third coat filling outside.
(10) Fit light quarters, net racks and mirrors, stain outside as guide to coach rubbers.
(11) Fit heater and seat rails, paint roof outside third coat.
(12) Fit seats and backs, lay linoleum.
(13) Clean interiors.

Vehicles which leave site 13 are finished inside except for the installation of the seat cushions, which are fitted after the coaches have

B•

been finally painted in Southern Region Malachite green. The painting prior to this stage has consisted of three coats of lead colour, stopping and filling. The wet rubbing-down process prior to the application of the finishing coats of green is done in the bays adjacent to stations 12 and 13.

After completion of painting in the paint shop, coaches go through a final inspection routine including the testing of the electrical equipment and brakes.

This example of railway coach building is most interesting, because the sponsors had such a very hard nut to crack. They made exhaustive studies of the job and they applied knowledge garnered from many sources. They have succeeded and, in their success, they encourage all those who manufacture assembled components to study their own activities from the aspect of flow production.

The managers of concerns that have only short runs of work are usually under the impression that flow production can hold no interest for them and that batch production is the only method suited to their needs. This is obviously true of general engineering and similar types of workshop work, but it is not true where repetition work, even in small quantities, is concerned. Progressive firms are finding there are many useful lessons to be learned from flow production techniques which can be applied to small outputs and that when this is done a very near approach will be made towards achieving flow production costs. Products based on engineering practice usually fall into recognizable categories, such as casings, covers, shafts, pulleys, gears, cams and so forth. Moreover, since most concerns deal with allied or at least similar products, these components although varied are, quite frequently, suitable for flow production under what is known as the group system.

The method employed is to analyse and classify the running jobs and to group the components in such fashion as to permit a layout of the machines in operation sequence. This means that work is moved from one machine to the next instead of travelling between departments. Then by studying the machine equipment, the fixtures, jigs, tools and gauges can be modified to reduce the change-over time to a minimum. The other advantages are that there is less work in progress, giving not only a smaller inventory but a quicker through-put, especially as there is no need to wait for batches to finish before passing to the next operation. Since inspection will naturally be in line with the machines, faulty work will be found almost immediately and the necessary adjustments made.

The system highlights the need for standardization both of components and tooling; the simplification of which will help to reduce the set-up time when changing over from one job to the next. The system also makes planning easier and simplifies production control, since the work is virtually self-progressing. Moreover, the movement of material, by whatever means adopted, can be properly organized. The balance of plant, or the lack of it, will be much more obvious than in the original layout.

Those who wish to set up a group production system may find the following detailed suggestions of interest:

(1) Make a survey of all the components that are in general production.

(2) Pick out those components that appear suitable for operating on the same line of machines.

(3) Analyse the operations under the following headings:
> Process times,
> Routing,
> Machine utilization,
> Fixtures and jigs required,
> Tools and gauges required.

Reference to the original operation cards should provide most of this basic information.

(4) With the data available make a machine layout for the largest or most complicated piece. Machines to be laid out in operation sequence without regard to type—the line to end with an inspector's bench.

(5) Match the selected components to the chosen part.

(6) In case of difficulty, ascertain if the components can be made to match by reorientation of the layout, by the introduction of additional operations into the line or by redesigning the components.

(7) Redesign the equipment where dictated by necessity. This applies particularly when fixtures have to be changed quickly to permit the use of one machine for several jobs.

(8) Change of fixtures need not entail dismantling—slides, turrets or other indexing mechanisms can be effectively used.

(9) When revamping, great attention should be paid to job simplification, particularly when new tools and fixtures are contemplated.

(10) The lines can be served by slides, gravity roller track, slat, pendulum or other types of conveyor. Fork trucks can be used for large components.

(11) Aim to have a supervisor over each line of production, or over two lines if the number of machines is very small.

(12) Having established the groups, continue to carry out time and motion studies on each operation and so, by modification as and when possible, lift the lines to the utmost efficiency.

Sometimes, in the interest of total efficiency, it may be found profitable to install, in the line, machines which will be occupied **for**

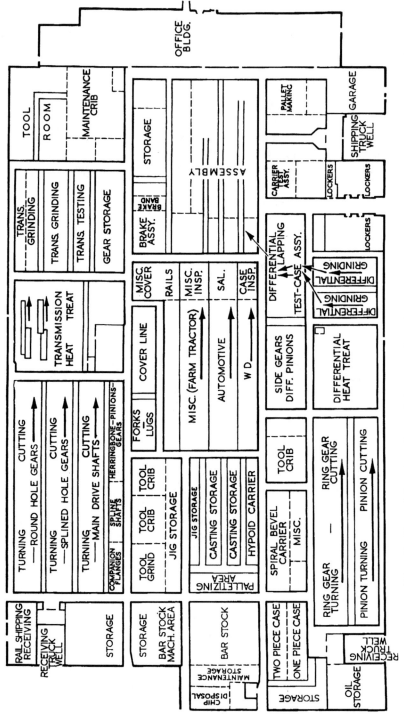

Fig. 28—Plan of American transmission manufacturing works in which, during the course of one month, up to 130 different transmissions are made on the flow production system

44

quite brief periods. It is, however, not individual machine tool efficiency but the overall utilization of man-hours that gives the desired results.

The Scania-Vabis Company of Sweden can be quoted as an example of this system. This concern builds some 2,000 heavy vehicles per annum. The company employs all three systems—30 per cent of the machines are on group production; 40 per cent are on batch; and the remainder are operating individually. They claim that on group production there is a reduction of the cycle time of some 40 per cent; that the morale on these lines has been improved; that the workmanship is of a higher quality; that the training time has been reduced, and that a greater degree of expertness is acquired. They say that this latter is largely due to the greater interest engendered by several jobs flowing through the line. It is true that certain machines are working at 10 per cent to 15 per cent less efficiency than would be achieved on the batch method: but, if that be all, it is a small price to pay for the general improvement due to the group production system which they are hoping to extend.

An American concern which makes transmissions and rear axle parts has to deal with as many as 110 to 130 different transmission sets per month. They have laid out their shops on flow production lines and it is said that despite the short runs they can approach mass production costs. (Fig. 28.)

In this country, B.S.A. Tools Ltd. find that flow-line assembly has great advantages even for such slow moving products as machine tools. The method adopted is essentially simple: a narrow rail track—some 18 ins. wide—is arranged on three sides of a rectangle with turntables at the corners. The machine bases are set up on trolleys which run upon this track. The trolleys are pushed from station to station where there are sub-assembly benches. On arrival at the appointed station, the sub-assembly is installed and the trolley is moved to the next location. This scheme is so flexible that it has been found possible to handle as many as five different sizes, and even different types, of machines on the assembly line at the same time. This is achieved by the adoption of a simple colour scheme for identifying the components and assemblies. The work bins and the racks and boxes on the assembly benches are given a distinctive colour for each type of machine. The Gridley range for instance, have all-red for the 1 in. size, yellow and white for the $1\frac{1}{4}$ in., yellow and red for the $1\frac{3}{8}$ in. and all-yellow for the $2\frac{1}{4}$ in. machines. The fixtures and jigs, on which the machined parts are made, also conform to this colour scheme. (Fig. 29.)

It is easy, with this device, immediately to identify the many diverse components. The major advantage of this flow production method is that it throws into high relief any shortages which might jeopardize the time schedule for the production of the machines. Knowing what

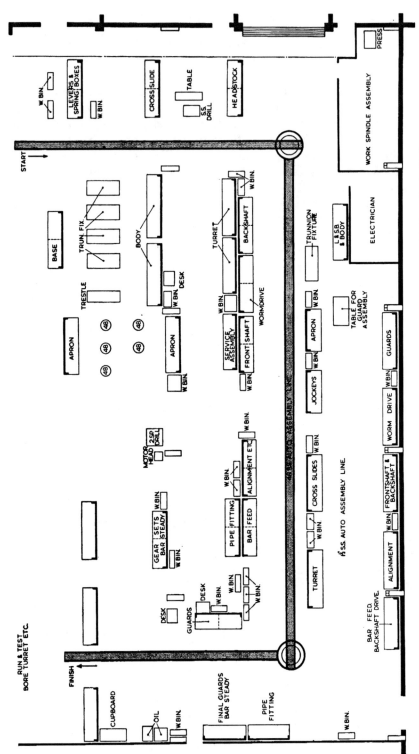

Fig. 29—Building machine tools on flow production methods in the works of B.S.A. Tools, Ltd.

46

machines are coming down the line, it is a simple matter for the foremen or charge-hands to glance through the material in the assembly bins to assure themselves that there is either a sub-assembly awaiting the machine or that all the necessary parts for producing the same are available. The scheme has the advantage of reducing work in progress and making the whole operation self-progressing. It also avoids much lifting by overhead cranes, which are only required to lift the bed on to the trolley at the commencement of the assembly and to off-load the finished machine into the test and storage bays.

CHAPTER THREE

THE PRINCIPLES: A GENERAL SURVEY

Having reviewed the historical development of mass and flow production and having noted that the system is much more widely applicable than is generally appreciated, we can direct our attention to the principles that underlie these methods of production. Before doing so, however, it is essential that the full implications of the operative words "mass" and "flow" should be appreciated.

Mass production implies the method of making vast quantities of similar articles—simple or complicated—by a series of individual acts which are not necessarily connected with each other. For example, the first operation on certain components could be forming under a press. The pressings might then be transferred, for a turning operation, to a machine shop 300 or 400 yards away. A third operation might be done on a multiple drill in another section, followed by case-hardening in the heat treatment shop and a grinding operation in yet another department. Given large quantities of standardized pieces, this method can be described—quite correctly—as mass production.

Flow production, on the other hand, envisages the passage of the part from operation to operation in a direct and uninterrupted sequence.

The ideal arrangement for flow production should resemble a watershed; the river being the main assembly track, fed by tributaries in the shape of sub-assembly lines which, in turn, would be supplied by streams representing the machine lines fed by brooks typifying the material conveyors. Each part should flow continuously forward. There should be few bends, no eddies, no dams, no storms, no freezing should impede the inevitable flow to estuarine waters—the dealers—and ultimately to the sea—the consumers.

Needless to say that riverine ideal is not automatically achieved. Eddies may be present in inspection rejects. Material supplies, held up, may dam the stream. Changes in design may make bends unavoidable. The economic situation may provide the frosts or competition the storms. These troubles will occur and the success of the company concerned is a measure of the skill by which such adverse factors are overcome.

While flow production is a comparative innovation in engineering, it is by no means new in other industries. Foodstuffs, textiles, lubricants, soap, newspapers and even steel rails are all, of necessity, produced by

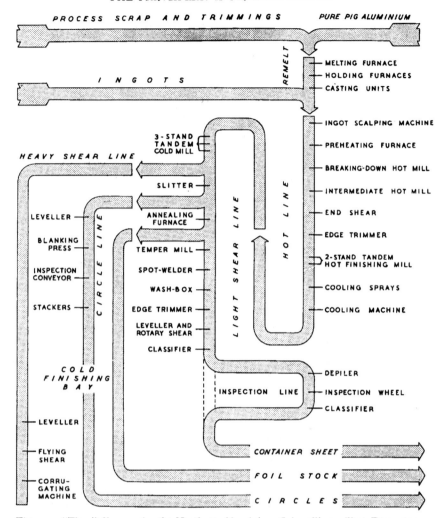

Fig. 30—"Flow" diagram for the Northern Aluminium Co's rolling mill at Rogerstone

this system. It will be noted that all these flow readily. Some, like beverages and lubricants, are actually liquid. Others, such as flours, powders and preserves are, in effect, fluid; while textiles, newsprint, steel rails, rolled and extruded metals readily lend themselves to flow manipulation. Engineering products, on the other hand, do not flow easily because of their hard unyielding nature; the varying and frequently awkward shapes of the components; the divergent character of the operations to be performed thereon, and the accuracy that is required in most engineering operations. Yet, given a sufficient quantity of similar parts to be produced over a reasonable period, without alteration, the mechanism to promote flow can be set up and worked economically. (Fig. 30.)

The idea of flow, which is another name for continuity in operation sequence, may not always be conspicuously apparent to visitors to factories employing such methods. It is, nevertheless, the guiding principle in establishments that use this system as a logical extension of the mass production method.

Again before considering the principles, let us see if we can define the objectives of flow production. In general, the aim is to produce goods more economically and more quickly with less stress or strain on the producers than that which is inherent in the older methods. In particular the following achievements can be claimed for the system.

Primarily there is the advantage of continuous production arising out of processing in operation sequence, which means that there is no waiting for the completion of a batch on one operation before the components can be taken to the next stage. This in itself is a very considerable gain: take, for instance, a component which requires five operations that are based on a 4-minute time cycle. On the continuous process the first finished piece will be available in 20 minutes. On the batch system—if there are 100 in the batch—the first finished part will come off the last machine in 1,604 minutes; even then the rate of delivery will be no greater than that of the flow production set-up. This, moreover, is on the assumption that there is no delay between operations due to inspecting, trucking, waiting for available machines and so forth. Further, on flow production, inspection is in line with the machines, which means that it is promptly carried out so that some five or six pieces is all that would be scrapped at worst. If the batch system is functioning as usual, it would be 400 minutes before the first piece was inspected, and there would be a chance that 100 pieces would be scrapped.

This prompt correction of faults greatly reduces the liability of a hold-up in the assembly shop owing to unforeseen faults in processing; thus flow production provides a much closer control of processing than any other method. In addition there is much less work in progress and consequently a smaller inventory and less capital locked up in stock. The saving in area of operation is also very considerable. The method reduces that terrible bugbear of "waiting time", a cost item which is disliked by men and management alike, to insignificance. It also makes for the balanced output for which we all strive. So far as control is concerned the flow production system has tremendous advantages. Planning is relieved of short-term tactical considerations and can therefore become, as it should, long-term strategy. Flow production is "self-routing" and "self-progressing"; in fact the "progress" function in a flow production factory is virtually limited to stores control.

There are also other benefits to be gained from the high-lighting of many problems. Owing to the essential simplicity of the system there

THE BASIC PRINCIPLES

(1) *(a)* Mass production demands mass consumption.

(b) Flow production requires continuity of demand.

(2) The products of the system must be specialized.

(3) The products of the system must be standardized.

(4) The products of the system must be simplified in general and in detail.

(5) All material supplies must conform to specification.

(6) All supplies must be delivered to strict timetable.

(7) The machines must be continually fed with sound material.

(8) Processing must be progressive and continuous.

(9) A time cycle must be set and maintained.

(10) Operations must be based on motion study and time study.

(11) Accuracy of work must be strictly maintained.

(12) Long-term planning, based on precise knowledge, is essential.

(13) Maintenance must be by anticipation—never by default.

(14) Every mechanical aid must be adopted for man and machine.

(15) Every activity must be studied for the economic application of power.

(16) Information on costs must be promptly available.

(17) Machines should be designed to suit the task they perform.

(18) The system of production must benefit everyone—consumers, workers and owners.

is high visibility on material shortages, on the balance of manpower, on the balance of plant and on the suitability, or otherwise, of the fixtures, jigs, tools and gauges. If any of the items are at fault or inefficient, the flow production layout will throw them into high relief and, in this respect, diagnosis may be properly considered as more than half-way to cure.

When setting up a flow production plant, there are certain basic principles that must be obeyed. They are all simple and virtually axiomatic but, naturally, they are not all of equal weight; and some of them depend on the state of the art in the particular establishment at the time of application. There can be several stages in the application of the flow production system and, obviously, many concerns will start in an elementary and less efficient stage and grow to the fully organized and highly efficient concern. The principles enunciated relate to the fully organized establishment, but that should not deter anyone from commencing even in a tentative fashion because, if the attempt at flow production is an honest endeavour, the highly organized state can eventually be attained.

In the list on page 51 the principles of both mass and flow production are stated, but items 6, 7, 8, 9, 10, 12, 13 and 17 apply more particularly to flow production.

The successful establishment of mass production—whether on the flow system or otherwise—commences at top-level management in the choice of a product which is readily and continuously saleable or which can be brought into that condition by skilful publicity and marketing campaigns.

The articles which immediately spring to mind in this category are many and various. Here are a few: bacon slicers, bicycles, binoculars, cameras, calculating machines, cash registers, duplicators, electric appliances, guns, games, meters of all kinds, motor vehicles, mowers, paint sprayers, portable power tools, movie projectors, radio receivers, refrigerators, television, toys, typewriters, vacuum cleaners, washing machines, watches, clocks.

These items, culled at random, are only a small section of the complete list, but they serve to show what a wide range of possibility exists for the application of these newly evolved methods. In passing, it may be remarked that the domestic utilities offer a major field for flow production operations, providing as they do that regular demand without which it is impossible to set up the necessary plant and equipment for flow production—or even to work such a plant if it were available. This, then, is the appropriate point at which to consider in detail the implications of the first principle in the art.

CHAPTER FOUR

LAUNCHING A NEW PRODUCT

Principle 1(a) Mass Production demands Mass Consumption
     (b) Flow Production requires Continuity of Demand

UP TO THE PRESENT the majority of the mass-production concerns have grown from small beginnings, developing through fairly clearly defined stages. Many stemmed from existing companies and, starting in a somewhat tentative fashion, built up strength, as they gained experience of their product and their markets, until they ultimately graduated to flow production. Others commenced without the advantage of a parent company but succeeded because they had a new commodity and no established competition. Among this class were many merchants who became producers. Starting with an assembly shop, in due course they acquired existing production plants or set up their own fabricating departments to feed their assembly lines. Eventually they graduated to flow production.

A point to observe is that starting small and growing large is the natural development, but one which becomes increasingly difficult (although not impossible) as industries arrive at maturity. To break into an existing line of business it is necessary for a new company to spring into being like the goddess Minerva—fully grown and fully armed. This may not be serious in the case of concerns making small and simple articles, but for those making the larger and more complicated products the vast amount of preliminary work that is necessary, and the large amount of capital required for launching a new project in a competitive market, is truly formidable.

Obviously, then, if it is intended to produce any new article on mass production lines, it is essential that the fullest possible market investigation should be made to ascertain not only the bulk consumption but the pattern of general distribution, the proportion of home and export demand and the incidence of consumption, at divers times, in various territories. This makes necessary the acquisition of as much factual evidence as possible in regard to consumers, distributors and dealers.

When breaking into a market in which trading has already been established—or even into one which, although new, is associated with an existing market—it is possible to conduct a market research, in the usual sense of the term, which will form a useful guide to the probable demand. When entering into an entirely new field no signposts are available, and the imagination plays a very considerable part in policy decisions. It is therefore vitally important that the consumer viewpoint is kept well to the fore, since the vision of the protagonist inventors, designers and promoters must inevitably be coloured by their own faith and desires.

The proportion of home and export sales is significant, for observation indicates that export goods are, on the whole, more satisfactory when backed by experience arising from a sizeable home demand. The incidence of consumption—whether at home or abroad—is even more important, particularly in respect of seasonal goods, since it brings in such questions as the need for shift working, overtime (and occasional short time), warehousing and stocking by distributors and dealers. If home and overseas requirements tend to balance each other, the problem of keeping production on an even keel is greatly eased. It is desirable, also, that markets and techniques should be considered together, for, in the endeavour to promote continuity of flow, they are indeed close partners.

On the technical side it is highly important that the designs should be fully developed, all details being worked out to a logical conclusion. This must be done if changes, which may be disruptive and which are always expensive, are to be avoided. In particular it is essential to see that the presentation of the article is attractive and that it is, moreover, likely to remain in fashion for a reasonably long period. Here, in fact, is the proper field for the industrial designer, who should preferably be a member of the design team. Styling after the completion of technical design, or what may be called the *appliqué* method, is never satisfactory, and dressing up a product, in addition to being technically unsound, is liable to be much more expensive than—as the artist would say—"designing from the inside outwards".

Again, the economics of design are tremendously important but not always obvious to the designer of the end product, who, rightly, is thinking primarily of the customer. In this connection, consultation with the suppliers of the raw material is invaluable but should take place before the design is crystallized. So often minor changes can be made in components, which mean little to the producer of the end product and nothing at all to the purchaser, but which can make, in total, a very substantial difference in cost. Suppliers are able to draw upon the wide experience gained in serving a variety of trades and, as will be shown later, they can frequently indicate the not-so-obvious methods of effecting economies.

When mass production and particularly when flow production is contemplated, it is most desirable that the working drawings should be completed to the very last detail, and that careful estimates of costs should be made before the project is launched. It is also essential that prototypes should be built and thoroughly tested. The component parts should be made in precisely the same manner as the bulk production. There should be no "cutting out of the solid" or other such devices to save the time and expense in making dies or patterns, which might have to be altered, because it is precisely these "short cuts" that are so apt to lead to subsequent trouble.

This may appear to be a counsel of perfection but, to show that it is quite practicable, the particulars of a system evolved by the author, for the production of prototypes, is given here—for the first time. As it may appear to be somewhat elaborate it should be noted that, in the result, it proved to be a great time saver. It also had the effect of reducing drawing office alterations to a minimum.

The method was developed in connection with the production of automobile power units—that is to say, the engine and gearbox combination.

The general features were, of course, settled by the board of directors when deciding the seasonal policy. Such features would include the cubic capacity, number of cylinders, bore and stroke, number of speeds in the gearbox, limiting dimensions, expected horse power, targets for production, and the anticipated cost. This information was then formally remitted to the director in charge of power-unit production, who called together under his chairmanship a committee comprising the chief engineer, designer, head draughtsman, jig and tool designer, planning and plant engineers, production manager, general works manager, buyer and cost accountant. (The order in which these officers are listed is an indication of the order in which their contributions would become effective.) The first meeting would note the instructions from the board and would proceed to make decisions on certain fundamentals, which would be minuted and advised to all concerned. In due course the discussions would embrace design, materials, methods, machinery and equipment, plant layout, production schedules and purchase policy. Eventually estimates would be considered and these subsequently would become the basis for standard costs. The designer, with his assistants, then prepared a rough layout of the unit, and a number of studies of various important components.

In actual practice, these studies were continually being made, as exercises in design, in the intervals between new models. The rough layout and the relevant studies were approved by the resident director in consultation with the chief engineer, after which the designer prepared the first general arrangement drawings. These, when completed, were considered by the committee, each member of which would comment on such aspects as would affect his department. In due course the arrangements would be passed for detailing.

The first items to be detailed were those which would take the longest to make—such as forgings, large and complicated castings and other items which required elaborate pattern-making or intricate die-sinking. Meanwhile the material bill was compiled and mnemonic identification numbers were adopted and published. As the details were finished blue prints were issued to the buying, planning, jig and tool and estimating offices. Further blue prints were issued to the tool room to which the machining of the prototypes was entrusted. The detail drawings were carefully checked for dimensions and for limits and tolerances and any necessary special instructions were added at this point. Then—and this is very important—the designer personally proceeded to build up a final general arrangement from the issued blue prints. This constituted a double check, but yet a third check was imposed in the interests of accuracy.

As the components were completed and inspected they were sent to the experimental department where they would, in due course, be assembled under the supervision of the designer who, knowing every part intimately, would decide on any adjustments that might be necessary either in regard to dimensions, limits or tolerances. Such adjustments were carefully noted and transferred to the drawings and thenceforward no alterations of any sort were permitted except by the express consent of the designer. It will be noted that this method of assembly constituted a very practical and searching third check.

Two of the engines then went through an elaborate type test. The other four (six prototypes were usual) were, after a normal "pass-out" test, assembled in cars for road testing, usually conducted by relays of drivers to ensure maximum mileage in the shortest possible time. Test reports were regularly received from both road and test beds. These were carefully considered and checked against the preconceived standards laid down for performance and, of course, any necessary adjustments were made. Sometimes a pilot order would be put in hand to provide preliminary test models for certain of the larger dealers but normally this was considered neither necessary nor desirable.

Meanwhile jigs, tools, fixtures and gauges were being made, additional machines were ordered, the new shop layout evolved and a detailed timetable for the changeover (usually fixed for a holiday period) was prepared.

The foregoing represents a fair sample of what is required (whether the same routine is followed or not) to launch a new model in an existing industry. A similar routine would be necessary in dealing with a new invention except that more prototypes might be desirable and testing on a larger scale advisable; while pilot production for both home and abroad might be essential. The procedure depends on the nature of the commodity, the scale of operations and the permissible element of risk.

It is not suggested that the routine set forth is the only way to handle a new product but the example is given to bring out, clearly, certain fundamental points which must be observed if maximum efficiency for flow production is to be attained. The noteworthy points are that (*a*) every department is brought into consultation at the earliest possible stage; (*b*) the final design is carried out by *one man*; (*c*) the designer is responsible for a second check on details in making the final general arrangement drawings; (*d*) the first of the prototypes is built under the immediate supervision of the designer, which constitutes a third check; and (*e*) no-one is permitted to change dimensions, limits, tolerances or material specifications except with the consent of the designer.

Thus in the most vulnerable period of translating new ideas into commodities the responsibility for carrying out the work lies with the one man who can visualize the project as a whole. This is important in ensuring an integral article and one which will not suffer those modifications and alterations to detail which are troublesome and wasteful at all times but particularly so when applied to flow production. Some may object that the precautions outlined would cause a prohibitive delay in developing a new job. Experience, however, goes to show that a well-tried team working on these methods can produce new designs in record time and with the minimum of subsequent alteration to details—a matter which all who are engaged on flow production will know to be one of the most important considerations.

So we establish that, in order to be assured of success, it is necessary to lay plans based on market investigation involving consumer and dealer research at home and abroad. In such investigations it is essential to be able to forecast the demand and, more particularly in the case of articles which have seasonal sales, the incidence of the demand. Parallel with this it is essential that the product should be designed in such fashion that it will remain substantially the same for specified periods, and that it should be designed under such conditions as to avoid, as much as possible, the necessity for internal modifications. Also, testing should be carried out to the fullest possible extent and, where new products are concerned or where considerable departures from an established design have been made, pilot batches for testing in actual service, in controllable territories, should be undertaken. All this is necessary to ensure that the flow of orders shall be maintained within economic limits. Again, this may appear too idealistic a conception for the rough and tumble of commercial life, but in aiming at flow production we are striving for a mechanistic ideal and the most notable feature of flow production is that it shows, so unmistakably, where any divergence is made from ideal conditions.

CHAPTER FIVE

SPECIALIZATION: STANDARDIZATION: SIMPLIFICATION

THE FLOW production techniques are based on repetition processes which demand standardization. Standardization covers simplification and specialization, which are particular aspects of standardization. To make this clear it is necessary to define these three terms.

Standardization originally meant the making or maintaining of uniform shapes, sizes and tolerances. It now has a much wider meaning, as will appear later. After a time it was found that standardization of itself was insufficient to control the situation, as there might easily be too many standards. So, in due time, simplification was introduced. This is the process of reducing the number of types and varieties of the standardized products. It is a winnowing, culling or selecting of standards. Later still, and largely due to the growth of flow production, came specialization, which is the process whereby particular firms concentrate on the production either of one product only or on a narrow range of products. Let us, then, examine the suggestion that the second principle in flow production should be specialization.

Principle 2—The Products of the System must be Specialized

Although, historically, the order of development was firstly standardization, secondly simplification and thirdly specialization, production policy calls for specialization as a first consideration. It is a prime necessity when accepting the idea of flow production that the firm concerned shall determine, precisely, what it is proposed to produce. In the case of an existing company this would mean a rationalization of existing products. It may mean the total elimination of certain lines and a reduction in the number of models in others. It may also involve a certain amount of domestic standardization and maybe a change of appearance.

For example, the XYZ Company (a fictitious concern, needless to say) may have been marketing five models of gramophones, seven radio receiving sets and four radiograms. They might resolve to abandon the production of gramophones, to reduce the receiving sets to three types and to make only two radiograms. They would probably agree that while certain chassis components would be common to all the sets, each cabinet would differ in certain respects. This is typical of the process of specialization, which is a matter that is entirely within the province of the particular producer. In this it differs from standardization as generally understood, for that is a matter for agreement between all the interests concerned.

Although, told in these brief sentences, specialization would appear to be the acme of simplicity, it is a matter of life or death to any firm concerned. Such steps, as indicated, could only be taken in the light of knowledge revealed by a searching market investigation, but, when there is sound evidence that the distributors and consumers will, in general, react favourably, there is no other step that will yield such gratifying results. When considering specialization it is as well to remember the shrewd advice of that famous iron-master Andrew Carnegie: "Put all your eggs in one basket but . . . watch the basket."

The national standardization of end products would be a form of specialization but it is not to be recommended. Such a totalitarian objective would lead to a drastic reduction in variety which would be undesirable for the purchaser and therefore, in the long view, disadvantageous to the producer. Moreover it is not necessary, since competitive firms can, by limiting the range of their activities, promote efficiency and economy and yet retain the individual character of their goods—and that is the function of specialization.

Specialization need not act to the detriment of the smaller producers of consumer goods. Indeed it should promote a much healthier condition than that induced by the spread-the-risk attitude which fosters the production under one roof of a number of diverse articles which, logically, should be made in separate establishments.

It is true that there is a growing tendency towards the group concern of the type in which a number of firms are bound together financially by a holding company. Whether this is a desirable system is not an issue here, but it is noticeable that in such concerns there is a definite trend to the smaller, more compact, specialist unit. There is, of course, an optimum size of unit, varying with the nature of the product, and at this size there is nothing to prevent the individual producer from competing effectively with the group concern.

This argument, so far, has dealt with consumer goods as sold to the public, but specialization also applies to producer goods sold to the manufacturers of consumer goods. These fall into fairly well-defined categories, for example:

(1) *Ancillary components* such as ball and roller bearings, pressure and vacuum gauges, stop valves, dynamos and starters and the like. These are either complete machines or integral assemblies but they only serve a useful purpose when embodied in some other machine or apparatus.

(2) *Finished parts*, for example bearing bushes, gaskets, pistons, valves, screwed components and so forth.

(3) *Semi-finished parts*: Castings, forgings, stampings, pressings and the like.

(4) *Fabricated materials*: plate, sheet, strip, rolled and extruded sections, bar, rod, tube and wire. These may be produced in ferrous or non-ferrous metals or maybe in plastics.

(5) *Miscellaneous*. A variety of materials such as paint, adhesives, fabric, hides, etc., with which this book is not concerned.

For economic production, specialization is desirable in all these classes. In class (1) there is a very high degree of specialization and a marked tendency to rationalization by company mergers. In class (4) the nature of the product demands specialization. In both these classes the capital that would be required to set up competitive establishments is so great that the existing firms can be said to be in control of their own destinies. Classes (2) and (3) are not so sheltered. They are, in fact, subjected to intense competition which rather militates against specialization, for these trades prefer to insure against the possible withdrawal of large contracts by covering as wide a field as possible.

In U.S.A. specialization has been carried much farther than in this country. One company, for instance, specializes in rods. They make any size of rod with a screwed end, a forged eye or a fork. They make nothing else so it can be readily understood that they could be very vulnerable to competition. Their only safeguard is to put down the very latest machinery for intensive production and so, by low prices, keep off all intruders. Nevertheless, as indicated in the Anglo-American Council of Productivity Report on "Simplification in Industry" there is some anxiety—even in America—on this subject.

When economic pressure becomes too great the answer is usually found in the merger, which may, in the absence of competition, lead to increased prices. Purchasing firms that wish to foster competition would be well advised to avoid putting too much direct pressure on their suppliers. There are less hurtful ways of obtaining their legitimate objectives. Arising out of the foregoing it would seem that the third principle in the art of flow production should be to standardize.

Principle 3—The Products of the System must be Standardized

Standardization, in this context, originated with the screw-thread system and was initiated by Henry Maudslay. In his autobiography (edited by Samuel Smiles) James Nasmyth refers to the situation as it was in 1829 in these words:

"Before his (Maudslay's) time no system had been followed in proportioning the number of threads of screws to their diameter. Every bolt and nut was thus a speciality in itself, and neither possessed nor admitted of any community with its neighbour. To such an extent had this practice been carried that all bolts and their corresponding nuts had to be specially marked as belonging to each other. None but those who lived in the comparatively early days of machine manufacture can form an adequate idea of the annoyance, delay and cost of this utter want of system. . . . In his system of screw-cutting machinery, and in his taps and dies and screw tackle generally, he set an example and in fact laid the foundation, of all that has been done in this most essential branch of machine construction. Those who have had the good fortune to work under him have eagerly and ably followed him and his admirable system has been established throughout the entire mechanical world."

Sir Joseph Whitworth was one of those who worked under Maudslay's direction, and it was he who carried on the work which culminated in his paper to the Institution of Civil Engineers in 1841 urging the adoption of a uniform system of screw threads throughout the world. For a time it seemed that the Whitworth thread would become universal, for it was accepted in Germany and in the United States, but the Continent of Europe, not unnaturally, evolved a metric system while, less logically, the Seller's system ousted the Whitworth thread in U.S.A.

The need for standardization in screw threads was self-evident, but there was little further co-operative effort in this field until the formation of the British Engineering Standards Association, which was founded in 1901, to deal, in the first place, with steel sections. In 1929 this body, which had extended its activities over much of the engineering field, became the British Standards Institution. At the present time the B.S.I. deals with the products of 50 major industries and has 1,500 active committees with 11,000 committee members.

In America a similar development has taken place. In 1910 the Society of Automotive Engineers of New York appointed a committee to set up standards to simplify automobile production. When the U.S. entered the First World War (April, 1917) standardization became an urgent necessity because of the placing of large contracts for a wide variety of components in factories scattered over the country. The American Engineering Standards Committee was formed in October, 1918, for the co-ordination and correlation of the work that had hitherto been done by independent bodies. Although the British led the way in the earlier days of the standardization movement, the U.S. was, in 1921, first in the field with simplification, to which further reference will be made.

Standards can be usefully divided into (a) fabricating standards dealing chiefly with materials and their processing, and (b) constructional standards relating mostly to component parts. These can each be sub-divided into (1) domestic standards as adopted by individual producers, and (2) trade standards agreed by a number of interested concerns and most frequently issued under the aegis of the B.S.I. as a British Standard Specification. These divisions and the material specifications are the points needing consideration in relation to flow production, but the B.S.I. deals also with methods of test, terms, definitions, codes of practice and so forth.

The fabricating standards which deal with the "run-of-the-piece" materials such as sheet, strip, sections, tubes, wire, etc., cover shape, size limits, tolerances. The material specification covers chemical composition, condition (heat treatment, for instance) and the physical and mechanical properties. Occasionally B.S. specifications, which are framed to meet a wide range of requirements, are not sufficiently close for certain processing. In this case it is not unusual for a domestic standard to be set up for an individual producer. Where this arises it would seem that there is a call for a "higher" standard in addition to the average specification. It is not desirable that private domestic standards should exist concurrently with B.S.I. standards because this indicates that one producer is unusually hard to please, or alternatively, that a number of producers are suffering from a particular disadvantage. Nevertheless, it must not be forgotten that standards are established to assist the ultimate producer and the consumer, and that, in some cases, mass and flow manufacturers may have to make stringent demands on the fabricators for what, to them, is their particular raw material.

Constructional standards relate chiefly to component parts and their installation. Standardization in this respect is important not only to the maker of the end product but also to the user. The importance to producers lies in the fact that standardized parts, by reason of the greater volume made, are cheaper than non-standard parts. This is not only true in respect of finished parts "bought-in", but also of material purchased for making such parts. The influence of standardization is not confined to one stage of production, but affects the whole chain of costs from the raw material to the stocks in stores and the locked-up capital that such stocks entail. Standardization also, owing to greater concentration in fewer lines, helps to improve the average quality of components.

Standardization is a great boon to the user and, incidentally, to the distributor, to whom service stocks are liable to become a nightmare. Naturally standardization opens the door for what are termed "spurious spare parts", that is replacements not supplied by the original manufacturer, but there are means for overcoming this disability. There was, however, a period when certain firms sought to help their spares turnover by deliberately making replacement components as non-standards. This short-sighted policy quickly built up a surprisingly strong sales resistance and, like Æsop's fable of the dog and the bone, the practitioners of this expedient found that for the shadow they had lost the substance. Within the author's experience was a case where sales difficulties were being encountered more than 20 years after the non-standard policy had been reversed, despite the fact that all advertising and every catalogue stressed the fact that all parts were—at that time—made to the trade standards.

The reason for this attitude is understandable, for when replacements are required the user is in some sort of trouble and if a dealer offers a part which, although standard, will not fit—it leaves the user with a "so-near-and-yet-so-far" feeling that will never be forgotten. The buying public has a singularly long and unforgiving memory for any concern playing this kind of trick.

The standardization of repairs has many ramifications, particularly in the motor car industry where everything is done to give the user prompt service. These range from the exchange of complete mechanical units to the providing of second and third standards of oversize pistons and rings for rebored engines and undersize bearings for reground crankshafts. Even standardized patches for repairing bodies damaged in accidents are made available.

Only those who have grown up with the development of the system of flow production can appreciate the tremendous efforts that went into the standardization of dimensions, limits and tolerances, resulting in the total abolition of hand fitting both on the assembly line and in subsequent service. Perhaps the high spot was the introduction of finished crankshaft and big-end bearings for automobile engines which entirely eliminated hand scraping and made running-in an obsolete operation.

This degree of accuracy which arises from the standardization of dimensions, limits and tolerances has been of the greatest service to the assembly lines, for although inspection adequately covers individual components it has never been possible to inspect the "closed job". The duty of ensuring that the "closed job" was correct had, perforce, to be left to the assembler, and with hand fitting there was always the possibility of cumulative inaccuracy. This made testing a definite necessity. Now the test has given way to a few minutes' running to make sure that the oil circulation is satisfactory, to wash out the pipe lines and to deposit an oil film on the interior surfaces.

It is sometimes alleged that standardization must lead to stagnation in design, but such charges are not warranted by the facts. It would, of course, be true if a total standardization of end products were contemplated, but there is no evidence that this is likely in a western civilization, and even if attempted it would meet with vigorous resistance from the buying public.

The standardization of detail has many advantages, not the least being that it imposes the moral obligation that no departure from a recognized practice should be made unless there is a very good reason for the deviation. This is important, for there is no value or justification in merely being different. After all, "originality consists in thinking for oneself; not necessarily differently from other people", and true originality does not consist in adding a centimetre here and subtracting a millimetre elsewhere. Design is based on broader concepts and it is an excellent discipline to have established standards for reference, even though we may decide to ignore them.

Moreover, it can be assumed that standard components have stood the test of time and that they will, in consequence, give the desired service. Ball and roller bearings, for instance, are prime examples of complete standardization and everybody knows that they can be relied upon, if fitted according to established practice, to give precisely the service expected of them.

It must also be remembered that even established standards are not immutable. In the "Aims and Objects" of the British Standards Institution it specifically states:

"The underlying principles covering the preparation of British Standards are: (*a*) that they shall be in accordance with the needs of industry and fulfil a generally recognized want: (*b*) that the interest of both producer and consumer shall be considered: (*c*) that they shall be periodically reviewed."

Standardization thus provides stability for detail design over a given period, but the standards are not mandatory: they carry no enforcement. Anyone who wishes can depart from standard, the only penalty being that in so doing a higher cost—perhaps considerably higher—will be incurred. The non-conformist will, however, be in a position to judge if his deviation is justifiable. This is not a quibble, for in large-quantity production the quantities are such that internal standards are practicable if desirable.

Principle 4—The Products of the System must be Simplified in General and in Detail

Dealing with the general aspect it must be recognized that the logical outcome of standardization is simplification because, in itself, standardization does not go far enough. It is possible to have so great a variety of standards that the original aim of standardization is in danger of being lost. Then we introduce simplification which is a standardizing of standards.

Now standardization is in its nature creative, requiring as it does careful analysis, technical investigation, frequent research and a logical synthesis. Simplification, on the other hand, is a commercial procedure involving selection to determine what varieties and sizes of component or article will serve the widest market.

Simplification originated in the U.S.A. when, during the First World War, the Conservation Division of the War Industries Board took action to curtail non-essential uses of labour, material and equipment throughout the industries in U.S. It was found that, in consequence of this action, production was enhanced and very considerable economies were made in other directions. Manufacturers then realized that, even in normal times, much waste in industry was due to the unwarranted production of many non-essential varieties of the same types of commodities. So, at their request, in 1921, Herbert Hoover, at that time Secretary of Commerce, established the Division of Simplified Practice within the Bureau of Standards to supervise this work. How effective this movement has been in U.S.A. can be gauged from the report published in the *Cost and Production Handbook* edited by L. P. Alford (The Ronald Press Company of New York, 1934 edition).

Although in this country the interest has been of more recent date, the brochure *Simplification in British Industry* issued by the Anglo-American Council on Productivity gives some remarkable facts. Examples are quoted of reductions of automobile dynamos from 48 to 3, starters from 38 to 5, distributors 68 to 3, batteries 18 to 3, camshaft chains from 6 to 1. In bolts, nuts, screws and rivets it is claimed that British simplification has gone further than U.S.A. Two interesting items are cycle chains 40 to 4, and gas cookers 33 to 1 with four hot-plate arrangements.

As previously remarked, when used in the specific sense, the word simplification means a reduction in standards or in types. There is, however, a wider interpretation which deals with the simplifying of the product and the process. Since the whole aim of flow production is that of process simplification that theme need not be pursued. On the other hand, the simplification of the product is an important factor in the development of the flow production technique. The system can, of course, deal with the most complex forms, but since it is employed for the purpose of producing more goods more quickly and more economically saving in all directions is implicit.

It is obvious that the simplification of form is of the utmost importance. This lies within the province of the design-draughtsman who will decide upon the shape, size and material that will give the best service to the user. He will also consider and decide whether two or more components can be combined with advantage or if it would simplify matters to divide an awkward or large component into smaller pieces . . . but design for flow production does not end at this point.

Due regard must be given to the method of production and this involves consideration of many points which may call for consultation with the planning department, the jig and tool designer, the machine tool or plant engineer and the materials handling section. Further than this some components may involve consultation with the makers of the raw materials—castings, forgings, stampings, pressings, and the like.

It is not suggested that formal consultation is necessary for the foregoing or that it relates to each and every component but, particularly on the large and complicated components, it is essential that there should be clear understanding on such matters as the method of locating the component on the machine or in the fixtures, on the question of the jigs, on the presentation of the workpiece to the tools, on the approach of the tools, on the clearing of swarf and the methods by which the components will be handled. The location of the

c

component is important to the draughtsman, who should set out the dimensions from the locating points. The operation of the jigs may be helped or hindered by the design of the component. The approach of the tools may be very important when dealing with easily broken pieces, moreover the first cut may have an influence on the cleaning-up of the material. The necessity for clearing the swarf is important when a chain of operations is contemplated, such as on automatic transfer machines. Handling methods may influence the design of fragile pieces.

Going beyond the factory door, design for easy and economical replacements in service is a matter of great importance. In the other direction, consultation with the supplier may be even more important, for three reasons. First, the producer of raw materials for end products can help very considerably if he knows what processing is intended. Second, he may be able to help by making minor adjustments—which have no bearing on the end producer's methods and which would not even be noticed by the customer—to save labour or material or, more important, the wasters for which the end producer and ultimately the public have to pay. It is essential to note, however, that these matters must be raised in the early stages of the design. Third, the supplier himself may be working on flow production lines and may be able to make suggestions for modification which would be mutually helpful both in easing the production problem and reducing the cost of the component.

In designing for flow production sufficient attention must be given to the process by which the rough material is produced. Limits should not be closer than can be reasonably maintained in the conditions obtaining in foundry, forge and mill where hot metal is associated with fragile sand in the case of castings or with other difficult conditions in stamp shop and rolling mill. The production engineer and the jig and tool designer are, in particular, apt to forget that the earlier processes in the production chain are not so amenable as the machine shop, for occasionally the laudable desire for economy outruns discretion, with the result that a farthing off the machining cost may mean pence on the material price for which, providing the supplier makes a profit, the purchaser pays. There is, of course, no reason why the buyer should not specify what he requires, but there is an inexorable law which ensures that it is paid for. It is a good plan firstly to establish allowances and tolerances with the supplying concern and thenceforward to buy per piece and not per pound. Moreover, sample components should be agreed as satisfactory, marked for identification and kept for reference. These simple rules will save much argument, much misunderstanding and much money, to say nothing of time and temper.

Closely associated with the foregoing is the necessity for the utmost regularity in raw materials which brings us to a principle which, described in the next chapter, is vital to the success of flow production.

CHAPTER SIX

RAW MATERIAL REQUIREMENTS

Principle 5—All Material Supplies must Conform to Specification

I T IS ESSENTIAL that raw material supplies must be regular in so far as chemical, physical and mechanical properties are concerned. In a word, they must conform to the specifications laid down by the purchasing company. Such specifications may be, and preferably are, those sponsored by the British Standards Institution, or they may be domestic specifications introduced by the buyer to meet some particular difficulty arising in the course of production. These specifications must, of course, be observed, or trouble is bound to ensue.

Incidentally, the phrase "raw material" needs some explanation, since the raw material of one firm is the finished product of another. Here it is used in its broadest sense as being the material bought by the concern under consideration—not necessarily the makers of the end product.

The purchaser, for his own protection, usually institutes some regular routine of inspection, testing and analysis on a percentage basis. Strictly speaking this should not be necessary since, if proper control is exercised at the supplier's works, a second check at the buyer's factory is redundant and merely adds to the cost of production. Maybe a method for dealing with this aspect of the matter will be evolved in due course.

For instance, it would be possible for a group of purchasing companies to arrange to establish a buyer's inspectorate at their supplier's works. It would then be unnecessary for the suppliers to inspect the goods, since this would be done for them, thus saving one element in the total cost of production. Moreover, if work should be rejected the rectification could proceed without delay. The cost of booking out the rejects, the transport to and from the buyer's works, the inspection, rejection, booking out and booking in again, and all the letter writing and argument in respect of the faulty work would be avoided. At the buyer's end there would, in addition, be the saving of congestion and delay on the receiving deck and in the rough stores which would be a distinct advantage.

Some supplies are held to such rigid standards by their producers that they can be accepted on trust. In raw materials there is the example of the Mazak zinc die-casting alloys. In this instance high purity is so essential for a satisfactory end product that the makers have taken it upon themselves to set the very highest standard of control.

Ball and roller bearings offer another example, in as much as the purchasers of these finished components would almost as soon query their own reference gauges as suspect their suppliers of providing a bearing that was not up to size and quality in every particular.

Again, roller chains are finished goods that are acceptable without examination, as are a number of complete assemblies that are never inspected because the makers have gained the complete confidence of the purchasing concerns. Under this heading come such auxiliary equipment as electrical units, stop valves, pumps, clutches, pressure gauges and so on. Rough material is, naturally, in a different category, for which it would appear that buyers' inspection will always be necessary, but, as suggested, there is a possibility of organizing it for greater efficiency.

In addition to conforming to the chemical and physical specification, materials must be within certain limits of size, consistent as regards surface condition and uniform in heat treatment which, of course, includes annealing. This is a necessity because large-scale flow production makes the correction of irregularities in shape, size or conditions virtually impossible. Remedial operations which *may appear to be* merely a nuisance in batch production, may, in flow production, result in serious stoppages and the return of the material to the supplier would have a like effect. Incidentally, the phrase "may appear to be" is used advisedly, for delays caused by irregularities are probably just as serious in batch as in flow production, although the effect is not so dramatic.

In brief, everything that impedes the flow must be eliminated, or at any rate reduced to a condition where it is regarded as an out-of-control calamity. From the foregoing it will be seen that the suppliers are swept into the orbit of flow production in no uncertain fashion, and that they are links—most important links—in the chain of operations that lead to the satisfaction of the consumer. It is important that this should be fully recognized, especially by the works force of the supplying concern who, being remote from the end product, have little or no knowledge of their importance in the scheme of things.

Among other matters it is important that the weight of the articles should not be allowed to grow. This applies to castings, forgings and even to rolled and extruded products, not excluding bar, tube and wire. It is important because it implies a wastage of material and may entail additional machining. The modern practice of buying components by the piece and not by the pound has had a good effect in checking unwanted growth in weight because the situation is watched by the supplier as well as the buyer.

Methods for checking specification and condition have been developed, but these are more appropriately dealt with under the section devoted to the eleventh principle, which deals with quality.

Meanwhile the quality of the material is not the only control required since, for flow production, it is almost as important that the incidence of deliveries of supplies shall be precisely regulated. Therefore the sixth principle may be cited as follows.

Principle 6—All Supplies Must be Delivered to Strict Timetable

The primary reason for this dictum is obvious, since any failure in the delivery of materials will stop the flow of work throughout the factory. There are, in addition, some very important secondary reasons for the observance of this principle.

It has been pointed out that one of the many advantages of flow production is that it reduces the inventory, that is the stock in stores and the work in progress. This is very important since, with the exception of plant and equipment, these stocks are liable to be the largest single item in the balance sheet; sometimes the amount is even greater than that for the plant and equipment. The ideal objective, therefore, is an inventory kept to the lowest figure consistent with the maintenance of the flow of supplies to the production lines. The reduction of working capital or the improvement of the liquid position due to a smaller inventory is not the only advantage; the lesser bin capacity absorbed, the smaller stores area required and the saving of double handling and of multiple paper-work are all very real economies. Incidentally with flow production methods the reduction of inventory may be as much as 75 per cent and even more.

Usually flow production concerns place what are known as blanket orders for their annual or seasonal requirement of materials. These orders are, normally, accompanied by an estimate of the daily, or weekly needs of the plant. The actual delivery instructions are given by periodic "releases" which are, in effect, controlled by the sales and stock position; hence the supplier is made to feel the ebb and flow of the market.

Now, another advantage of the flow production system applied to an end product factory lies in the fact that it highlights the waste and inefficiency arising from interruptions to output or, in other words, hindrances and stoppages in the rhythm and flow of production. This is made so conspicuous as to be unmistakable, not only in general, but specifically by pin-pointing the precise cause of the trouble. This trouble may occasionally be due to a hiatus in the supply line which must be remedied with the least possible delay. (Fig. 31.)

Although perhaps not so dramatic in its manifestation, the same situation is reflected in the factories of the suppliers who, when subjected, as they sometimes are, to violent changes of delivery instructions, are forced to sacrifice efficiency to expediency whenever the "stop-start" technique is applied. This is not always recognized, for when suppliers carry a large part of the inventory they cushion the shocks for the end

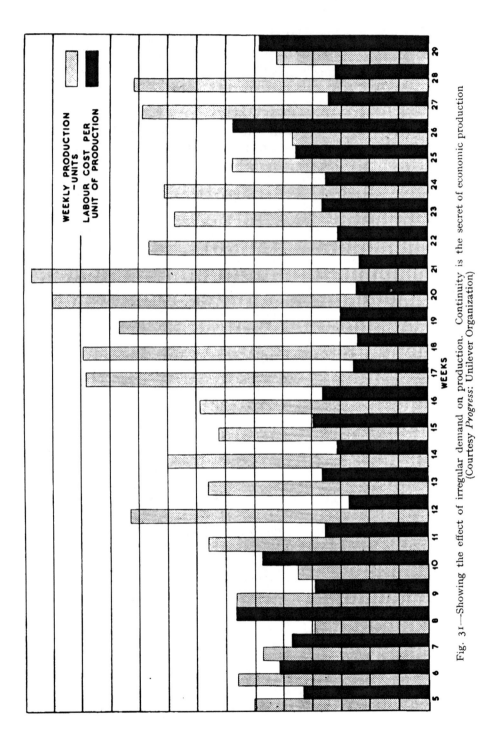

Fig. 31—Showing the effect of irregular demand on production. Continuity is the secret of economic production
(Courtesy *Progress*: Unilever Organization)

product factory—but not for love. The sooner that there is recognition of the fact that efficiency cannot be divided or isolated, the better it will be for industry as a whole. Inefficiency, no matter where it occurs, demands its price and the fact that it is hidden from sight does not, in any way, mitigate the penalty. This is, possibly, a divergence, but it must be recognized that flow production in the suppliers' factories will have the same important effects as in the end product factories—that is the production of more goods more efficiently and more economically.

As the volume increases, with the growth of the production unit, the movement of material in and out of the factories becomes a more formidable task. This calls for systemization on behalf of the producer of the finished goods and co-operation by the suppliers of the materials. It is patently foolish for suppliers to organize their factories to near-perfection internally only to have railway wagons and road vehicles held up for a place at the loading decks at either end. At a certain stage a strict timetable for the delivery and receipt of goods becomes an essential item of organization. It is well known that the major economies to-day come from the reduction of material handling, so external transportation is as important in this respect as internal handling. The ideal situation will arrive when the supplier is incorporated into the flow production line of the makers of end products, and this is the modern trend.

As previously indicated there is a tendency on the part of the end producers to accept materials without inspection—in other words to rely on the inspection at the suppliers' end. This, if it becomes accepted practice, will speed up the handling of inwards goods and, where palletized, the material could, if desired, travel direct from the suppliers to the producers' machines with the least possible delay.

In this connection there is an interesting development in U.S.A. and Canada where non-ferrous metals, including zinc and copper, are delivered in palletized form. Wooden pallets have been discarded in favour of ingots designed to provide floor clearance, which enables fork trucks to pick up the load. Thus the pallet becomes a consumable ingot. There are no returns and none of the paper work which returned empties are apt to entail.

The methods, all simple and effective, differ somewhat in different concerns. The patented system used by the Anaconda Copper Mining Co. of Great Falls, Montana, appears to be the most highly developed. Four base slabs, with feet, are laid down to form the pallet. These are overlaid with the normal type of slab, which only differs from the earlier types in having a projection at one end and a hole at the other. The projection is in the shape of a truncated four-square pyramid, the hole being the same shape in reverse. These slabs are built up on the base slab in criss-cross fashion—projections engaging with holes—which interlock gives the bundle horizontal stability. (Fig. 32.)

The normal thickness of the slabs is 1¼in., but the base slabs—cast integral with the feet—which provide 2½ in. clearance for the truck fork, are 3¾ in. thick. The slabs are piled 18 high (25 in) including the base slabs. Thus there are 72 slabs in the bundle, which weighs 3,320 lb. The whole is held together by steel straps which are stretched and crimped, in a seal, to prevent slipping of the banding. Methods of making up the bundles to economize time in handling have been worked out to a nicety at the supplier's end; while at the receiving end the bundle can be checked, weighed and, unless bonded for analysis report, passed direct to the processing department. (Fig. 33.)

In this country palletized delivery of metal is not unknown. Mazak zinc is forwarded from Avonmouth to Meccano, Ltd. in Liverpool, on wooden pallets which are checked into stores and straight out to the pressure die-casting machines just as received. The consumable pallet has been introduced by the Imperial Smelting Corporation, Ltd., for zinc die-casting alloys and by BKL, Ltd., for aluminium ingot.

These examples serve to stress that the idea of flow need not be confined to the end product factories, but that it can be projected backwards to the secondary and primary industries. It can also be projected forward into distribution and even into after-sales service.

To sum up—the delivery of material to a predetermined timetable is an essential if the flow is to be maintained without interruption and, in

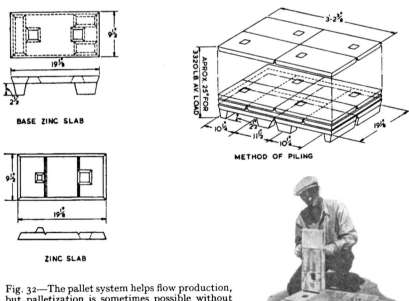

BASE ZINC SLAB

ZINC SLAB

METHOD OF PILING

Fig. 32—The pallet system helps flow production, but palletization is sometimes possible without pallets. The diagram on the left shows how the Anaconda Copper Mining Co. make ingots serve as pallets; that on the right shows how the ingots are piled. The photograph shows a parcel of ingot being built up

Fig. 33—This shows how easy it is to handle Mazak zinc ingot when it is palletized. Each of these parcels weighs 448 lb. There are no "returns". The steel binding strip is the only wastage. (Courtesy Imperial Smelting Corporation Ltd.)

the grosser instances, to avoid both glut and shortage. Flow production cannot be flooded with material at one time and starved at another. In most factories it would be a physical impossibility to hold the flood; while starvation of only one component could easily bring a whole plant to a standstill.

The seventh principle will now be dealt with. It is really an extension of the sixth, bringing us on to the factory floor and within the ambit of the operators of the machines and other plant.

Principle 7—The Machines Must be Continually Fed with Sound Material

It goes without saying that every machine must regularly be provided with usable material. This is the only way to ensure even flow. The provision of appropriate quantities of castings, forgings, bar, sheet or what-have-you in the proper place at the right time poses problems of material movement and control. These problems largely consist of handling quantities of material expeditiously, and of keeping sufficient reservoirs of stock to cover predictable shortages of supplies from outside and to provide against local mishaps on the production lines. Predictable is the operative word because large margins of safety are undesirable since they represent frozen capital locked up both in goods and in accommodation. This matter of accommodation is so important that some concerns have cut down the margin of supplies behind machine and assembly lines to almost unbelievably small quantities; figures as low as three hours in hand have been quoted for U.S.A. but no factory in England works within quite such fine limits as yet.

Consideration of this problem reveals how the idea of continuous flow is a stimulus for the elimination of the causes of obstruction and delay. Here is an illuminating example taken from a concern which had to carry a comparatively large buffer stock. One of the major difficulties of carrying the stock arose from the fact that the easiest

Flow production is assisted by "storage" that flows.

Fig. 34A—*Above*: Cellular bunkers for the storage of components which must be used in sequence. Input end of the installation is shown here. *Below*: The side of the cellular bunkers for the storage of components which must be used in sequence

Fig. 34B—The delivery end of cellular bunkers for the storage of components

approach to the stockpile was from one side or the top. This meant that the bulk of the buffer stock was not drawn upon until an emergency arose. Then, owing to the length of time that the material had been on hand, it was found that the remoter portion of the stock was obsolete. This may have been due, perhaps, to a detail modification in the design, to a change in the material specification, or to trouble arising from a hidden fault not discoverable by the raw material inspection. These could all be responsible for a hold-up despite the stocking precaution.

This disability was overcome by the use of a specially designed storage bunker. The bunker was divided into some 80 cells, 20 horizontally and four vertically. Each cell was approximately 65 ft. in length and 20 × 30 in. in cross-section. The floor of each cell was made up of roller track set at a sufficient angle to ensure that the contents would gravitate from the inwards to the outwards end. Upon these tracks the larger components went bare or were carried on skids. The smaller parts were loaded into tote boxes. Stacking machines, at each end, were used for loading and unloading and, since the cells were always filled at the one end and emptied at the other, the material was used in exactly the same sequence as delivered. Incidentally, the method of using open bins with an "in" and "out" side is a very useful device for packages and boxed goods which, preferably, should not remain too long in stock. (Fig. 34.)

Fig. 35—Another aid to flow. Gravity lowering device for use in feeding flow lines in storeyed buildings

The method of delivering the material to the machines varies with the shape and size of the components, the position of the machine line and the distance that has to be traversed. For instance, in storied buildings the stores can be on the top floor when the parts can be delivered by chutes, conveyors, or gravity lowering devices which, when the lowest piece is lifted from the arms or platform, automatically bring the next piece into position. (Fig. 35.)

On the level, the components can be delivered by conveyors which may follow the piece through the machining operations or by tote boxes, trolleys or fork-lift trucks, the latter being favoured where there is a "lift" on to the machine. Fork-lift trucks have gained much ground owing to their flexibility in use and it would seem that for many purposes they compete heavily against the conveyor. The conveyor has, however, the great advantage that it is a "stores in transit" from which parts can be taken—or left—as required by the situation of the moment—but here we are encroaching on the subject matter of a later chapter.

CHAPTER SEVEN

ACHIEVING CONTINUOUS OPERATION

Principle 8—Processing must be Progressive and Continuous

IN SO FAR as the individual factory is concerned, this is the principle that goes to the root of the whole matter of flow production. All the other principles are contributory to this central idea of a progressive and continuous process. There are, of course, other aspects to be considered later, but at the factory floor level the ultimate aim of the establishment is summed up in the words "progressive and continuous processing"—progressive in the sense that the work advances from stage to stage and continuous in the sense that it is never interrupted in its straight-line flow.

This phrase "straight-line flow" must not, of course, be taken too literally. The shape of the factory may not permit long machine lines or assembly tracks, and it may be necessary for them to go round corners, to double back, on themselves in U formation or to go up and down or across the shop several times. This, in particular, applies in storey buildings which, for natural lighting purposes, are usually restricted to a width of 60 ft. (Fig. 36.)

The term "straight-line" is used to indicate that there is no divergence from continuous and progressive flow, that there is no backtracking to a previous operation and no crossing of the flow line, for any purpose, by the components in operation. This is an essential condition in flow production and it is one which must be constantly and vigilantly watched, for it is so easy to make alterations in process without rearranging the plant to suit until the time comes when (as has happened) the works manager says, when examining a flow chart— "Huh! Looks like a wireless diagram struck by lightning."

As we have seen, flow production commenced with the assembly line and then spread to the machine shops, being applied first to the larger, heavier components and then to the smaller parts. In the beginning the machines were grouped more or less in operation sequence, the work being man-handled from one machine table to the next. Later the machines were joined to each other by slides, chutes or roller track. At this juncture certain anomalies became apparent. For instance, original layouts, which diverged from the straight-line ideal, came in for sharp criticism: machine tables were found to be at differing and sometimes inconvenient heights: frontal presentation of the workpiece was often extremely troublesome: power points were

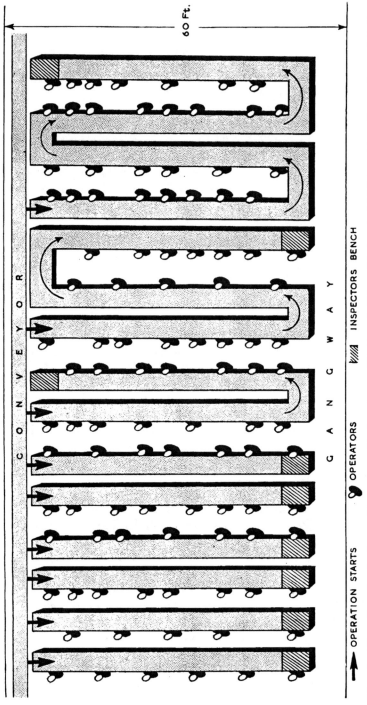

Fig. 36—Alternative planning for machine or assembly lines in a multi-storey building, showing straight lines—return lines and convolute lines. Where the inspector's bench is remote, an overhead pendulum conveyor returns the finished components to the gangway. The roller track on the gangway side is "gated" to give employees access to the gangway

frequently inconveniently placed: delays due to tool changing became conspicuous and swarf removal was (and, indeed, often still is) a major nuisance: moreover, inspection had to be brought into line with the new layout.

To-day every conceivable device is in use to provide ease of handling, swift operation and smoothness of flow. The old style of layout has vanished or is quickly disappearing—partitions have been swept away and departments have been merged. The most modern factory buildings with their broad open spaces of 100 to 200 ft. in width, without a stanchion, with a complete absence of shafting, seem to emphasize and indeed do typify the revolution that has taken place. It is common practice to find lathes, milling machines, shapers, drill presses, boring mills, grinding machines and even heat-treatment furnaces and shot-blasting apparatus strung out in line—each connected by gravity slides, roller tracks, pendulum conveyors and other handling devices—and now the inspectors' benches are in line with the miscellaneous collection of machines that are arranged to suit the evolutionary processing of the product.

In the latest phases we have the automatic transfer machines which—combining any and all types of cutting heads on a single bed—clamp, machine, release and move the workpiece from station to station without human aid or intervention. The sole manual work on these machines is that of loading castings, stampings or what you will, at one end, and removing the finished job at the other.

In many cases the components literally never touch the floor after they have once been lifted on to a machine for the initial operation—so the term "floor-to-floor time" becomes an anachronism. The workpieces flow from the machine lines to sub-assembly lines and on to the main assembly line, where they are embodied in the finished product. It is an essential of flow production that the machinery shall be laid out in the natural sequence demanded by the component.

To obtain continuous operation it is essential that every operation that stops or slows the operator must be removed. Tool changing must be organized. The smaller tools, such as drills and reamers, can be dealt with by quick-change chucks. Milling cutters, on the other hand, present greater difficulty, particularly when they are large in size. These should be examined during rest periods and replaced during meal breaks. They should be resharpened immediately so that they are available without delay for the next change. In one case, where very large cutters were used, it was found desirable to have the grinding machine alongside the group of milling machines on which the cutters were used, and such a method is justified in exceptional circumstances. The changing of jig bushes, the adjustment of machines, the lubrication and cleaning-down should also be effected during meal breaks, or otherwise when the normal working day is over.

Fig. 37—The removal of chips is not the least of the flow problems. This is a chip conveyor on an automatic transfer machine

The removal of cuttings is quite a problem.* In some of the transfer machines a screw- or other-type conveyor is used for chips removal, but the ideal method for handling the chips made by a miscellaneous group of high-production machines has not yet been conceived. Conveyors of the type which require troughs in the floors are not desirable in view of the fact that this prevents a quick change-round of the machines if demanded by a variation of product or design. (Fig. 37.)

The human factor should be given high, if not first, priority when considering the establishment of flow production. The removal of physical obstacles to continuity is indeed important, but to obtain the whole-hearted support and co-operation of those who operate the plant is still more important. In fact, many of the physical obstacles will, on analysis, be found to be those that also provoke a mental or moral reluctance, or even resistance, to the performance of a task. Too much exertion, over-reaching, a bad stance, uncomfortable conditions and the like have their undesired repercussions. The advantage of flow production is that usually these matters are brought to light because of the continuous study that can be applied, since the machine lines or assembly tracks throw up any weaknesses in the methods employed.

When working as a team to produce a completed article, the operators will, as a rule, impose the necessary discipline. A wise

* The new Ford-Cleveland engine plant has to deal with 185 tons of dry and 45 tons of wet chips each day.

manager will encourage this teamwork and will take into account all those matters which lead to interference with the normal task, particularly those which influence men to leave their stations. Among these is the desire to smoke or for refreshment. The remedy is found in permission to smoke at all times, except in dangerous areas, and the opportunity for a "bite and a sup" during the rest period. Some firms provide a cafeteria service at such times, but this can become a very expensive luxury. Other delays are caused by such miscellaneous matters as shutting doors and windows against draughts, wandering around in search of tools, lubricants, cotton waste, dealing with wage complaints and such like. Here the remedy is obviously in the hands of the management. Cloakroom needs present greater difficulty, but nearby accommodation reduces time spent away from the job and this, like gossip, is one of the things in which team co-operation can be so very helpful.

Absenteeism can best be mitigated by forming a "flying squad" composed of men who have knowledge of all operations. These can, normally, be employed in some occupation from which they can be spared for short periods; for instance, on rectification, service repairs or maybe the machine-tool demonstration bay. These men can be rushed to any danger point when accident, or illness, causes a gap in the operation line, and so the work can carry on without interruption. In a large concern, some of the flying squad may be permanently employed as relays. For brief periods the charge-hand may step into the breach, and this has a tonic effect on the remainder of the team who will see in their supervisor a man who is still with, as well as over, them.

There is another form of continuity which must be considered—that of continuous plant operation. Modern capital equipment is extremely expensive and is liable to become a tremendous burden when based on a week of 44 hours or less. (Incidentally it must be appreciated that 44 hours gross is just about 39 hours net.) This can be alleviated by the adoption of the two-shift or three-shift systems. The shift system can be operated successfully provided that it is framed in such a way that it does not too materially alter the habits of the workers; that is to say, when it does not too greatly interfere with the domestic arrangements of wives and families, when travelling facilities are available, when it provides some daylight hours for recreation and shopping, and

	A			B	
Shift	*Commence*	*Finish*	*Shift*	*Commence*	*Finish*
Morning	6.00	2.00	Morning	7.00	3.00
Afternoon	2.00	10.00	Evening	3.00	11.00
Night	10.00	6.00	Night	11.00	7.00

TABLE I: Timetable for double and treble shifts.

some hours of darkness for sleep. The most acceptable shift hours would appear to be either as tabulated at A or B in Table I.

The double day shift based on these hours is commonly worked in U.S.A. on a five-day week basis. The meal break is for 30 minutes only; thus the nominal working time is $37\frac{1}{2}$ hours per shift per week, or 75 hours against our more usual 44. Saturdays and Sundays are only worked when the nature of the process precludes a shut-down. The three-shift system is not very satisfactory in machine shops for two main reasons. First, there is no available time for adjustments; second, there is no period during which the machines can cool off, and they are not normally designed for continuous 24-hour service without attention. A third reason which is very real, although it may appear frivolous, is that when trouble ensues it is always: "George done it" and "George" can never be found. Further, the third shift tends to upset the habits of the household much more than either shift on the two-shift system.*

In double-shift working it is essential that a supervisory staff should work the same hours as the shift workers. Any other method is likely to cause trouble, for it must be remembered that superintendents, foremen and charge-hands are, to a continously operated plant, what the engineers, artificers and mechanicians are to a ship at sea. Indeed, in many ways, the ship analogy is very suitable for continuous production.

Another desirable feature in operating these systems is that of training operators to do several jobs. This is not only advantageous for the operators themselves but is of very considerable help in manning a continuously operated plant. There is, for instance, the formation of the flying squad previously mentioned. Operators who have had the opportunity of working on many and various machines and assembly lines make ideal flying-squad men.

A point to be remembered is that, in order to get the full co-operation of the works force, redundancy must be dealt with in a realistic fashion by studying the placing of those likely to become redundant before new plant or methods, which are likely to cause displacement, are put into operation. This is most important since flow production is not merely a matter of machinery or material handling or systemization: it is a *marriage of mechanism and management*, and it is the exercise of the more advanced methods of management that ensures the success of flow production.

In this connection it must be remembered that flow production does

---

* A night shift of four nights of 11 hours per night with two meal breaks is in favour in some localities in the British Isles. This means commencing at 6.00 p.m. and finishing at 6.00 a.m., or perhaps from 7.00 p.m. to 7.00 a.m., or even from 8.00 p.m. to 8.00 a.m. The actual times will be dictated by the available transport and local works conditions. The advantage of this system is that the workers have from Friday morning to Monday evening free and it does provide a 44-hour week.

not necessarily mean the installation of expensive plant and special machines. On the contrary, quite ordinary plant with simple tooling, properly arranged and suitably operated, can give some quite surprising results. It is true that the large and costly automatic transfer machines represent the zenith, the culmination of the system, but these are only installed where the nature of the operations and the quantity of components to be handled justify the use of super-machines. All the present flow production factories started in a modest fashion, building up their techniques and their equipment step by step, only taking the greater strides as and when new designs or greater demands created the opportunities.

In the earlier stages of flow production it is essential that the lines should be kept flexible, so that alterations can be made without difficulty. In general, there should be little difficulty in modifying assembly lines, but machine lines can be troublesome unless foresight is exercised. To ensure the utmost flexibility, standard machines should be used and they should be of the individual motor-drive type in order that there will be no shafting to consider when revamping the layout. Machines should not be bolted to the floor except where absolutely necessary (e.g. drilling machines). Troughs and channels in the floor should be avoided—much better to raise the machine where normally there would be a pit, but this, of course, does not apply to such pieces of plant as large presses which must have deep foundations.* For these the pre-planning must be as far-sighted as possible, since once they are sited they must remain. Arrangements should be made for all machine tables to be at common height for specific components; this may involve the packing-up of the machine and maybe a platform for the operator. The machines can be connected by chutes or roller track in the first instance, and conveyors can be installed when circumstances invite this addition. Portable conveyor units, now available, offer considerable advantages.

Electric power connections should be made by down-droppers from an overhead grid. Electrical conduits should never be laid in the floor. In laying out a machine line, it should not be forgotten that, given suitable jigs and fixtures, the pillar drill is one of the most adaptable of the simpler machine tools, and also that many minor types of special machines can be improvised with the aid of powered portable tools.

Except where the product is so firmly established that long-period forecasts of required production can be made, freedom to change the layout of both machine and assembly lines to suit the changing character of, and the modified demands for, the product must be retained.

When planning for flow production, it is essential to take into account

---

* The smaller power presses are sometimes mounted in a grid foundation. These can be moved to match a new sequence when necessary.

all differences and variations that would disturb the straight-line flow. If this is done it is remarkable how many variations of the same type of product the flow production system can deal with concurrently. At one period, for instance, the Ford Motor Co. handled, in sequence, all current types of cars and trucks—without pause or intermission—on one assembly line. To-day, in their automatic assembly plant, the Austin Motor Co. handle three body types and right- and left-hand steering on the same assembly track. One American concern assembles 500 different sizes and types of air cleaners on one conveyor line. They do not, in this instance, come in sequence but by a changeover limited to a 24-hour run for any one model. These mutations can be matched on the machine lines provided sufficient care and attention is given to jig and fixture design, and the method of changing the tools is carefully studied. It will, of course, be appreciated that where this method is adopted the product has, so to speak, the same common denominator. It would not, for example, be feasible to machine or assemble baby carriages and bacon slicers on the same line: even to attempt it would violate the ninth principle.

CHAPTER EIGHT

TIME PLANNING

Principle 9—A Time Cycle must be Set and Maintained

IN FLOW PRODUCTION it is essential to have an overall time cycle for the factory. This will be based on the number of finished units that are passed to the despatch department or to warehouse during a normal working week. Thus, should the figure be 800 in a week of 40 hours net, the factory will be on a 3-minute time cycle, and all operational activities will be based on, or rather geared to, this three-minute period. In other words, each operation, or series of operations, will be a factor or a multiple of three minutes.

This brings in that most important question of balance which is the secret of the efficiency of flow production. Efficiency is largely a matter of timing, and the virtue of the flow line layout resides in the fact that it helps us to take control of the time that we are buying. It does this by making explicit the losses of time incurred in the activities of men, in the functioning of machines and in the movement of material.

Assembly lines are usually models of synchronized activity, especially when they are mechanically operated. The assembly track immediately reflects the efficiency of the organization, for it is not, within itself, subject to the causes of breakdown that fall to the lot of the machine lines. Hence the final assembly line can be regarded as a factory metronome—beating out the time and marking the pace for all the tributary lines. Every foreman, charge-hand and operator throughout the plant is well aware that unless in each hour "x" pieces or sub-assemblies go from his department to the assembly line the output stops!

To return to this matter of balance: before the establishment of a flow line, the operations on the particular component must be reviewed. They must be broken down into their elemental forms and production times, actual or estimated, must be set against each operation. Then the necessary machines and their equipment can be allocated to each task.

In some instances, it will be possible to combine operations by grouping certain elements together. Some operations may take double or treble the time cycle, in which case the machines or the machine heads will need to be duplicated or triplicated. Some operations which cannot be combined will take only part of the time cycle; this situation can be met by arranging for one man to handle two or three machines. Other jobs may take just that fraction more than the allotted span: for

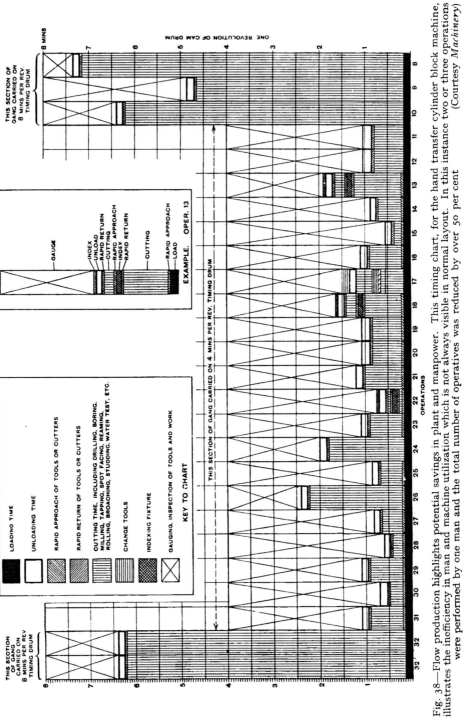

Fig. 38—Flow production highlights potential savings in plant and manpower. This timing chart, for the hand transfer cylinder block machine, illustrates the inefficiency in man and machine utilization which is not always visible in normal layout. In this instance two or three operations were performed by one man and the total number of operatives was reduced by over 50 per cent

(Courtesy *Machinery*)

this an increase in speed and feed coupled with the use of a more powerful machine and perhaps super-high-speed cutting tools may be the answer. Possibly a change in operation sequence or the introduction of a sub-operation will solve the problem. Frequently these troublesome fractions of time can be eliminated by modifying the fixtures to permit the more expeditious handling of the workpiece. Power clamping devices, operated hydraulically or by compressed air, may solve some such difficulty. Then again aluminium or magnesium might replace steel, cast iron or brass to reduce the cutting time.

Despite all the care and trouble that may be lavished on the original layout, there is every possibility, when the flow line is established, that desirable modifications become glaringly obvious. This should cause no anxiety, but should rather be a matter for rejoicing, for, as frequently stated, the virtue of flow production lies in the fact that it brings all inconsistencies into the light of day and so provides the opportunity for correcting them. Those responsible for any line layout can be very sure that, at least, they will have removed the grosser incongruities which were not apparent when operating under the batch system.

It is unlikely that automatic transfer or multiple-unit machines would be installed, except in circumstances where information respecting operations is very complete. It is, in fact, usual for these machines to be the outcome or, so to speak, the culmination of considerable experience in line production on a particular unit. It is, obviously, essential that this should be so, since the multiple unit machine has no flexibility comparable to a flow line built up of standard machines.

An example of the lack of balance of machine operations is indicated by the illustration of a timing chart detailing certain operations on the original cylinder block machine. Owing to the nature of the component the combination of the shorter operations was not possible without major alterations to the design. Nevertheless, when it is known that the 53 operations were handled by only 22 machine operators, it will be realized what a large saving in manpower was effected. (Fig. 38.)

Returning to the normal flow line, it is possible that there are danger points where machine lines may be unable to cope with certain conditions. In such circumstances a small stock of components may be carried on the floor, in racks, or as "stores in transit" on conveyors. It is the duty of the shop supervisors to see that these buffer stocks do not grow, either in the number of points or in the quantities carried, because they are an indication of inadequacy in material, in tools, in machines or in men and, more especially, in management. This again illustrates how the flow-line method throws into relief the faults of organization, for, if there is a hold-up at any point, it is due to some lack of foresight, to some remedial accident or to some want of co-operation.

Finally, working to a time cycle demands discipline. This discipline cannot be relaxed when demand is scarce. It is essential that, whatever other adjustments have to be made, the time cycle must be held. When demand is low it may, unfortunately, be necessary to work short time. When the demand is above normal, overtime will look after small increases, while the greater increases may demand an additional shift or an extension of the works. Many variations can be met by a combination of judicious stocking coupled with increased working hours. However this may be, the time cycle, once set, must be strictly maintained.

Nevertheless, there is a moral force about flow-line production which, if properly understood, and rightly used, should make for better order and for more equity and justice in works administration.

The tenth principle is closely allied to that relating to the time cycle and is dealt with next.

Principle 10—Operations must be Based on Motion Study and Time Study

This is an unmistakable truism, since the whole of flow production is an exercise in motion and time study; being, in fact, motion and time studies carried to their logical conclusions.

Yet, even in the most advanced flow production establishments there will be a considerable number of individual jobs where the whole operation is carried out on one machine, or where a minor assembly or fitting operation is performed by one man. These will, of course, be subject to the classic motion and time study techniques on which there is such ample information. Again, in flow lines which are built up of individual machines, standard or otherwise, the normal methods will be used for the balancing of the various operations. Naturally a close study will be made before the flow line is set up, but even when it is established it may be desirable to check and recheck the methods and movements employed; particularly in striving for the equalization of time and task. The approach will follow the well-tried analysis of those tasks which take the longest time, and the breaking of them down into manageable proportions, coupled with the endeavour to combine or amalgamate the shorter operations.

With the multiple-unit and automatic transfer machines the situation is very different, since in these the mechanical element preponderates so greatly over the human factor. It is true that the loading and unloading of the components may be subjected to the normal method of rate fixing, with the object of seeing that the machine is never retarded by manual lack of dexterity or by inefficiency but, more often than not, the time permissible will be large enough to compensate for any human failings. In automatic transfer machines the whole of the timing sequence must be pre-planned with exactness and precision, and for this time and motion study must be combined with operation study and machine capacity analysis, and the whole integrated with design for production studies. In brief, the layout of these machines calls for

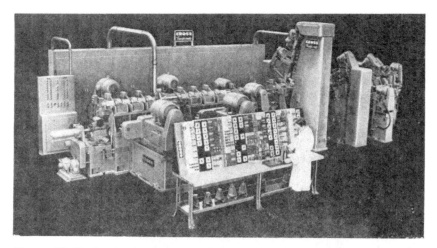

Fig. 39—The Toolometer is a special tool crib allotted to an automatic transfer machine. It combines storage with an automatic reminder of necessary tool changes Note the appliances in foreground.
Right: A Toolometer panel with gauges on left, tool "cartridges" in centre and meters at right of picture.
Below: A general view of the Toolometer panel with the tool setting fixtures in the foreground (Courtesy *Machinery*)

the total co-operation of all those concerned with design and production, and with the machine-tool designer and builder as well.

In this class of machinery there is a further factor to be studied. The feeds and speeds must be so set that the cutting tools will not need to be changed during a working day. For real efficiency, tool changing can only be permitted at meal breaks or after work is finished for the day—not, be it noted, between shifts. The between-shift changeover may necessitate a pause, but it should not be the occasion for a break in continuity of operation. A correspondent from the Ford Motor Co., in U.S.A., stresses this point when writing about automatic transfer machines. He says:

"Of course, there are some disadvantages to this type of equipment. Perhaps the worst is idle time resulting from changing tools. This has been somewhat overcome by using rapid change chucks and collets; nevertheless, this is not possible when using milling cutters. Best results are obtained by following a pre-determined schedule."

In order to solve the problem of organized tool changes the Cross Company of Detroit have introduced the Toolometer. This is, in effect, a special tool crib which is allocated to a specific automatic transfer machine. The Toolometer carries a series of dials with indicator hands which are operated by the "cycling" of the machine. When the safe limit for tool operation is reached a warning is given; in some instances the dial mechanism is set to stop the machine, in others there is a pre-set hand which, when overtaken by a sweep hand, lights a red lamp to call the attention of the operator to the need for a tool change. There is also a segment on each dial, marked in red, to show the minimum and maximum life allotted to the tools. When the machine is stopped for a tool change the operator will, in all probability, change all the tools that are "in the red", thus avoiding unnecessary breaks in production. (Fig. 39.)

The tools, which are in duplicate to avoid lengthy stoppages if a tool should fail before the resharpened items are available, are accommodated in pockets in the control panel. Colours help to identify the various panels with the section of the machine to which the tools belong. This helps the operator to make a quick tool change, since he knows where to look for tools and where to find the heads. The Toolometer includes a bench upon which are mounted setting fixtures for obtaining the correct length of tools in the adjustable tool holders. These gauges, when not in use, are held on the panel adjacent to the tool housing. It is stated that the Toolometer system enables tools to be changed in as short a time as 2 minutes from stop to start. Here is an outstanding example of the solving of a problem by management aided by mechanism.

For checking results when flow lines are first installed, the Servis Recorder is a very useful instrument. Applied to a machine or to an assembly track, this clockwork mechanism will record all stoppages and, if the charts are completed, by the addition of detailed reasons for any time lost in production it becomes easy for those in charge of the plant to work back to the originating causes. (Fig. 40.)

The author is much impressed by the ability with which a gang of operators will find their own best methods of handling their work when engaged on a flow-line set-up. This is particularly noticeable under incentive systems of payment. This aptitude, like the self-imposed discipline mentioned earlier, should be encouraged by management, since it gives an added interest to a repetitive task. If the motion and time study engineers will assist by timely suggestions, they will probably

find that this self-help method is more profitable than the more professional approach; moreover, it is in line with the modern co-operative technique of management.

Fig. 40—On flow lines the Servis Recorder is invaluable for locating the incidence of lost time, particularly on assembly lines. The photograph below shows a Servis Recorder applied to a printing machine. (Courtesy Servis Recorders, Ltd.)

CHAPTER NINE

ACCURACY OF WORKMANSHIP

Principle 11—Accuracy of Work must be Strictly Maintained

FOR THE FOLLOWING reasons, accurate workmanship is an essential for flow production. Firstly, belt assembly does not permit of individual fitting: therefore the components must be correct within the limits and tolerances set by the engineering department, who are responsible for the allowances which determine the class of fit. With the aids that now exist for the production of accurate work, it is well within the capacity of the modern machine shop to produce work that needs neither file nor scraper to make the fit perfect. Indeed, it is true to say that no hand fitting can equal the machine on normal work. It is equally true to say that such perfection is only maintained by constant vigilance.

Secondly, reprocessing cannot be tolerated in a flow production establishment since it is liable to throw the whole plant out of balance. In the past, instances have been known where an entire factory has had to close until one department had recovered a lost situation; and it can happen to-day. Thirdly—and this is vastly more important than the foregoing—mass and flow producing units serve very wide markets; therefore, troubles arising from bad or indifferent workmanship have extremely wide repercussions. It is exceedingly difficult to give prompt and satisfactory service when epidemic trouble arises and this is always a possibility unless the utmost care is exercised.

Since the control of quality is of such prime importance, it will be found that inspection, in such establishments as we are considering, is regarded as one of the major functions of management. As this is so, it follows that the officer in charge of quality should have full managerial status that, in fact, he should be in a position which renders him independent of other departmental heads. It is obvious that as a subordinate to the production chief it would be difficult for him to take an effective stand on border-line cases. (Incidentally, it has been wisely said: "Production is responsible for quality: inspection measures the achievement".) Similarly, if he should be subject to the chief engineer there might be difficulty in establishing that certain details of design tend to more wastage than need be. For these reasons, in many concerns, the inspection manager is solely responsible to the highest executive.

It is also desirable that all functions concerned with quality should come under the inspection manager. This covers raw material, bought-in finished components, own production components, complete end products and the routine testing of the same. It should, preferably include the inspection of machine tools and small tools including, under this heading, jigs, fixtures, tools and gauges. Travelling inspectors who visit distributors and customers should, of course, report to the inspection manager. While this wide range of duties may not be recognized in every flow production concern, it must be conceded that it is only logical to have all matters—concerned with the control of quality—centralized, and the responsibility for quality definitely and unequivocally assigned.

In so far as minor repetition parts are concerned there is, frequently, no difference between the flow production and the batch method of inspection; but the conveyor is being pressed into service as evidenced by the following description. In one plant the machines are arranged on both sides of a conveyor which is divided longitudinally into a series of troughs, the sides being wooden slats while the bottom is the actual conveyor belt. Each machine is provided with a chute into which the finished parts are placed to gravitate to the allotted trough or channel. By this means the parts travel to the inspection bench where they are deflected into their own small bins which are gated so that the parts can be discharged into tote boxes. The inspector sits on a chair—mounted on ball-bearing wheels running on rails—which can be effortlessly propelled from one end of the bench to the other. The inspection appliances are arranged in appropriate places on the bench so the inspector can pick up the parts, in rotation, as they are received from the machines. If any are out of standard the operator is notified and the tool setter takes charge. This method, with local variations, can be found in several modern factories. (Fig. 41.)

The methods on flow lines, where a large number of operations have to be performed, differ considerably from normal practice. Intermediate inspection is not so necessary as in batch production because, despite the fact that inspection is delayed until the finished component reaches the end of the line, there are so few parts in process of operation that, in event of trouble, it is possible to stop the machine with probably only a half-dozen pieces out of standard. Moreover, it is usual to station an inspector at all points where there is likelihood of trouble. For instance, it would probably be desirable, on a cylinder block line, to have inspectors gauging the bores immediately after the finished boring or honing operation. It is obvious that the procedure on a flow line must be dictated by the possibilities, or rather the probabilities, of inaccurate work arising from a specific operation. In many cases a patrol inspector is able to watch all these key points and so to keep the line free from trouble.

Sometimes it may be desirable to combine inspection with a minor operation; for example, de-burring is frequently necessary before

Fig. 41—The following four photographs show how components continuously
flow from machines to inspection and thence to assembly

In a pressure die-casting shop chutes lead from the machines to a slat conveyor
which takes the castings to the inspector
(Courtesy Birmingham Aluminium Casting (1903) Co. Ltd.)

Chutes from these machines feed the conveyor belt with finished components.
The conveyor delivers them to the viewer
(Courtesy Fisher and Ludlow, Ltd.)

Conveyor from a line of machines to inspection bench. The inspectress
is on right of photograph
(Courtesy Automotive Products, Ltd.)

The inspectress is seated on a mobile chair. The components are delivered
into standardized tote boxes. A power-driven screw gauge lies by her
right hand
(Courtesy Automotive Products, Ltd.)

gauging is possible. Again, minor assemblies may serve the dual purpose of inspecting by actually putting the pieces together. These are practical and economical methods of making the best of flow production.

There are, today, many aids to improve the quality of inspection and to accelerate the gauging and testing operations. Among the former the X-ray and ultrasonic methods for revealing internal defects must be counted. The X-ray method is not generally used on production runs except for aircraft parts. It is, however, invaluable when developing new casting techniques in zinc and light alloys, particularly in the pressure die-casting field. It is to be hoped that the ultrasonic method may prove equally useful with iron castings. Miniature testing by means of the Hounsfield Tensometer and the smaller impact machines is also a great help in the development stage. Crack detectors are useful for both raw material and for inspection of finished parts. They can be used "in line" with the production machines. To speed up raw material inspection there is chemical analysis by the spectroscope and one American concern has developed a direct-reading "spectrometer" by which a molten charge of steel can be chemically analysed in 40 seconds.

In the machine shops the sampling methods of "statistical quality control" have made considerable headway with the resultant elimination of an enormous amount of handling, while multi-dimension inspection machines would appear to be able to keep pace, on a 100 per cent basis, with the terrific output of modern automatics.

Additional help in this difficult task is provided by receiver gauges which will not permit the component to enter the next operation stage unless it is correct in vital particulars. Direct-reading and dial recording instruments also reduce the chances of gauging errors while speeding up the operations. In order to keep an uninterrupted flow of operation, some concerns have adopted the method of allowing the operators to inspect their own work. Coupled with this is a system of rewards for work properly done and a penalty for allowing "out-of-gauge" work to pass. The reward is in the form of a bonus and the penalty that of losing the bonus and having official inspection re-imposed. Other firms have adopted the method of making the next operator the inspector of the previous operation. This has much to recommend it, since it is frequently difficult, and sometimes impossible, for men to be entirely objective about their own work. Such methods may help, very considerably, to reduce the high cost of inspection without lowering the standards.

Balancing is frequently regarded as a function of inspection and for this the Gisholt Co. have introduced a "line operation for measuring and correcting the out-of-balance in automobile crankshafts". The "unbalance" measurements made on the Dynetric balancing

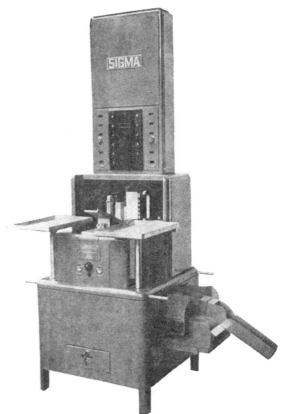

Fig. 42—In flow production inspection should match production speeds. The Sigma automatic multi-dimension inspection machine, as illustrated, makes this possible. These machines can be chute-, hopper- or magazine-fed, with delivery into tote boxes or on to conveyors. Rejected parts which can be reworked are separated from those which are completely out of standard. The machines can be reset for a different component in 12-15 mins. (Courtesy Alfred Herbert, Ltd., and Sigma Instrument Co. Ltd.)

machine are used to control, automatically, the depth of the drilling by which the correction is made, thus eliminating the possibility of human error. This reduces handling so considerably that it can be regarded as a part of the flow-production line, whereas in the past this operation was liable to be a bottleneck. The method of balancing clutch parts employed by Borg & Beck is noteworthy for the simplicity that can be introduced by a study of flow production methods. The balancing of the clutch part is one of the operations on the assembly line. The part is removed from the conveyor belt, placed in the balancing machine and plugs of different colours are inserted in that portion of the component where the drilling for balancing takes place. The component is then passed to a drilling machine where the exact amount of metal is removed in accordance with the colour indication and the part is replaced on the conveyor belt for subsequent operations. (Fig. 43.)

Earlier it was suggested that machine tool and small tool inspection should lie within the province of the inspection manager. This is a logical development. In the first place the inspection department should be responsible for gauges. From there it is only a short step to

Fig. 43—The Gisholt crankshaft balancer is an "in-line" machine. The instrument on the left locates and measures the "out-of-balance" and the machine on the right corrects it by drilling

(Courtesy B.S.A. Tools, Ltd.)

responsibility for jig bushes and finally for jigs, tools and fixtures. Ultimately, it is only a short remove for the inspection department to be responsible for the inspection of the machine tools themselves. There should, of course, be a complete liaison with the tool room and machine repair departments.

In large-scale production there is always the question of salvage of parts which have been rejected as faulty. In oversizes these can be reworked and put back into the line of production, but in undersizes this is not usually possible. Some companies, however, have found that it is economic to restandardize such parts for other purposes. Be this as it may, all salvage should be kept apart from the normal production run and, again, it is logical to regard the salvage section as part of the inspection department.

Incidentally, it is a prime mistake to be too easy with borderline production, for rigid standards are necessary to ensure good work. It needs considerable strength of will to resist the temptation to "let up" on inspection, but to do so is to enter on a very slippery slope whose destination is disaster. It might here be remarked that such troubles as are experienced are much more liable to be due to indifferent assembly than to poor machining. This is particularly so with "closed jobs" which, while they may permit of testing, do not lend themselves to inspection as such. The moral is obvious—assembly should be done by well-trained and reliable workpeople who should not be unduly hurried.

CHAPTER TEN

LONG-TERM PLANNING

Principle 12—Long-term Planning Based on Precise Knowledge is Essential

ROME WASN'T BUILT in a day, nor does flow production arrive overnight; but it can be achieved, even by small concerns, provided they have the potential demand, by careful long-term planning. In batch production, planning is a short-term day-to-day process involving continual changes in routing, machine loading, machine equipment, operation instruction and so forth. The long-term planning of a flow production plant is well defined at the Westinghouse Electric Corporation as: "(a) placing the right equipment, (b) coupled with the right method, (c) in the right place, (d) to permit the processing of a product unit in the most effective manner, (e) through the shortest possible distance, and (f) in the shortest possible time". To do this the planning department must, through its members, have knowledge of the product, of the capabilities, limitations and capacity of the machinery which the company can afford to purchase, of the machining and ancillary processes to be employed, of the operation times and the motion and time study analysis which help to build up those times, of operation sequence and routing, of material handling, of assembling and of plant layout. The chief planning officer must have the ability to visualize complete operation sequences and the processes required in such sequences. This information may be scattered in other departments of the factory according to the company organization set-up, but it must, ultimately, be collected in the planning department in order for the department to function efficiently.

Planning should be long-term. There should be a master plan, a five-year plan; a ten-year plan is not too long. It is within the writer's recollection that a 20-year plan was consummated in half that time. The overall plan is, of course, a matter of high policy; it is a matter for the directorate. Nevertheless, it must be available to those who are responsible for putting the plans into operation. To disclose a long-term project in its entirety might be, in certain circumstances, a premature action, but such plans must have substance and they must be on record. They can then issue as required, the advantage being that they will form a coherent pattern and will cover the strategical situation. Short-term planning will, in the nature of things, be subject to continual adjustment of detail, but if the long-term plan is sound such adjustments should fall well within the framework of the original

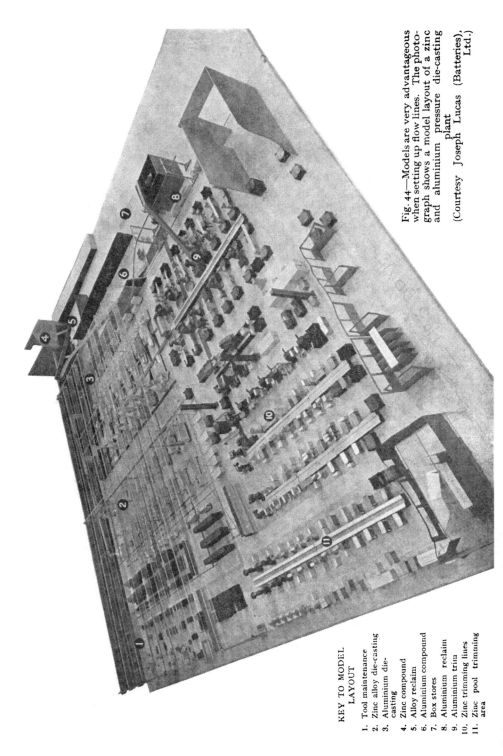

Fig. 44—Models are very advantageous when setting up flow lines. The photograph shows a model layout of a zinc and aluminium pressure die-casting plant

(Courtesy Joseph Lucas (Batteries), Ltd.)

KEY TO MODEL LAYOUT

1. Tool maintenance
2. Zinc alloy die-casting
3. Aluminium die-casting
4. Zinc compound
5. Alloy reclaim
6. Aluminium compound
7. Box stores
8. Aluminium reclaim
9. Aluminium trim
10. Zinc trimming lines
11. Zinc pool trimming area

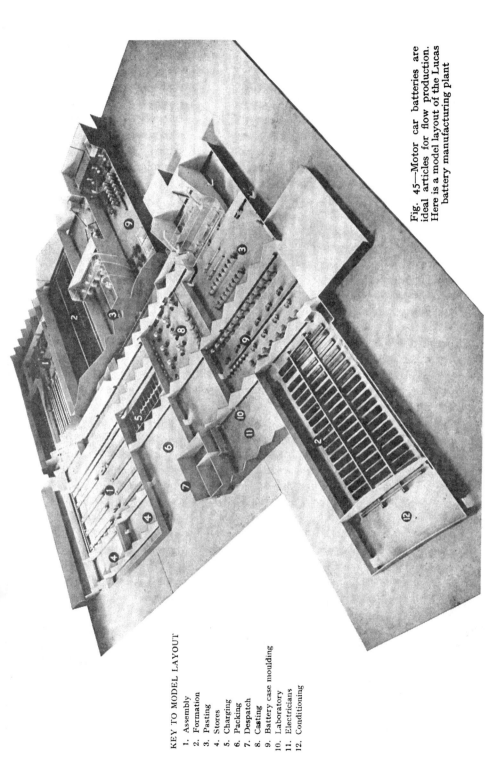

Fig. 45—Motor car batteries are ideal articles for flow production. Here is a model layout of the Lucas battery manufacturing plant

KEY TO MODEL LAYOUT

1. Assembly
2. Formation
3. Pasting
4. Stores
5. Charging
6. Packing
7. Despatch
8. Casting
9. Battery case moulding
10. Laboratory
11. Electricians
12. Conditioning

scheme. The adjustments will be due to minor changes in detail design, to differences in materials, to improved tooling and to the availability of new and improved machines. It is a healthy sign to have such changes provided that they are made with due care and deliberation.

Models, which can be regarded as drawings in three dimensions, are extremely useful for the layout of flow production lines. The third dimension is very important for indicating the position of the various services and particularly the run of the conveyor lines. Models have become even more valuable now that management has become conscious—in the words of the Report of the Materials Handling Productivity Team—"of the 'air-rights' of the factory".

In the Rootes Group assembly plant at Coventry the overhead route is not only used for conveying but for live storage of power units which otherwise would be occupying valuable ground-floor space. It is an awe-inspiring sight to see 350 engines suspended on a moving conveyor 26 ft. above the floor level and each moving to its appointed station in due time.

The use of models for planning layout of plant has everything in its favour. It is more economical of time than making drawings and, as the model stock is built up, it becomes more economical in cost. If the layout is shown to the foremen and charge-hands they can appreciate what is proposed and can frequently offer very good advice in connection with handling and so forth. When a new layout envisages many changes, it is wise to exhibit the model in the department to which it applies and to encourage the workpeople to make comments through the "suggestion box". Even when no suggestions are received, the fact that they know what is going to be done accustoms them to the idea and eliminates that hidden resentment to change of conditions which is a psychological factor we must all recognize as existing within us. (Figs. 44-45.)

The value of the model layout is quickly realized when a rapid revamping of machines or plant is necessary, e.g. owing to a seasonal change. The millwright staff can see at a glance precisely what moves have to be made and the order in which they should be undertaken. That models are not merely a fancy, but really serious business, is exemplified by the fact that the large American companies use this technique. Among them are the Ford Motor Co., Oneida Ltd., The Philco Corporation and the Dodge Division of Chrysler Motors. The latter is reputed to have a model stock of some 25,000 pieces of miniature plant. The model layouts are used to ascertain and illustrate how to economize in movement and how to make the most of available space.

The author used the model technique 30 years ago and was firmly convinced of its advantages. On one project, a contour model of a 40-acre site was made and hung on the wall like a picture. The pro-

KEY

A. Loading dock inwards
B. Loading dock outwards
C. Stores
D. Machine shop
E. Machine lines

 Flow of work

Conveyor

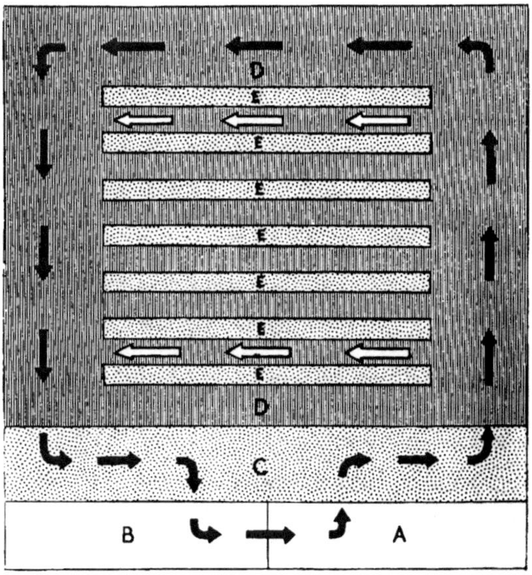

Fig. 46—This "inwards-outwards" conveyor layout shows how flow can be maintained in a machine shop making small components. The conveyor brings in raw material and takes away finished components

jected railway siding, roads, building, and so on, were painted in white on the green field background. As these became actual, a model was superimposed on the painted area so that the state of progress—virgin land, projected work and completed buildings—could be seen at a glance. Other more detailed models represented the interiors of the various shops showing the supporting columns, doorways, side wall windows, cloakrooms, lavatories, all the services and other essential information. On these floor layouts the models of the machinery with their roller track and conveyors were assembled in due order.

It was astonishing how frequently these models were visited by the senior members of management, but possibly "astonishing" is the wrong word, since here was the plant in miniature for immediate reference when any alteration was in contemplation or when any difficulty was encountered. Nothing suggests the complete effectiveness of the model layout so well as the French phrase *coup d'œil* for, literally, all the information required is, by these means, conveyed in a "blow of the eye".

Nowadays, models of machines can be purchased from model makers. These are representational and to a scale of ⅜ in. to the foot, which would appear to be ideal. Representational models may not be considered essential, but they add to the sense of reality and thus have considerable advantage over the template when the complete layout is being shown to those who are not well versed in the symbols of the drawing office. Moreover, as soon as the template is abandoned for blocks in three dimensions, the claims for the representational model become irresistible.

In planning it is necessary to arrange for reception of the incoming materials and to decide upon the method of handling, storing and issuing to the shops. The storage must, of course, be kept down to the minimum. That really means that planning starts with the suppliers. In one factory the inwards supply and outwards goods are both handled on different portions of the same loading dock and a conveyor of the pendulum type circulates right through the works, taking the raw materials on the outward half of its journey and bringing back the finished goods on the return half of its journey. This, of course, is only possible for the smaller finished products, but it is an excellent illustration of intensive planning. (Fig. 46.)

Then it is necessary to determine the most efficient arrangement of the essential machines and plant in the available space. This entails operation planning and an appreciation of operation sequence. It is essential that there should be a proper balance of machine capacity, but the full employment of the operators should come before studying the balancing of the machine capacities, the cost of manpower usually being considerably greater than that of machines. In fact, in many instances some idle machine time is extremely economical in saving the great expense of setting up the machines. Naturally, distances travelled will be as short as possible and all movements will be in straight lines. Wherever possible the movement of material should be mechanical and, when circumstances permit, materials should be handled automatically.

It will be appreciated that, although the routing of material is an essential part of planning, there will be no need for a progress department within the flow production works for flow production, being pre-planned, is self-progressive.

Those who are about to commence planning for flow production must not be disheartened if the whole product does not lend itself to this method. They must remember that, even in the most highly integrated factories, there is still a percentage—sometimes a fairly large percentage—of work that is not handled on flow production lines. This should serve as an encouragement to start flow production on those components where advantageous possibilities can be seen rather than to wait for the perfect product. Once started the system can be gradually extended to its reasonable limits. The golden rule is to commence with the assembly lines and work back. That is to say, start with the assembly lines so far as the internal arrangements are concerned: actually, as we have already noted, flow production starts with the sales department and extends throughout the whole organization.

Two warnings may be desirable, the first being that all flow production planning must be on a factual basis. Those about to plan must avoid falling in love with the mechanism of planning for its own sake. No mechanical handling devices should be installed unless there is a very clear view as to the reason why they are being adopted and a specific knowledge of the amount they are going to save. This applies to every item of mechanical equipment except where it is installed for safety reasons or to ease unduly hard labour. The other caution is that all experimental work should be conducted outside the production departments. The machine lines should never be interrupted in order to handle work of an experimental nature. Finally, if the company has had no experience of flow production, much trouble and grief might be saved by employing a consultant who has had the previous handling of such matters.

After the machine and assembly lines are set up, there is still a considerable amount for the planning engineer to watch. Every change in design and material, to say nothing of improvements in method, will make it necessary to consider the balance of the units of production throughout the line. But this is possible for, as mentioned several times before, high visibility conferred on the company's activities by flow production will lead to unceasing and continuous improvement.

In a word, flow production is another name for super-planning.

CHAPTER ELEVEN

MAINTENANCE

Principle 13—Maintenance must be by Anticipation—Never by Default

THAT MAINTENANCE is a matter of primary importance in flow production cannot be denied, since the efficiency of the system depends on the whole plant working in unison. It might appear that the advent of the transfer machine makes it more important still. This, however, is an inversion of the facts, the truth being that flow production and transfer machines both serve to stress a significance which has always existed but which has not been recognized for the vital matter that it is. These new methods throw into high relief the fact that proper and timely maintenance is essential for any form of quantity production.

In batch production the breakdown of the odd machine would not appear to be more than a slight inconvenience, because the considerable amount of work in progress tends to obscure the real issue. Fixtures and jigs can be transferred to another machine (the work on it can await a more convenient season). The operators can work overtime to catch up (at some extra cost). Moreover, it will not hurt the customer to wait a day or so longer. In other words, here are all the elements that make for loss of time, money and prestige—an epitome of inefficiency and delay.

In the flow production line there is no volume of work in progress and rarely, if ever, any machines to which fixtures and jigs can be transferred. If the breakdown is of a major character it will speedily affect the main assembly line. Thus flow production makes any delay due to failures in plant, machinery or equipment highly visible to everyone throughout the factory.

It will be seen from this that the haphazard maintenance which awaits failure before a repair is undertaken cannot be tolerated. It must give way to preconceived "timetable" or scheduled attention so that breakdowns never occur except as absolutely unforeseeable accidents. This applies to every item likely to cause delay; from faulty electrical contacts to slack bearings, and from sharpening cutters to changing jig bushes. Preventive maintenance may in the early stages be somewhat difficult of achievement because there may be no existing information upon which to base the scheduled attention. It will then be necessary to make an estimate of the number of pieces that can be made before attention becomes necessary and to correct the estimate as experience is gained.

Take, for example, jig bushes. At one plant, a considerable amount of trouble, found on testing a power unit, was due to sporadic seizures. This was traced to worn jig bushes in which the tools normally centred correctly, but would on occasions run to one side, thus causing subsequent difficulties. Investigation revealed a number of other components which were liable to suffer from similar trouble. The situation was met by setting a date—based on the projected output—on which the bushes were to be changed. And changed they were whether they showed visible signs of wear or not. The bushes were then carefully gauged and a fresh estimate of the probable length of life was made, this being extended at intervals until there were signs that the safe limit was reached. From this figure of longevity a percentage was deducted to cover contingencies and thus the basic timetable was established. In the first instance a few vital components were chosen for observation and the information gained therefrom served to "bracket" the figures for all the jig bushes throughout the plant. Used bushes were naturally always scrutinized to ensure that full advantage was being taken of the service of which they were capable.

This simple example serves to show how such data can be established without endangering production schedules. Success is dependent upon adopting a quite conservative estimate in the first instance and gradually extending it to suit the known conditions.

To cope with breakages and the wear and tear of machine tool components it is essential to carry, in stock, spare parts of such items as may be expected to give trouble. This emphasizes the desirability of standardization for machine tool components which, in turn, indicates the need for a well-considered policy for the purchase of plant.

It is essential that all machine tool components which are subject to wear or damage should be regularly inspected. This can be done by the line supervisors or by the maintenance department or, as earlier suggested, by the inspection staff, but—in order to avoid misunderstandings—it must be the definite and sole responsibility of one department. Much inspection can be done between shifts or at mealbreaks. The Saturday morning, with a five-day week, gives an excellent opportunity for remedying defects. Log books should be kept to show the dates of inspection, the conditions found and the adjustments or replacements made. These log books will be invaluable for formulating maintenance schedules.

It cannot be too strongly emphasized that the keynote in machine tool maintenance in a flow production plant is anticipation. It is fatal to deal with maintenance by default. The same method should apply, not only on the machine lines, but throughout the whole plant; and not only so far as mechanical devices are concerned, but in everything about the factory—even down to door latches and window fastenings. It is amazing how careless handling and even malicious damage are apt to grow where insufficient care and attention is paid to the property. The "spit and polish" of the Royal Navy and the Army establishments has a psychological aspect which can, with advantage, be adopted by industry. The flow production system performs a service in as much as it gives high visibility to all these matters and so assists in the discipline necessary to good housekeeping in the factory.

Maintenance is also closely related to the replacement of worn and obsolete by new and improved machines and plant. This most important matter in a flow production factory demands specialist attention, which is discussed under another heading, but the key to the situation lies in the maintenance department, because properly documented repair records will provide warning when the time for renewal approaches. Such records also give pointers to what should be avoided in the purchase of new plant. They are particularly useful in indicating where machine components are too highly stressed, where wear and tear could be avoided by better distribution of load or by the provision of larger bearing surfaces and where careful study of lubrication would result in longer life.

A proper appreciation of the policies governing plant replacement is desirable in any manufacturing undertaking and the flow production factory is no exception to the general rule. Flow production, however, makes it easier to visualize the fact that depreciation and obsolescence are direct factors in production cost. It has always been accepted that the cost of cutting tools must be met from revenue and that jigs and fixtures must be amortized over a given period or quantity and it should be recognized that the same methods ought to be applied to machine tools. These wear out or become out of date in precisely the same way—except that the period is longer. Toll is levied on bearings, slides, gears, screws, etc., just as it is on the cutting edges of the actual drill or milling cutter. In other words, machine tools are consumable. Change of design may necessitate new machine tools in much the same manner as it may necessitate new jigs and fixtures. Availability of more efficient machines may, in a competitive market, bring obsolescence into the picture long before depreciation by wear and tear has become an operative factor.

The situation can best be met by building up a replacement fund out of revenue. That is to say that the figure for depreciation and obsolescence should not be apportioned at the end of the year in accordance with a fixed formula, or as dictated by financial affluence or stringency, but by making every sales unit that leaves the factory contribute its quota—in due proportion—to a replacement fund to cover its obligation to the machines, plant and buildings which made its production possible.

The amount which should be charged for depreciation can be established by classifying the assets and setting rates for each class.

When each asset has been multiplied by its rate, their sum will be the amount to be provided. If this is divided by the estimated output of production units the amount that each unit should contribute will be ascertained and can be included in the price make-up of the sales unit. This means that the depreciation account is brought into the budgetary realm of actuality and foresight and can be dealt with by anticipation rather than by default. Suggested rates applicable in a general way to flow production factories are given in Table II. This presupposes an annual running of machinery equal to 3,500 hours on high-rate production but under good conditions and with a reasonable maintenance. This figure approximates to one year's work on double shift with overtime.

The author favours the deduction of an equal proportion of the original cost of the asset at each accounting period—i.e., the straight-line method of depreciation. This has the advantage of simplicity and,

TABLE II

SUGGESTED BASIS FOR ANNUAL DEPRECIATION RATES
(Straight-line Method)

Class of Asset	Estimated life in years	Depreciation rate per cent
Buildings (permanent)	40	2.5
Fixtures and fittings (average)	10	10
Machinery, ordinary	10-15	10-6.6
Machinery particular purpose*	7-10	14-10
Machinery, special†	2-5	50-20
Electric motors	15-20	6.6-5
Electric installations	20	5
Compressed-air plant	20	5
Hoists and lifts	20	5
Portable tools	7-10	14-20
Installations and foundations	As life of the machine	
Office equipment	10-15	10-6.6
Motor vehicles	8	12

* E.g., cam shapers and grinders, crank grinders, gear cutters etc.

† Special to a particular model.

These figures, which include allowances for obsolescence and for salvage value, are based on a double day shift of 70 hours effective on intensive production. The obsolescence and the salvage values have been merged in the general figure, but it will be appreciated that these are intended as a guide only. In due course an evaluation for the particular plant will become available in full detail. The figures given are, if anything, on the low side for a plant of this description.

in practice, it has been found to be reasonably accurate for flow production concerns. It can be used in assessing the amount to be incorporated in the factory cost of the sales unit. Once established, the table of depreciation, in which there is an allowance for obsolescence, can be adjusted in accordance with the knowledge gained during the operation of the plant. It might be advisable here to issue a caution against the use of the reducing balance method of depreciation, which has three bad features:

(*a*) A too-rapid depreciation in the early life of the assets.

(*b*) Too slow a depreciation in later life.

(*c*) Too high a residual value when the time comes for disposal of the asset.

Rapid changes in product may involve heavy plant expenditure. Therefore the depreciation fund should be invested in easily realizable stocks. It should never be allowed to become a book figure or be merged into a general reserve. This particularly applies to flow production plant where product changes may involve large expenditure and where temporary expedients are apt to break up the flow sequence, thus disturbing the smooth efficiency of the plant and increasing the costs in an alarming fashion.

CHAPTER TWELVE

TRANSFER MACHINES AND AUTOMATION

Principle 14—Every Mechanical Aid must be adopted for Man and Machine

FLOW PRODUCTION has been responsible for much intensive study of materials handling because, once established, it becomes so apparent where time is wasted and, be it remembered, the entire aim of the flow-line is to use time—that priceless commodity—to the best advantage. Indeed, for flow production, we might well amend the old proverb to say: "Take care of the seconds, the profit will take care of itself". One sure way to take care of the seconds is by adopting mechanical assistance for all movement of material whether as bodies in space or material for removal by cutting implements.

Turning to the former:one of the most interesting features arising from flow production is the integrated use of conveyors. These may be quite simple, being dependent on gravity, and taking the form of mere slides or troughs, a piece of plate, channel or even rain-water gutter, set at such an angle that the component will slide or roll from one operation to the next. Roller track is substituted for slides when larger and heavier pieces have to be handled. Gravity roller track may be supplemented by power "humpers" or elevators placed at intervals

 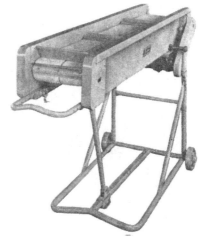

Fig. 47—In flow production the conveyor is an indispensable piece of equipment. *Left*: This example of a modern assembly or packing conveyor is made on the unit principle and is extensible and portable. *Right*: An elevator conveyor serves to raise workpieces to a higher level and also to regain lost height for roller track
(Courtesy Fisher & Ludlow, Ltd.)

Fig. 48—In this highly mechanized foundry the castings are poured on a pendulum conveyor and, when cool enough, are knocked out and transferred to the chain conveyor for despatch to the dressing shop. This picture shows the transfer point
(Courtesy Dartmouth Auto Castings, Ltd.)

Fig. 49—A close-up of the pendulum mould conveyor which carries boxes up to 36 in. × 16 in. wide. Travelling at the rate of 20 ft/min., it serves four pairs of moulding machines producing 270 complete moulds per hour
(Courtesy Dartmouth Auto Castings, Ltd.)

Fig. 50—A modern assembly conveyor with individual work tables and inspection
at the end of the line
(Courtesy Fisher & Ludlow, Ltd.)

to restore lost height. These tracks may be gated horizontally or vertically or bridged by steps to allow easy access by the personnel. Turntables and "roll-overs" can be used to offer alternative presentation of the components to the tools. (Fig. 47.)

Overhead chain conveyors find great favour, particularly when used for stores in transit. The hangers take many forms, such as trays, baskets, hooks, clips or quite special devices, and they have the merit that these appendages can be mixed. Thus all the components necessary for feeding an assembly line can follow in sequence no matter what type of holder, carrier or container may be required. (Fig. 48.)

A development of the chain conveyor can be found in the pendulum conveyor which will carry pallets sufficiently large to support fair-sized moulding boxes and so provide for almost continuous pouring operations. (Fig. 49.)

Power-driven belt-and slat or pallet conveyors are in great demand for assembly operations. These may carry small jobs like electric fans, speedometers or clocks down the centre of a bench, across which girl operators sit face to face; the inspector being at the end of the line. Or they may take the form of large floor conveyors able to carry anything up to a public service vehicle for erection or dismantling for repair. (Figs. 50-51.)

The use of roller-track and belt conveyors makes a common height

Fig. 51—A packing conveyor. Normally the operators sit *vis à vis,* but cross tables are used for specific operations (Courtesy Meccano, Ltd.)

for machine tables an essential, and standard machines may have to be packed up to achieve this. In some cases where there is a miscellaneous bunch of machines in line, a belt conveyor behind the operator may be more convenient than a linkage of the actual machines. The conveyor in this case becomes a moving bench which carries the components but requires the workman to make an "about turn" for each operation. This, of course, is a divergence from true straight-line flow production. (Fig. 52.)

The foregoing—i.e., the sequence of operations; the line-out of the machines; the common table level; the use of power conveyors; the discipline of the time cycle—were the logical steps leading in the direction of the automatic transfer machine, which is essentially a group of machine heads mounted on a common base and fitted with an "in-built" conveyor system supplemented, of course, by locating and clamping mechanisms. The conveying system is special in that it is a

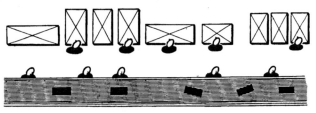

Fig. 52—Miscellaneous groups of machines can be linked by roller track or belt conveyor behind the operators who make an "about turn" between each operation. Quite practical, but not ideal flow production

shuttle system, with a short movement, operating in a prescribed area. In the form of "automation"—to be described later—it can also be used for interoperation transfer; that is, for the transfer of workpieces between machine and machine.

The mechanism for transfer machines and for automation devices is so similar that the description of one will serve for both. It is much less complicated than would appear on first acquaintance and may consist of a reciprocating bar fitted at one end with a spring-loaded pawl. On the outstroke the pawl passes under the workpiece, the pawl being depressed by the weight of the same; it rises when it is free to do so and on the instroke carries the workpiece to the operating position. There may be one transfer bar for a narrow and two for a wide workpiece, this latter to ensure proper presentation of the component to the machine. Some of the Archdale machines replace the bar by a chain mounted on two sprocket wheels; these rotate to give the outstroke and the instroke. The pawl lies neatly between the chain links. Some machines are fitted with a shaft having one or two fingers. The shaft is rotated through an arc which is sufficient for the fingers to clear the workpiece on the outstroke but to engage it on the instroke; an arc of about 90 degrees is usually sufficient. All these methods are, of course, merely variations on ratchet mechanisms. (Fig. 53.)

When the transfer bar makes its instroke, it carries the workpiece to a stop where dowels engage holes which have previously been drilled and reamed for the purpose. These dowels, which have a tapered lead, will locate the workpiece in accurate relationship to the cutting tools.

Fig. 53—Flow production was responsible for the development of the automatic transfer machine. Workpieces are moved from station to station by means of ratchet mechanisms; this is a chain transfer device introduced by Archdale on the Bedford cylinder head plant installed at Vauxhall Motors Ltd.

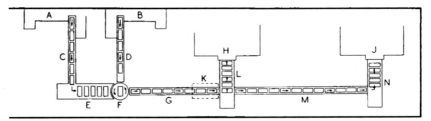

Fig. 54—Automatic handling ("automation") at Ford Motor Company, U.S.A.
Cylinder blocks are taken from machines A and B by lengthwise shuttles C and D.
Shuttle E takes priority over D to avoid interference at turntable F. Turntable
F transfers blocks to lengthwise shuttle G. Then overhead shuttle K passes
blocks to broadside shuttle L for machine H or via lengthwise shuttle M to
broadside shuttle N for machine J

Fig. 55—How the operations depicted in Fig. 54 are carried out. The overhead
shuttle at the right of the picture is more clearly seen in the photograph below

Fig. 56—The overhead shuttle
is picking up the blocks from
a lengthwise shuttle and
feeding them broadside to the
machine. The overhead
shuttle is essential to avoid
interference at junctions

Fig. 57—A close-up of the overhead shuttle at the point where it takes over from the lengthwise shuttle, the transfer bar of which can be seen at the bottom of the picture

Fig. 58—This overhead shuttle is picking blocks off a broadside shuttle. It has a long stroke which enables it to move two blocks at the same time thus removing the first from the rest station and pushing the second into the orbit of the machine tool transfer bars

This done, the workpiece is clamped by a pneumatic or hydraulic device. Sometimes it may be clamped to the ways on the bed of the machine or it may be lifted to top rails. The transfer bar will also be operated hydraulically or pneumatically and it may be controlled mechanically or electrically.

When necessary, turntable and roll-over devices can be built into the transfer machine so that the work can be presented to the tools squarely or at any angle on any face. This is where the automatic transfer machine differs from the normal automatic or automatic cycle machines. It is this flexibility, which, incidentally, need not be confined to a short series of operations, which makes the auto-transfer machine such a valuable contribution to flow production. The automation devices naturally dispense with the locating mechanisms since they only serve for interoperation movement of the components from machine to machine.

Automation is a contribution to the art of flow production which comes from U.S.A., and in the Ford Motor factories at Cleveland and Dearborn there are a large number of these devices in operation for loading and unloading machines and for moving the buffer stock or "float" between the machines. These devices are not part of the machines but self-contained adjuncts to them. The means employed are similar to those in use on the automatic transfer machines—they consist of shuttles built in to a frame which can operate as lengthwise or broadside movements. These manoeuvre the workpieces into the required positions while turntables and roller-overs provide the proper orientation of the workpieces to the tools. This mechanism converts a miscellaneous collection of machine tools into a complete automatic

Fig. 59—The turntable plays an important part in automation. These three photographs show the stages in turning blocks delivered broadside to the lengthwise direction

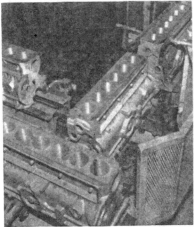

Fig. 60—The turntable may be combined with a roll-over device; the roll-over operating during the rotation of the turntable

Fig. 61 (*below*) shows the mechanism of the combined turntable and roll-over. It shows also how the shuttle bars pick up the workpiece for transfer

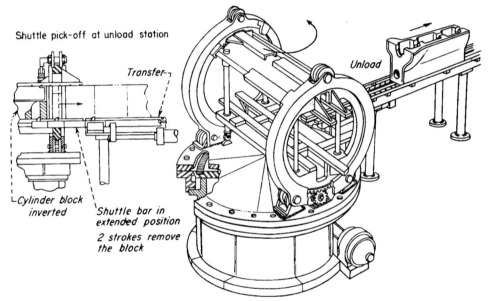

Shuttle pick-off at unload station

Transfer

Unload

Cylinder block inverted

Shuttle bar in extended position

2 strokes remove the block

transfer plant, and it has the advantage that it permits the purchase of machine tools from a wide variety of makers. (Figs. 54-62.)

The details of the shuttles are largely standardized but they can be varied as required. The framework that carries them is made up from standard structural steel. These shuttles feed into the orbit of the machine transfer bars, completely coupling up the external tracks with the mechanism that is built into the machine. The pushing speed of the transfer bars is about 7 in. per sec. It is kept low to avoid the inertia of the workpiece, causing an overrun beyond the intended location.

The timing sequences are controlled in such a manner that parts can be marshalled for one short operation on one machine, or for a longer

Fig. 62—The Hautau-Turndex turntable is a "package" unit which will index from 10 to 180 degrees in a time cycle of $\frac{1}{2}$ to 2 seconds and will carry a maximum load of 2,700 lb.

operation which, for balancing purposes, must be carried out on two or more machines. This control is exercised by electro-mechanical devices of various kinds, the movement of the workpieces being selected according to the number of pieces at each station and priority being in accordance with the requirements of the situation. (Fig. 63.)

Transfer mechanisms may be operated mechanically or they may involve pneumatic, hydraulic and electric means for operation. The preference appears to be for pneumatic or hydraulic power units with electrical controls, largely by limit switches. Vickers Incorporated of Detroit have evolved what they term a hydraulic "package" unit consisting of a driving motor, pump and necessary valves mounted on a tank to make an integral piece of equipment. This unit can be installed with the very minimum of fitting. (Fig. 64.)

Another American package unit is the Bellows air motor: a pneumatic device providing a push-pull action controlled both for direction and for speed by solenoid-operated valves. The valves are integral with the unit and only two electric cables and one compressed-air pipe have to be connected. The exhaust air can be used to blow away the chips. The bore sizes range from $1\frac{1}{4}$ to $4\frac{1}{2}$ in. in diameter, with any required length of stroke. Such units will work under any conditions—even when flooded with coolant or buried in chips and dust. Vickers units are made in this country by Stein and Atkinson Ltd., and the Bellows type units are supplied by Benton and Stone Ltd. (Fig. 65.)

Many other types of automation are in use. These are for the most part based on the conventional conveyor or on hopper feed mechanisms but, in general, they are not unusual. This adjective can, however, be applied to the extraordinarily ingenious Iron Hand introduced by the Sahlin Engineering Co., of Birmingham, Michigan. This is a self-contained, fully-automatic unloader, for medium- and large-size presses, handling such parts as automobile roofs, door panels, side panels, bonnet tops, or, in the domestic field such items as bath tubs, sinks, stove-tops and refrigerator parts. There is a small size which

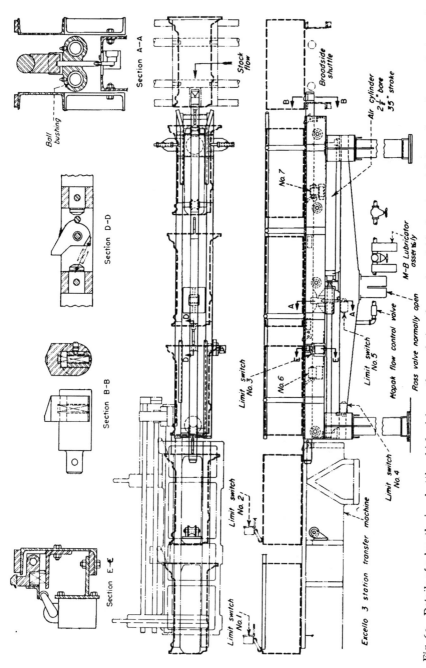

Section A—A

Stock flow

Ball bushing

Section D-D

Section B-B

Section E-E

Broadside shuttle

Air cylinder
2¼" bore
35" stroke

No. 7

M-B Lubricator assembly

Limit switch No. 3

Limit switch No. 5

No. 6

Hopak flow control valve

Ross valve normally open

Limit switch No. 2

Limit switch No. 4

Limit switch No. 1

Excello 3 station transfer machine

Fig. 63—Details of a lengthwise shuttle which picks up the workpiece from a broadside shuttle and delivers it to the transfer bars of an Ex-Cell-O machine. If limit switch LS.3 is depressed by the workpiece and LS.2 or LS.1 signals that the station is empty, the shuttle bar moves left to unload the broadside shuttle—the latter must be at rest. The workpiece on LS.3 is delivered to LS.2 and the shuttle bar returns to rest at LS.5; LS.4 and LS.5 control the length of the stroke

KEY TO DIAGRAM

A. Vickers adjustable time delay and reversing pilot valve model SP.135. Reverse cam F must be arranged to delay plunger return after table or head is reversed

B. Vickers series C-8-53 back pressure check valve (for pilot pressure)

C. Vickers motor-pump and combination valve unit

D. Vickers cycle control panel, series C-1245 or C-1265. Connections for series C-1245 shown

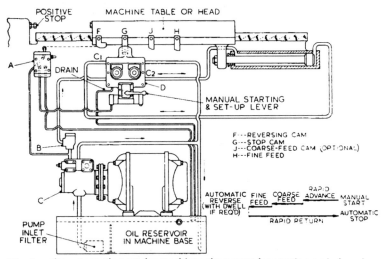

Fig. 64—On automatic transfer machines the power for moving and clamping the workpiece will probably be hydraulic or pneumatic. The photograph illustrates a Vickers hydraulic "package" unit. The diagram shows the connections operating cycle and the connections

(Courtesy Stein & Atkinson, Ltd.)

can deal with pressings up to 20 lb. in weight at the rate of 20 per min. The larger sizes can handle panels up to 80 × 120 in., weighing 100 lb. or even more, at 12 to 15 per min.

It is claimed that production, when presses are unloaded by the Iron Hand, is increased by at least 30 per cent. Moreover, the mechanical handling of such awkward, heavy and sharp-edged shapes makes for safety in operation. Production costs are therefore reduced, not only by speedier operation, but by the avoidance of accidents to the personnel.

When in operation, the claw of the Iron Hand takes a firm hold of the pressing. It first lifts the piece out of the die, with a vertical movement, and then swings it through an arc to clear the press. According to the timing, the Iron Hand can release the piece so that it falls on the obverse or reverse. After releasing the component it returns to the "ready" position to await the completion of the next pressing operation. The claw is adjustable inwards and outwards to suit pieces of differing widths, and up and down for different loading heights.

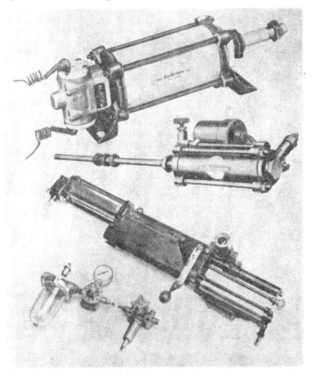

Fig. 65—Compressed-air "package" units such as are used for operating transfer mechanisms. The two upper items are push-pull units; the lower is for a rotary movement

The travel into the press is adjustable, as is the distance; the claw travels upwards before the arm swings out from the press. The arm can be locked in the "up" position when changing dies or tools. The Iron Hand can be fitted to existing presses by any competent millwright. The operation is by compressed air actuated by solenoid-operated air valves. It is controlled by limit switches. Normally, it works on a 110 V, 60-cycle, electric circuit. Most engineers would have considered this press-unloading operation to be one which would be extremely difficult, if not impossible, to mechanize, and yet, as evolved, it is beautifully simple and wonderfully effective. (Fig. 66.)

It is not intended to describe all the mechanical aids that are

Fig. 66—Flow production is assisted by the Iron Hand, an automatic device for unloading large presses

(Courtesy Nuffield Organisation)

The Iron Hand mounted
on a press

The pressing has been
raised by the extractor
pins and the Hand
is about to grip

The Hand has a vertical lift to raise the pressing clear of the die

As the arm swings back the Hand opens to drop the pressing, obversely, on the conveyor

The Hand, by releasing the pressing somewhat later in the backward swing, makes a "reverse" drop on to the conveyor

available. The aim of these examples is to illustrate principles rather than to be a documentary of practice. Yet it is essential to mention some of the lesser appliances that are available and which in their sphere are great economizers of time and effort. The first place must be given to the electric and pneumatic portable tools used for drilling, reaming, tapping; as stud-setters, screwdrivers and nut runners; and for sanding, grinding, buffing and polishing operations. These portable tools are mostly in evidence on assembly lines, but they can serve a purpose in the machine lines for minor operations; they are, in fact, extremely useful small "package-units".

Nor should the lesser tools be forgotten, such as a light power drive with reverse to operate screw gauges and the automatic tension wrench

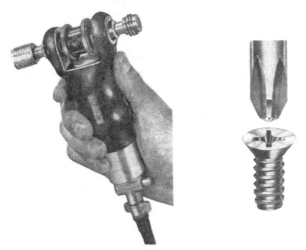

Fig. 67—The minor tools and appliances are an immense help to flow production. For example, this power-operated screw gauge, driven by a Desoutter Mighty Atom air motor, is claimed to give a throughput five times greater than the manual method. (Courtesy John Harris Tools, Ltd.) The Phillips recess screw shown with its driver (*right*) has also proved highly effective for flow production. Machine screws, wood screws and self-tapping screws of this type are available
(Courtesy Guest, Keen & Nettlefolds (Midlands), Ltd.)

which ensures that all nuts are tightened to a predetermined degree. Even the universal recessed-head screwdriver has a place in the economics of flow-line production. (Fig. 67.)

It is not perhaps out of place to mention the joining and fastening developments which have helped the straight-line principle in assembly, not only in matter of speed but also by the avoidance of subsidiary operations which break into the truly straight-line sequence. In this connection there are, to name a few only, such aids as Hi-Shear rivets, self-tapping drive screws, self-locking nuts, speed nuts, welding nuts. The growth of the art of fastening quickly and securely has very greatly

Fig. 68—Flow production has called forth the quick
fastening methods illustrated below
(Courtesy Simmonds Aerocessories, Ltd.)

A

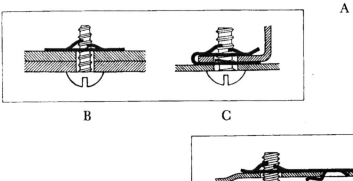

B   C

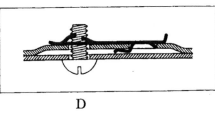

D

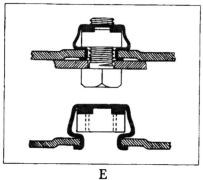

A. Flat Spire speed nut with Nettlefold-Parker-Kalon screw

B. The self-locking flat speed nut in position

C. A self-retaining speed nut for blind assembly

D. The latching type used when holes are remote from the edge of the plates

E. This captive speed nut is more quickly applied than a nut welded into place

E

assisted flow-line assembly, and as such must be given due credit. It is, in fact, a very material example of the many continuous methods which are being developed because flow production technique makes the necessity so obvious. Another of these minor details which are so important concerns the solving of lubrication difficulties. For instance, new cutting oils are available which will perform all duties and can be used where there is a possibility of cross-leakage between the cutting, lubricating and hydraulic systems. Even, though, when set against the larger issues, these matters may appear trivial they, in aggregate, assume very considerable significance as essential aids and accessories to the operation of the highly mechanized flow production plants. In practice, success may depend on some quite subsidiary detail; therefore no item should be regarded as too small for close attention. (Figs. 68-73.)

Principle 15—Every Activity must be Studied for the Economical Application of Power

The amount of work that can be accomplished by man's unaided power is so small in comparison with the needs of our civilization as to be almost negligible. For instance, a labourer raising weights with a rope and pulley will exert about 1/20 h.p. Turning a winch or pushing and pulling in a vertical direction he will develop approximately 1/14 h.p., or pushing and pulling horizontally, 1/10 h.p. Working in the manner most favourable to his physical structure the average human can only produce an effort to match a motor of 1/8 horse power. As draught animals it needs four men to equal a horse, and two men and a boy measure up to an ass.

Obviously human beings are wasted if used as machines for hauling, pushing and lifting and they should not be so used except when there is no other means for accomplishing a given task. Men are only economically employed when they control the power producing and using machines that we have inherited from the great engineers of the past.

The slave societies of bygone ages arose from the desire, by the more intelligent of the human species, for a civilized life. Their intelligence, however, did not prevent them from regarding their less fortunate brethren as beasts of burden. It is doubtful whether any political system could prevent this exploitation in circumstances similar to those existing before the introduction of power machinery, for no one can achieve political ends without economic means. It is, therefore, not without significance that Wilberforce, who died in 1833, lived just long enough to know that the second reading of the Bill abolishing slavery was carried in the House of Commons, nor that this was followed some 30 years later by abolition in North America. The vital significance resided in the fact that steam power, applied to rotative engines in 1783 had developed in 50 years to such a remarkable degree that it challenged the economic as well as the moral justification for the use of slave labour; now our slaves are reckoned in terms of electrical, mechanical and hydraulic energy, eventually to be reinforced by nuclear energy.

Today the economic factor—the cost and value of manpower in industry—makes it more necessary than ever that we should study methods for the prudent utilization of more and more power. In this respect we have much to learn from U.S.A., for it is generally recognized that the high productivity of U.S.A. and Canadian factories is chiefly due to the greater horse power available. There are no strictly comparable up-to-date figures that can be quoted, but in 1930 (U.S.A. 1929) it was known that the horse power per worker in the factory trades as a whole was 70 per cent greater in U.S.A. than in Britain.

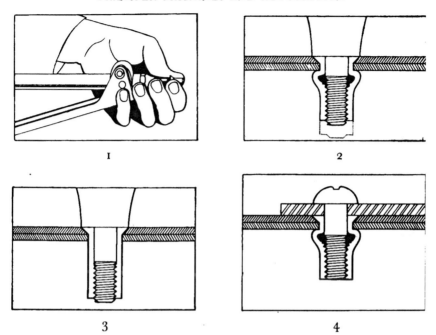

Fig. 69—For flow production, quickly assembled rivets or rivet bushes are a great help. For example, the Rivnut, which serves as rivet or nut, or both, is particularly useful for working on one side of a blind assembly

    1. The simple closing tool has a threaded mandrel
    3. Mandrel and anvil in position for clenching
    3. The Rivnut is clenched
    4. Mandrel is withdrawn and another component attached by a
       normal machine screw

                                       (Courtesy Linread Ltd.)

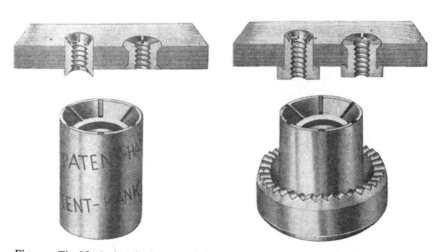

Fig. 70—The Hank rivet bush is a useful attachment device. This serves as a rivet and screw attachment or it can be used instead of a weld-nut
(Courtesy Guest, Keen & Nettlefolds (Midland), Ltd.)

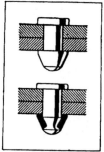

Fig. 71—The Hi-Shear method of riveting (*left*) is another of the quick methods. The shank is shaped like a knob and an aluminium collar is squeezed over it to make a neat rivet head. The closing tool brings the sheets closely together

(Courtesy Hi-Shear Rivet Tool Co.)

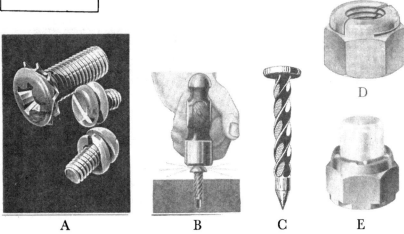

A   B   C   E

Fig. 72—Some flow production time savers: (A) Sems captive locking (or plain) washer which saves time and prevents maladroit handling. (B) Nettlefold-Parker-Kalon hammer drive screw. (C) Nettlefold-Parker-Kalon hardened screw-nail. (D) Aerotight stiff nut which, being self-locking, makes split pins superfluous. This system is also applied to the Hank rivet bushings. (E) Simmond's Aerocessories make three types of self-locking nuts. In the one shown the locking insert (of moulded nylon) also forms a cap, making a completely leak-proof seal

(A: courtesy Linread Ltd. B, C, D: courtesy Guest, Keen & Nettlefolds (Midlands), Ltd. E: courtesy Simmonds Aerocessories, Ltd.)

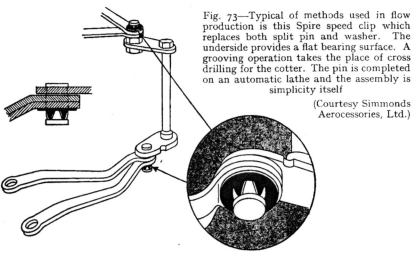

Fig. 73—Typical of methods used in flow production is this Spire speed clip which replaces both split pin and washer. The underside provides a flat bearing surface. A grooving operation takes the place of cross drilling for the cotter. The pin is completed on an automatic lathe and the assembly is simplicity itself

(Courtesy Simmonds Aerocessories, Ltd.)

Fig. 74—Flow production lines emphasize the desirability of machine tools of ample power. Each of these massive vertical mills, by Archdale, has a total 52.5 h.p. available. The components are Bedford cylinder heads, made at Vauxhall Motors

(Courtesy *Automobile Engineer*)

In cast-iron foundries the figure was 120 per cent and in the motor car industry 290 per cent in favour of U.S.A. There is every indication that U.S.A. still leads the way by a very considerable margin.

To increase applied power it is necessary to use more machinery and machinery with greater capacity, also more handling plant, more ancillary machines, more portable tools. Dealing first with machine tools, it has been a common failing for British machines to be under-powered. To use a phrase which is common on the factory floor, "We expect a boy to do a man's job". In America they tend to the other extreme and equip their machines with unusually powerful motors. If it is a fault it is a good fault. This reserve of horse-power not only reduces the cutting time but frequently makes it possible to avoid subsidiary operations. For instance, a correspondent from U.S.A. writes:

"In our foundry considerable time was spent in chipping gates and cleaning the joints on cylinder blocks before machining. With the new Ingersoll mill these operations are no longer required because the machine is 'built sturdy' to remove this excess stock."

The practice of using greater power for machine tools is, however, growing in this country. An example is found in the Archdale vertical milling machines installed at Vauxhall Motors for use in the Bedford cylinder-head line. Forty horsepower is the rating of the spindle motor, while to provide for the feed drive and the quick power traverse (300 ft/min.) there are motors of $7\frac{1}{2}$ h.p. and 5 h.p., or $52\frac{1}{2}$ h.p. in all.

Under normal production conditions these machines are capable of removing $\frac{3}{16}$ in. of cast iron over a width of $7\frac{1}{2}$ in. at a feed rate of 39 in/min. A much higher feed was obtained under test conditions. (Fig. 74.)

In addition to the larger motors for machine tools, much power can be gainfully absorbed by handling appliances such as cranes, hoists, lifts, power and fork-lift trucks, portable elevators and conveyors of all kinds. Also by "iron hands" and automatic transfer and clamping devices which are, of course, handling appliances built into the actual machines.

Much power can also be usefully employed in operating ancillary machinery, particularly machines which are only occasionally required. The ancillary tools would *inter alia* include that wide range of electric and pneumatic tools which by reason of their adaptability and small size help so much to assist the installation of aids to production. In U.S.A. such labour-aiding equipment is really lavish. It is not suggested that handling plant and ancillary machines are not used to any extent in Britain, but undoubtedly their use could, with advantage, be considerably extended. One of the greatest benefits of the flow production system lies in the fact that it renders highly visible the points at which ancillary machinery and labour aids should be installed.

Spending capital to save revenue is good practice; hence the attitude of mind which must see "every spindle in the shop turning" is out of date—although it was valid when there was one man to one machine in batch production shops. For flow production it should be avoided like the plague and the installation of machines and appliances for occasional use should be encouraged.

Successful operation of flow production is dependent on well-chosen equipment, and the adage that "true economy consists in wise expenditure" is particularly apt in this connection. Extravagance is certainly a grave pitfall but no more so than false economy, and no economy is more false than that which denies labour the use of ancillary machinery.

CHAPTER THIRTEEN

COST-KEEPING

Principle 16—Information on Costs must be Promptly Available

NATURALLY, in a flow-line production factory, costs are meticulously kept and carefully studied, for where every other activity is so closely co-ordinated it would be the height of folly to neglect such a plain indicator of efficiency. Cost-keeping under these conditions is a very satisfying process, for with the regularization of routine and a steady flow of production it is possible to make comparisons and draw deductions with a degree of accuracy unattainable under other conditions.

Standard costs for material, labour and the various expenses should be established with which current costs must continually be compared. If there is a rise above normal, the reason must be sought and the cause remedied. Should the costs fall below those already established, the favourable conditions should be analyzed and standardized. The responsible executives being advised of the cost-efficiency of their departments are able to gauge their past efforts and guide their future progress.

The advantage of flow production in relation to costing lies in the fact that a complete story is available and that the effects of modification and alteration can be visualized and studied in detail. Meticulous analysis is possible while correction and re-analysis will provide a connected and conclusive picture of a mechanism that can, by continuous application, be brought very near to perfection.

It will be appreciated that flow production is admirably suited for group bonus whereby the gang is paid for the net number of pieces passed correct by the inspector. The bonus is earned by the group effort and distributed according to individual rating. This method encourages the team spirit and team discipline, in other words it encourages co-operation within the group. It has all the advantages of piece-work without its complexities. This scheme is very much to be preferred to the measured-day work system which is based on the knowledge arising from time-studied flow production because, in addition to the urge to get the utmost out of the machine, it avoids that element of "driving" which must always be present with day work systems framed against a set target. It also dispels that feeling, so much disliked by the worker, of having "someone always breathing down your neck".

Naturally, flow production concerns apply the flow technique to the office as well as to the factory; making use of continuous operation wherever possible and applying mechanization wherever this is economically possible. Adding, calculating, accounting and punched-card analyzing machines assist cost-keeping, while copying, addressing, duplicating, franking, dictating and stenotyping apparatus help in general office work, and the filing and card index cabinets serve as quickly identifiable storage.

Here again, in the office, flow production is the ideal; witness the following quotation from "Machines and Appliances in Government Offices" published by H.M. Stationery Office:

> "When a procedure is divided into processes carried out in sequence, equipment should be so arranged in the rooms that the work flows in one direction with no backward movements. For example, in a duplicating room, the stencil should be received at one end of the room, where it is rolled off on the machine. The copies should be passed to the collating tables and then on to despatch with a minimum of movements between operations and no criss-cross movements to cause obstruction to easy flow of work."

Machine accounting provides information with accuracy and with speed. This is a great, if not indispensable, help in the operation of a flow production factory, since the cost accounts reflect deviations from those standards which can be so readily established under the flow production system.

CHAPTER FOURTEEN

AUTOMATIC TRANSFER MACHINES

Principle 17—Machines Should be Designed to Suit the Task they Perform

THE LOGICAL development of the flow production principle is obviously continuity in operation sequence. Whether this is achieved by individual machines grouped together, by automatic cycle machines, by automatic transfer machines or even by a group of hand-workers depends on the nature of the product and the stage of development of the enterprise. There is, however, a constant urge towards complete automaticity in order to reduce the labour content and the burden of capital investment.

Where automatic machines can be effectively used they have many advantages over the standard types. They operate much more rapidly save much handling and largely eliminate the factor of human error. They take up less floor space and, in relation to the work done, are more economical of electric power. Despite their complications they contain fewer parts than the group of standard machines that would produce an equivalent output. It is, of course, their higher productivity at lower cost which is the determining factor in their utilization.

The normal type of automatic machine is restricted in its operations by the fact that the workpiece has to be held in chucks, collets, vices or on mandrels which are brought under the operating heads by an indexing mechanism. Alternatively the work is rotated and the tools are advanced on an indexing turret or carriage. The limitation in this class of machinery is due to the fixed position of the workpiece and to the relatively few operations that can be performed at one chucking. The automatic cycle machine differs from the full automatic only in as much as the latter is continously operating, whereas the former has a halt station for unloading and loading.

The automatic transfer machine differs very materially from the automatic and automatic cycle types. The limitation imposed by holding the workpiece in a more or less fixed position is overcome. The workpiece frequently travels "bare" (i.e., without a fixture) and, by use of roll-over and turntable mechanisms, can be made to present any face at any square or angular position to the operating tools. Moreover, there is virtually no limitation in the number of operations that can be performed in sequence, since the workpiece moves in straight lines which can be as long as may be required. Thus the automatic transfer machine does for the large awkward irregularly-shaped pieces what the normal automatic machine achieves for small neat circular components.

If the exigencies of the shop floor make it necessary, the straight-line flow can be varied by doubling back on itself once or many times. The Ingersoll cylinder block plant at the River Rouge Ford Works, where one imagines there could, if required, be all the room in the world, was actually installed in U formation. Thus it will be seen that automatic transfer machines will fit any layout, and they are also, within limits, flexible as regards the product. The limits are, of course, those imposed by such tools as multi-drills, which may be designed for fixed centres. On the other hand, they can have limited adjustment, or even be of the universal adjustable centre type.

The automatic transfer machine is, in essence, very simple, consisting, as it does, of a foundation or base which carries a table for supporting the workpiece, simple means of moving the workpiece from station to station, and equally simple means of clamping the workpiece for operations, which are performed by cutting heads reduced to the bare elements of a rotating tool with a fast approach, cutting feed and quick withdrawal. For milling operations it is usually possible, if the design of the part and the tooling is integrated, to provide for a single traverse, the keynote being simplicity of operation in the cause of the utmost efficiency both mechanically and economically. In these machines all the universal motions essential to the normal general-purpose machine tool can be omitted. As one prominent British engineer put it: "You aren't forced to have seven levers when you only want two."

It is on such lines that the American industry is building up the so-called package units. Since these package units are simplified standardized tools it is possible to arrange and rearrange the elements of any automatic transfer machine and so adapt it to suit the exigencies of any situation that may arise due to alteration in method or in design. In brief, the system is flexible, much more flexible than, at first acquaintance, would appear possible.

There is little doubt that when the flexibility of this new system is appreciated a new technique in machine design will be perfected which will combine all the virtues of automaticity with those of the older system. One can visualize the possiblities open to the producer of end products if he were able to keep a number of bases, machine heads, transfer and clamping units in store so that the next forward step in production or in change of design could be taken with the minimum delay. Alternatively the machine tool maker would be able to stock components to build up into automatics for special purposes without involving the long delay to which we are at present accustomed. In fact, if we allow our imaginations off the leash, we can conceive of flow production for standardized machine tool units which can be assembled after the same fashion and with something of the same freedom as a boy builds with Meccano.

Flow production, with its machines in line, led logically to the automatic transfer machine which imposes fewer limitations on the number and variety of operations that can be performed at one loading than any previous type of machine. The photographs in this chapter illustrate some of the various machines now installed

Fig. 75—Drilling oil holes in crankshafts might be called a problem operation. The problem is solved by this 35-ft. Kreuger machine which handles 60 crankshafts per hour with one man to load and one to unload. The view below is of the delivery end of the 28-station machine, installed at the River Rouge Plant of Ford Motor Co.

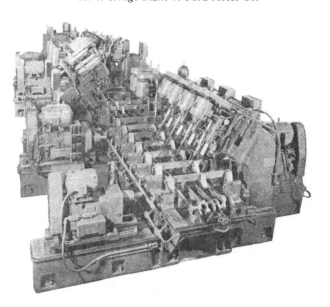

E*

Fig. 76—This Cross Transfer-matic drills 13 holes, taps two, counterbores two and reams one in the gearbox cover shown below. The rate is 180 per hour at 80 per cent efficiency. The lower view is of an operator loading the gearbox covers. The rough casting and the finished job are shown on the right

A brief description of two automatic transfer machines, namely the Archdale machines at Vauxhall Motors and the Cross Transfer-matic for axle casings, has already been given. It was also indicated that this type of machinery had developed to a far greater extent in the United States than elsewhere. This is due to three main factors: (*a*) the vast output of U.S.A. factories, (*b*) the shortage and high cost of manual labour and (*c*) the quicker industrial recovery of U.S.A. after the Second World War.

Among the items operated on automatic transfer machines are cylinder blocks, gearboxes, gearbox covers, hydraulic torque cases, differential carriers, axle case housings, aircraft cylinder heads, refrigerator components, crankshaft oilways. One of the latter made by the H. R. Kreuger Company for the River Rouge Plant is 35 ft. long and has 28 stations, the machine being made in such a way that it can be operated either as a complete machine or as four individual sections. For individual operations there are two idle stations between each working section to allow for the removal and inspection of crankshafts. Normally the crankshaft travels through all the 28 stations, being automatically turned to present different portions of the crankshaft to the tools as required. This machine drills the oil holes from the main bearings to the crank pins and at the same time drills and reams the connecting oil line holes through the crank pins from the ends. Its production is 60 per hour, with one operator for loading and unloading at each end. (Fig. 75.)

The Cross "Transfer-matic" for machining gearbox covers drills 13 holes and taps one, and reams and counterbores two other holes at the net rate (80 per cent efficiency) of 180 per hour. (Fig. 76.)

The 120 ft. Ingersoll cylinder-block transfer machine installed at the River Rouge Plant is of very great interest, since with this new plant five men produce 550 V8 cylinder blocks in 8 hours against the 200 produced by nine men in the same time on a normal flow production machine line. It is said that fatigue on the part of the operators has been greatly reduced and that some less tangible savings are realized. The operations are as follows:

1st Station—Rough and finish mill the bottom of the block.

2nd Station—Drill all bearing-cap stud holes, ream two locating holes, drill oil-pump holes, drill three oil-line lead holes, after which a turnover fixture positions the block for milling the upper faces.

3rd Station—Rough and finish mill top face.

4th Station—Drill oil hole and breather hole, mill off four locating stops, rough and finish mill the cylinder banks. The block is then turned automatically through 90 deg. to provide the correct presentation for the next operation.

5th Station—Rough and finish mill both ends of block. (Fig. 77.)

Fig. 77—The following six photographs show Ford V8 cylinder blocks on Ingersoll automatic transfer machinery at the Ford River Rouge plant
(Courtesy Ford Motor Co.)

Station 1: Rough mill and finish sump or pan face

Station 2: Drill various holes. Note automatic roll-over on the right

Station 3 : Rough mill and finish up face of block

Station 3a: Drill oil line and breather hole

Station 4: Remove, by milling, four location spots. Rough mill and finish cylinder banks. Block is then automatically turned through 90 deg. for following operation

Station 5: Rough mill and finish both ends of block

Fig. 77 (*continued*)—The cylinder block, after the operations illustrated on the previous pages, is transferred to the Ingersoll 8-spindle boring mill which also has power transfer and clamping mechanism

Attention must be called to the massive nature of Ingersoll machinery. The photograph of the Ingersoll two-way, eight-spindle boring machine is an excellent example of this, as can be seen by contrasting the size of the V8 cylinder block with the machine itself. Incidentally, this machine, which is arranged with power transfer and power clamping, bores 87 eight-cylinder blocks per hour at 100 per cent efficiency. (See above.)

France has also made very considerable contribution to the art. Régie Nationale des Usines Renault (National Administration of the Renault Works) have designed and built in their own workshops a large number of special machines which incorporate standardized machine heads of a particularly simple character. (See above.)

The standard heads, of which there are three, comprise a light single-spindle head, a heavier edition which serves for both milling and drilling, and a 24-spindle multi-drilling head. These unit heads are fitted with two electric motors, the larger for driving the spindles, the smaller for the feed mechanism. A cam mounted on the side of the head controls the feed cycle. The operation is commenced by pressing a push-button switch, when the cam motion takes charge of the rate and the depth of feed, the latter being controllable to 0.01 mm. Normally heads are made for one specific operation, but the gearing can be changed if this should be required. (Fig. 79.)

These heads can be used for many purposes. They can, for instance, form part of individual machines, such as pillar drills or milling machines. They can become units in automatic cycle machines or form components in automatic transfer machines of which there are several in the Renault works. Three of these are shown in Fig. 79. One performs all the drilling and tapping operations on the sump and

Fig. 78—Usines Renault of Billancourt have built, in their own workshops, a large number of automatic transfer machines which are remarkable for the simplicity of their "package" unit design (Courtesy Régie Nationale des Usines Renault)

Automatic transfer machine for the 4 h.p. Renault cylinder block

Automatic transfer machine for the cylinder block of the Renault Frégate car

Automatic transfer machine for steering boxes for the Renault 4 h.p. car. This shows the versatility of the standardized machine heads

Fig. 79—Three machine heads as used on automatic transfer machines developed by Usines Renault, Billancourt. *Upper*: Light single-spindle drill. *Middle*: Heavy single-spindle drill with milling attachment. *Lower*: Multi-drilling head with 24 spindles

(Courtesy *Machinery*)

side faces of the cylinder block. This embodies six transfer units providing 12 working stations with a total of 23 of the standardized heads. Another of these machines carries out a long series of operations on the cylinder head, while a third is used for the machining of the steering box.

The Renault transfer system has some very interesting features, in as

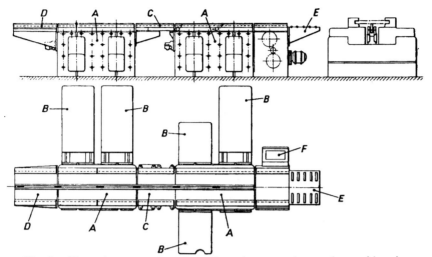

Fig. 80—The unit construction of the Renault automatic transfer machines is applied throughout. This diagram shows (A) the machine base; (B) platforms for machine heads; (C) the bridge piece; (D) the loading station; (E) the unloading station; (F) the indexing mechanism

(Courtesy *Machinery*)

much as they have adopted the unit system and have carried it to a logical conclusion, as shown in Fig. 80. Each transfer unit (A), which is mounted on a cast-iron base, has two operating stations. These are served by the appropriate machine heads mounted on the platforms (B) which are attached to the sides of the transfer base. Between the adjacent units a bridge piece (C) is mounted. This is spring borne to take care of possible differences in alignment of the transfer units. These bridge pieces will adjust themselves when receiving and passing the workpiece from one transfer unit to the next. Meanwhile, correct location of the workpiece on all transfer units is maintained as these are independent of the bridge pieces.

At one end of the machine there is a cantilever loading section (D) and at the other a roller conveyor unloading section (E). The gears which operate the indexing motion for the workpieces are contained in a box at (F).

In the Renault system the workpiece is always clamped to a jig-plate or pallet on which it remains during its passage through the transfer machine. These pallets are transferred from station to station by hinged pawls on a central reciprocating bar. The spring-loaded pawls slide under the jig-plates on the outward stroke, but push the jig-plates to the next station on the inward stroke. The jig-plates are located at each of the operating stations by a pair of dowel pins which engage bushed holes. Four plungers with pads lift the plate thus located to engage upper locating rails which give the required setting for height. The dowels and the plungers are operated by wedge members which extend the whole length of the machine.

As a rule only two operators are required for each transfer machine, one for loading and one for unloading. At the end of the run through the machine the workpiece is taken off the jig-plate, which is returned to the starting end, the heavier types being returned by a hoist. They are either cleaned by compressed air or soda-washed to rid them of grease and swarf before they pass through the machine a second time.

In these machines the cycle of operations is started by a simple push-button or lever, after which the machine takes charge. Indicator lamps mounted on the starting panel show the progress of the cycle or give warning if anything goes wrong. Safety devices are also incorporated to prevent damage to the mechanism, the tools or the components arising from clumsy loading or incorrect timing. The provision of fouling pieces ensures that the workpieces cannot be incorrectly placed on the jig plates. Electrical interlocks make it impossible for the work to be transferred until all the heads have completed their operation and have withdrawn to the starting position.

Fig. 81—The Usines Renault "package" unit machine heads can also be used on indexing machines, illustrating the versatility of this method of construction

The heads will not feed until the jig-plate is correctly located. All the machine heads are started simultaneously, but each has its own cycle of movements controlled by individual cams attached to the heads. Renault have an interesting system for preventing damage to taps due to holes being incorrectly or incompletely drilled. Before the tapping station is reached the work passes through a checking station where pin gauges are automatically inserted into the drilled holes. If the gauge does not "go home" the transfer mechanism will not operate until the fault has been cleared.

As previously noted, the Archdale machine for the production of the

Bedford cylinder heads dispenses with the jig-plate or pallet—the workpiece travelling through the machine "bare". This, of course, gets rid of the problem of cleaning and returning the pallet; a special form of location strip is used to ensure that the swarf is always scraped away from the bottom of the workpiece.

The transfer mechanism on these Archdale machines is both simple and effective. It consists of a chain mounted on chain wheels at each end of the machine table. These chain wheels rotate to give a forward and reverse movement. At five points in the chain the links are substituted by pawls, which act as pushers on the forward movements

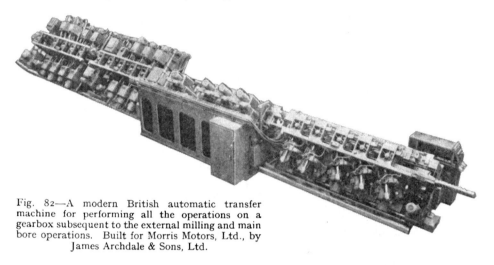

Fig. 82—A modern British automatic transfer machine for performing all the operations on a gearbox subsequent to the external milling and main bore operations. Built for Morris Motors, Ltd., by James Archdale & Sons, Ltd.

sliding under the component on the reverse motion. This ratcheting mechanism lies between two hardened steel slides which form the face of the machine bed. The cylinder head moves on these, being kept in place by two side rails. The approximate location of the component is obtained by stop mechanisms, the exact position being determined by dowel plungers which engage certain stud holes previously reamed to limit size. The clamping is done by compressed air. An interlock mechanism ensures that all four heads in operation on the machine are properly located and clamped before the motors of the multi-operating heads can start. As each operating head completes its cycle, warning lamps on the control box are lighted so that the operator knows when to manipulate the control lever.

An excellent example of automatic transfer plant, performing a large number of operations, is provided by the Archdale four-stage multi-station machine installed at the engine factory of Morris Motors Ltd. at Coventry. On it are performed all the operations on the gearbox castings, for the Morris-Oxford car, that are subsequent to the external milling and main bore operations. (Fig. 82.)

Fig. 83—Stage 1 of the auto-transfer gearbox machine shown in Fig. 82, viewed from the loading end. The five stations on this section are all concerned with milling interior surfaces

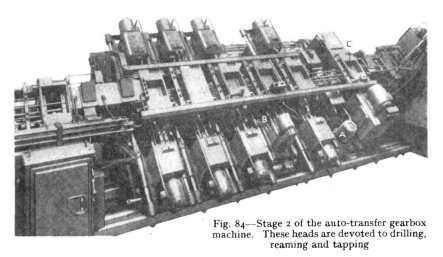

Fig. 84—Stage 2 of the auto-transfer gearbox machine. These heads are devoted to drilling, reaming and tapping

Fig. 85—Stages 3 and 4 of the auto-transfer gearbox machine (drilling, tapping, spot-facing, etc.). Note the shaker conveyors A and B delivering chips into the bin C

This machine, which is approximately 60 ft. in length, replaces a line of 18 standard-type machines which needed 13 operators to produce 750 gearboxes in a 44-hour week. Only four men are required to produce 1,600 boxes in the same time at 80 per cent efficiency. The original plant occupied 1,800 sq. ft.; the transfer machine occupies only 885 sq. ft.—less than one-half the space.

There are 20 machining and two gauging stations, plus a number of idle stations at which the gearbox can be removed for examination if desired. The locating rails which form the work table and, consequently, the machine heads are set at an angle of 45 deg. This makes it easy to get at all the mechanism and it is also helpful in the disposal of swarf.

The workpieces travel bare through the machine. They are loaded on to a roller conveyor whence they are pushed on to driven rollers which carry them to the transfer mechanism. The transfer bars rotate through 90 deg. to insert fingers behind the castings moving each, in turn, to its appointed station. The boxes are located by the main bores and the top cover face—the distance between the bore centres and the face being an important dimension. Hydraulically operated plungers enter these bores and another mechanism ensures that the castings are held in the right position against the hardened steel locating rails. (Figs. 83-85.)

All the machine heads have a cam feed with a positive return, with the exception of the tapping heads which are controlled by lead screws. Air blast clears the holes of chips before the taps are entered and there is a gauging station to ensure that all holes are drilled to the correct depth. Fixtures that rotate through 90 deg. and return are a feature in the last operation sequences. The actual cutting speeds are kept low, so that long cutter life is secured and stoppages during working hours are virtually unknown from this cause. Quick-release positive drive chucks of Morris design are in use for holding drills, taps and reamers.

The machine stops automatically if there is a fault and red signal lights indicate the station at which the fault has occurred. If, for instance, a plunger fails to go home, if an electrical contact is not properly made or if the hydraulic system falls below the pre-set pressure of 250 lb./sq. in., the machine stops and signals for assistance. All operations are interlocked so that no movement can take place unless all is in order. Hand-operated safety switches are provided at each station for the operators and a wandering lead with an "inching" switch is used for machine setting.

All service pipes and leads are exposed to full view and can be reached for service and maintenance without difficulty. There are no pits in the floor and overground shaker conveyors located on both sides of the machine carry the chips, which fall from the sloping surfaces to portable bins placed at the end of the structure. The floor around the machine is remarkably free from chips and dust.

The development of this automatic transfer machine represents a triumph in co-operation between James Archdale and Sons Ltd., and the Nuffield Organization—in particular the Morris Engines Branch of Morris Motors Ltd., and Nuffield Tools and Gauges Ltd.

To students of industrial development this example will have a particular interest, as the original automatic transfer machine, built in 1923-24—also for the production of gearboxes—was a co-operative effort between the Engines Branch of Morris Motors Ltd. and James Archdale & Sons Ltd. These pioneering firms set a fashion which is having a profound influence on the future of machine shop practice.

Today the Austin Motor Co. probably employ a larger number of automatic transfer machines than any other British factory. They, like Renault in France, build machine heads to their own design, in their own works. They, too, have developed the package unit idea and the machine heads can be applied to a wide variety of operations. These heads are not of the universal type that are, necessarily, the stock-in-trade of the machine tool builder. For instance, while the speeds and feeds can be changed if desired, this cannot be effected by pulling a lever. The head must be delivered to the machine tool department who will open it up and make the necessary adjustments. This makes for simplicity in design with its accompanying economy. The method is justified by the fact that such changes will only need to be made at very long intervals, as for instance, when there is a major alteration on a new model.

Sir Leonard Lord, now chairman of Austin, said 30 years ago: "What is required of a production machine head is that it shall rotate the tool and provide a rapid approach, a feed appropriate to the task and a quick return", adding that, "all else is superfluous".

The universal machine tool has its appointed place, indeed we could not do without it, but that place is not in the automatic transfer machine nor even in the highly developed flow production line.

The Austin heads are made so that they can be used in any required position. The spindle head is mounted on a slide which forms an integral base. There are two motors in the head; one of these provides the quick approach and return movements while the other turns the spindle and—by means of reduction gearing—controls the cutting feed. The automatic cycle is controlled by electric devices mounted on the base slide. These can be arranged to provide any required sequence of movement: for instance the cycle for tapping heads is: quick approach; feed at tapping speed; reverse feed; quick return; and stop. Multi-spindle heads are obtained by means of a cluster box attachment to the spindle head which has dowel and bolt holes standardized so that any appropriate attachment can be made. The machining times are not set to achieve the fastest cutting speeds but to give an all-round balance of economy in machining costs. Blow-out and gauging stations are interposed wherever necessary, e.g. before tapping blind holes.

Austin have not adopted the method of allowing the workpiece to go bare; they favour the use of a work carrier, platen or pallet. As previously remarked, this has certain advantages in respect of locating and clamping. It must also be remembered that certain awkwardly shaped components must, of necessity, be handled in fixtures. Chips are taken away by means of an endless tray conveyor placed beneath the operative part of the machine.

In addition to the Austin-designed machine heads a number of Archdale automatic transfer machines are in use in the Austin Works. Some of each (there are far too many to show all of them) are shown in the illustrations which have been chosen for the interest they will have for the student of flow production. A complete list of the automatic transfer machines in this plant is most impressive and should convince the most sceptical that these new methods are here to stay. (Figs. 86-96.)

Next we must consider how far these new techniques lead towards the automatic factory; but, before doing so, it is necessary to point out that automatic machinery is not an essential of flow production. It is the ultimate expression made possible by circumstances in which volume and continuity of product is in demand. The author's intentions would be entirely frustrated if, in his endeavours to show what can be accomplished, he should leave the impression that flow production is only possible with the aid of very elaborate and expensive machinery. It cannot be too plainly stated that while flow production is a marriage of mechanism and management the accent is emphatically on *management.*

The Austin Motor Co. employ a large number of automatic transfer machines, and a selection of interest to the student of flow production are shown in Figs. 86 to 95.

(*Courtesy* Automobile Engineer)

Fig. 86—A 12-station in-line auto-transfer machine performs sundry milling, drilling, reaming and tapping operations on the A30 cylinder block

Fig. 87—The semi-finish and finish machining of the A30 cylinder bores is accomplished on this 9-station auto-transfer machine. The loading station and control panel are on the right of picture

Fig. 88—A 19-station in-line auto-transfer machine for drilling, tapping and reaming cylinder heads. This picture clearly shows the fixtures that are carried on the pallets or platens

Fig. 89—Drilling, tapping and forming the ends of crankshafts are the operations carried out on this 7-station auto-transfer machine

Fig. 90—The loading station for the crankshaft machine shown in the previous illustration. The lifting rings are for slings for the return of the pallet by overhead gear

Fig. 91—An auto-transfer machine which drills and reams oil holes from main journals to crankpins. The indexing fixture mounted on the pallets presents the crankshaft to the machine heads at the required angle

Fig. 92—A 13-station auto-transfer machine is used for milling, drilling, spot-facing, tapping, counterboring and reaming gearbox castings

Fig. 93—The loading end of an 11-station auto-transfer machine for rear axles. After certain preliminary operations, the boring and facing of the banjo; screwing the ends and reaming the bores of the axle tubes; drilling and reaming the end flanges; and forming the oil return grooves are among the operations performed on this machine

Fig. 94—Auto-transfer machines are also used for the smaller components. This is a general view of a machine for the production of selector rods

Fig. 95—Rotary auto-transfer machines are used. These are built from the same unit heads as those on the in-line machines. These same unit heads are also used on individual head machines in the ordinary flow-line set-up. Facing the bell housing flange of the gearbox is done on such a machine

Fig. 96—Before tapping, the components pass through a blow-out and gauging unit of the auto-transfer machine. This unit is on the A30 cylinder block in-line machine

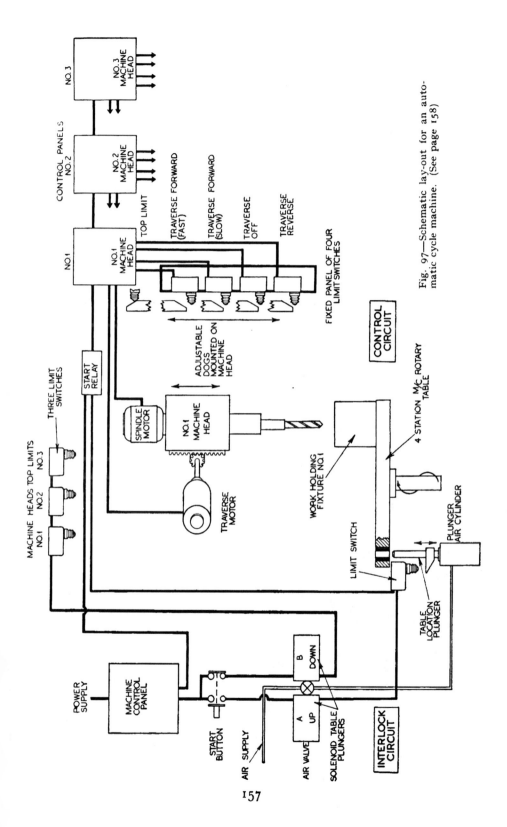

CONTROL PANELS

NO.3

NO.2

NO.1

NO.3 MACHINE HEAD

NO.2 MACHINE HEAD

NO.1 MACHINE HEAD

TOP LIMIT

TRAVERSE FORWARD (FAST)

TRAVERSE FORWARD (SLOW)

TRAVERSE OFF

TRAVERSE REVERSE

FIXED PANEL OF FOUR LIMIT SWITCHES

ADJUSTABLE DOGS MOUNTED ON MACHINE HEAD

CONTROL CIRCUIT

START RELAY

THREE LIMIT SWITCHES

MACHINE HEADS TOP LIMITS
NO.1 NO.2 NO.3

SPINDLE MOTOR

NO.1 MACHINE HEAD

TRAVERSE MOTOR

WORK HOLDING FIXTURE Nº1

4 STATION Mᶜ ROTARY TABLE

LIMIT SWITCH

PLUNGER AIR CYLINDER

TABLE LOCATION PLUNGER

POWER SUPPLY

MACHINE CONTROL PANEL

START BUTTON

AIR SUPPLY

AIR VALVE

A UP

B DOWN

SOLENOID TABLE PLUNGERS

INTERLOCK CIRCUIT

Fig. 97—Schematic lay-out for an automatic cycle machine. (See page 158)

157

Fig. 97—Limit switches control the movements of both automatic transfer machines and inter-operation mechanisms. On the opposite page is a schematic lay-out for an automatic cycle machine; the same principle being used on all such mechanisms. The cycle is initiated by a momentary depression of the starter button which de-energizes solenoid B and energizes solenoid A. The air valve operates the locating plunger to correct the position of the table. As the plunger goes home, a limit switch energizes the start relay which, in turn, energizes the table clamps (not shown in diagram) and starts all motors. The rate of travel of the heads and the distance travelled at that rate is set by dogs, mounted on the head, which actuate the switches. Thus any number of fast and slow feeds can be obtained, including momentary reverses to clear chips.

The forward traverse completed, each machine head automatically withdraws to top limit position when the motors are switched off. When all three top limit switches are depressed, solenoid B is energized and A de-energized; the table locating plunger withdraws and the start relay resets ready for the next cycle. Interlocking of the plunger with the top limit switches prevents the table from turning until all tools are clear of the workpiece.

Below are shown a micro-switch with a roller lever actuator, and a limit switch with an over-travel spring plunger   (Courtesy Burgess Products Co., Ltd.)

Fig. 98—Chemical plants provide good examples of highly integrated flow production systems. They are largely—sometimes completely—automatic. The following photographs illustrate the control of 76 motors from one central point
(Courtesy Contactor Switchgear, Ltd.)

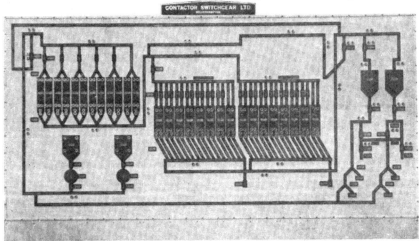

Fig. 98A—A mimic diagram of the storage and processing units and of the conveyor system. Automatically operated lamps indicate the position of all materials as they move through the plant

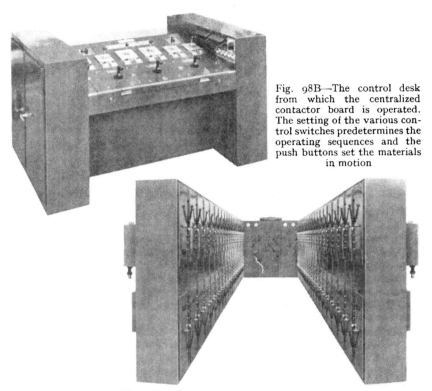

Fig. 98B—The control desk from which the centralized contactor board is operated. The setting of the various control switches predetermines the operating sequences and the push buttons set the materials in motion

Fig. 98C—The centralized multi-motor control board comprises a batch of direct starters for the squirrel cage motors. Each has its own interlocked isolating switch, the whole being arranged in two tiers. The cubicles at the far end contain the incoming electric supply and the bus bar interconnector gear from which the starters are fed

Fig. 98D—*Below*: A variety of limit switches, with a heavy-duty pattern shown in the centre. They can be arranged for self resetting as required

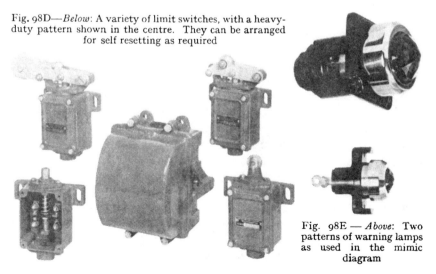

Fig. 98E — *Above*: Two patterns of warning lamps as used in the mimic diagram

CHAPTER FIFTEEN

THE AUTOMATIC FACTORY

PROBABLY the earliest serious reference to the possibilities of the automatic factory was made by H. E. Taylor—the then chief engineer of the Coventry branch of Hotchkiss et Cie—in his paper on "Factory Planning" given to the Institution of Production Engineers (see Proceedings for 1922-3). These are Mr. Taylor's own words:

> "Imagine a factory in which the structure is of standardized sections, this combination of steelwork, having cast iron facings, carrying standardized machine tool parts, such as grinding heads, drill heads, milling heads, and so forth. It is thus possible to conceive the factory itself as a colossal automatic machine in which the structure is the frame, the standardized machine tool parts being carried on the structure. Such a scheme readily lends itself to elaboration and it is not difficult to conceive units being driven by standardized electric power units, with automatic conveyors between the various tooling points, and with automatic assembly, so that it would be possible to run the factory as a machine with a staff of tenders. These units could be laid out in one plane which would be the natural development of the line system or, for compactness, they could be built in two planes which, for want of a better name, the author has termed a 'cubic development'. The whole structure would be enclosed by glass-filled panels and roofed with standard roofing panels.
>
> "The author conceives a factory of the kind referred to as being operated from a central control room, which is in itself a model of the factory having electrical indicators to all the tooling units, which immediately show if one of them is not functioning correctly. Any faulty mechanism will be at once provided for, by throwing out of action the whole set of machine-tool units for producing a component and by immediately fitting in another standard unit while the defective one is being repaired . . . assembly would not be interfered with, as provision would be made for these delays by a reserve supply of finished components which would always be in the conveyor."

Mr. Taylor dealt with difficulties and methods of overcoming them. He foresaw that such a scheme would, of necessity, come more or less gradually depending, as it would, upon demand on a scale to justify the capital expenditure. He said that: "the principle underlying the system is a gradual building up of simple details into detail assemblies which are again built into minor assemblies, and these in turn are built into major unit assemblies."

Mr. Taylor was, afterwards, concerned in the design of the cylinder block, gearbox and flywheel machines which were mentioned in Chapter 1. These were, in fact, the early editions of the automatic transfer machine of today. It will be appreciated that the automatic transfer machine is, in effect, a self-operating factory making one component. There is no reason why a combination of such units, if economically justifiable, should not evolve into a fully automatic factory.

More recently the E.C.M.E. (Electronic Circuit Making Equipment) plant was hailed in the Press as an automatic factory, but, in fact, it does not produce a complete end product ready for despatch to consumers which is the normal conception of an automatic factory. It is more analogous to an automatic transfer machine, and in the eyes of the student of flow production the brilliant conception and design of the components is even more remarkable than the machine that produced them. This, however, does not detract from the concept or the ingenious manner in which it was carried out.

E.C.M.E. is the invention of Mr. John A. Sargrove, who was for 11 years chief engineer with the British Tungsram Radio Works, Ltd. The E.C.M.E. plant originally housed at Sir Richard's Bridge, Walton-on-Thames, was designed for the production of radio panels by a method known as the "spray-milled" technique. The principle is not, however, limited to radio—the process can be applied to television, radar and other devices where similar types of compound circuits are required.

In brief, the compound circuit component is made by completely coating a moulded plastic panel with zinc, by the metallization process, and then milling the surface to remove all the metal except that in sunken areas. Preformed plastic panels, in which the circuit channels and other contours are moulded, are fed into the machine, passing first into a grit blasting chamber for the roughening of the surface to form a key for the metal spraying. This done, the panels travel through a photo-electric cell inspection section which will stop the grit blast operation if the surface is not properly conditioned. The panel then goes to the metallization compartment, where four jets spray the whole surface of the panel with molten zinc. After this the panel moves to a milling operation where groups of three diamond-tipped milling cutters take a very shallow cut; six such groups of cutters are used, thus avoiding the generation of heat which might distort the panel. The repeated milling operations remove all the metal except that in the circuit channels, the shallow round depressions—which will become condensers—and the spiral grooves which will form the induction coils. At the next operation the sockets, for holding those components which go to make up the complete radio, are hopper-fed past a photo-cell unit which rejects any that are faulty or wrongly positioned. (Fig. 99.)

Thence the panel passes through an electric inspector which, in 20 seconds, makes 50 separate circuit tests. If two consecutive panels are faulty the machine stops to await adjustment. After inspection, the panels are varnished and baked, and are ready for assembly with the other components—the valves, large condensers and loudspeaker—into

The so-called automatic factory is quite possible. It can come into being as soon as the industrialists consider it an economic possibility; all the means are available if the end is desired. The photographs in Fig. 99 show how near we have approached to fully automatic operation.

(Crown copyright photographs)

Fig. 99A—This Electronic Circuit Making Equipment (E.C.M.E.) is an automatic transfer machine for the production of elaborate compound electrical circuits by the "spray-milled" technique. These two machines, 70 ft. in length, are producing complete panels for radio. They could make any required compound circuit components

the cabinet. There are two different panels in the set, the other, in which resistors are formed by means of an automatic graphite-spraying operation, being rather more complicated. Both panels can be produced at the rate of 180 per hour. The method employed is said to save the making of 35 individual components and also wiring needing more than 80 soldered joints. It is estimated that to carry out this work by normal methods in the output quantity mentioned would require about 500 people. It is anticipated, therefore, that, given an economic quantity, the cost of production should be reduced by 33 per cent to 50 per cent.

It will be seen that this very interesting plant is not the wholly automatic factory visualized by Taylor. It is, nevertheless, a signpost indicating what is possible by integrating the design of the product with the design of special machines—in sequence, interspersed with automatic inspection devices—always providing, of course, that the demand justifies the method. In this instance the sponsor was aiming to supply the low-paid worker of the Far East with the cheapest possible radio set. To satisfy that market, enormous quantities would be required and this warranted an entirely new approach to the production problem.

Fig. 99B—The operator feeds the machine with pre-formed plastic plates. Only the valves, capacitors and loudspeaker have to be assembled with the finished panel to make a complete radio

Fig. 99C—The pre-formed plates are fed through a grit-blast chamber and then inspected by a photo-electric eye for the quality of the resultant surface. The plates then travel to this station where both sides are metallized by spray guns

Fig. 99D—When the plates leave the spray chamber they travel to this face-milling unit where surplus metal is removed by a battery of high-speed diamond-tipped tools, leaving the metal in the depressions that form the circuit

Fig. 99E—Completed panels leaving the terminal end of the machine

Fig. 99F—Fitting the valves, capacitors and loudspeaker. There are two panels, each having different circuits on both sides

Fig. 99G—The completed radio being fitted into its case

F•

The machine was made by Sargrove Electronics, Ltd., and it fulfilled all that was required of it, but it is not yet in operation owing to the fact that the political and social changes in the Far Eastern countries, for whom its products were intended, destroyed the potential market which was essential for its full exploitation. The firm—Sargrove Electronics, Ltd.—is at present busily occupied on special machines and electronic controls in other spheres of mass production, among which are electric cables, plastic products and food manufacture.

This example is of interest also in that electronic devices are predominant, thus foreshadowing a new method of control. Mechanical engineers are, as a whole, rather reluctant to use electrical apparatus if mechanical means can be made to operate to the same end, but this reluctance will no doubt disappear as easily replaceable spares of the package unit type become readily available.

If and when they are required, there is a wealth of such devices to draw upon in the shape of the military, naval, aircraft and anti-aircraft fire control mechanisms, but the automatic factory will have to be a very much more advanced proposition than it is before their use becomes a vital necessity. Automatic controls are used in modern chemical plants and in oil refineries. It will, however, be recognized that the manipulation of such plants is vastly different to the handling required by the mechanical trades.*

One of the greatest achievements in the automatic production of engineering components is the motor car frame-making plant of the A. O. Smith Corporation, of Milwaukee, U.S.A. The story behind this stupendous undertaking is full of interest. The corporation, which had made a name in the manufacture of bicycle frames, was required in 1903, by the Peerless Motor Car Co., to produce pressed steel automobile frames. Orders followed from the Studebaker, Pope-Toledo, Cadillac, Packard, Elmore, Reo, Locomobile and others, but the first real indication of the great future of the motor car industry came when the Ford Motor Co. placed an order for the then unheard-of quantity of 10,000 pressed-steel frames for their model N car.

The far-sighted president of the corporation of that day, Mr. L. R. Smith, foresaw the great demand which would ultimately be made by the automobile industry and, in 1915, called upon his engineering staff to construct a plant which would turn out frames automatically or as nearly so as human ingenuity could contrive. None of the staff had heard of such a plant, but the A. O. Smith concern had never followed convention when seeking better methods. Hundreds of engineers turned to this task. Six years of labour and 8,000,000 dollars were

---

* In the *Manchester Guardian* Survey of Industry, Trade and Finance for 1953 it is indicated that the Americans are devoting some 20 per cent of their capital expenditure on fixed plant and machinery to electrical control equipment. The British figure for 1951 is estimated as between 3 and 4 per cent.

expended on it; the result was astonishingly successful. Flat sheets of steel were fed in at one end of the plant and black-painted frames came out at the other at the rate of one every 8 seconds—more than 10,000 frames in a 24-hour day.

The entire plant, more than two city blocks in length (846 ft), can be considered as a series machine consisting of six essential operations as follows.

(1) The press line, where blanks are cut from steel strip previously rolled to the desired width and thickness, and the "kick-up" over the rear axle formed by cold-bending the blank edgewise, after which the blank is trimmed and punched for the fittings. (Fig. 100A.)

(2) The sidebar assembly line, where the left- and right-hand sidebar strips are made into channel beams by cold-forming in two presses. The chassis side-members, thus formed, pass on to the sidebar section which consists of a block-long line of carriages which move in unison

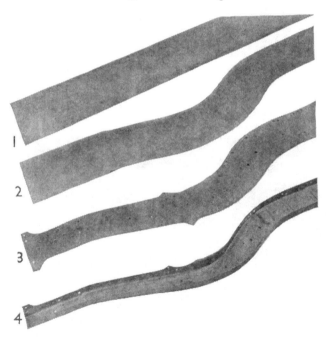

Fig. 100A—The A. O. Smith Corporation of Milwaukee, U.S.A., have an automatic plant for producing automobile frames, illustrated on this and the following pages. Above are shown four steps in the manufacture of a typical side bar for an automobile frame

1. The blank, cut to length from strip steel, rolled to desired width and thickness.

2. The "kick-up" over the rear axle is obtained by cold bending the blank edgewise

3. The blank is trimmed and punched

4. The U-shaped side bar is cold formed in a single operation

Fig. 100B—The side bars are placed on a conveyor which brings them to appropriate stations where they are thrust to and fro to have holes drilled, brackets added, etc. A parallel line prepares the transverse and cross members. In the foreground are the chassis carriers

Fig. 100C—On the carriage in the foregound is a frame which takes the place of the frame in the background. This is receiving rivets blown through the tubes. 150 rivets can be blown into place in rather less than one second

Fig. 100D—The frame passes, on a conveyor, through a line of riveting "bears" which advance, close rivets and retire. This line is automatic. The rivets are closed cold

Fig. 100E—A stock of finished frames awaiting shipment. The plant is sufficiently flexible to make a change of set-up for an order of as few as 60,000 frames an economical proposition

from station to station. At each station the carriages automatically present the sidebars to machines which perform various operations, such as punching holes, attaching hangers, placing and closing rivets and such like. (Fig. 100B.)

(3) The sub-assembly line, which consists of a number of machines, on a lower floor, which produce the other frame components, such as cross-members and "X" members which are built up and joined by welding or riveting. This line flows parallel to the sidebar line and they both meet at the general assembly line.

(4) The general assembly line, where the various parts of the frame are located on moving carriages to be picked up by the "nailing machine", which first pushes the parts into close contact and then, by means of tubes carrying air pressure at 90 lb./sq. in., blows the individual rivets into place. This machine can place up to 150 rivets in approximately one second. The frames continue to move, on carriages, to the riveting stations. Since the frame has become an integral unit, it cannot be handled in the same fashion as the sidebars; therefore, at each station, the riveting machines move up to the frame, close their particular rivet, and back away. (Fig. 100C-D.)

(5) The welding line is the final mechanical operation and here the frame passes through a series of booths for certain simple welding operations which, in this instance, are performed by hand.

(6) The painting line performs the last operation wherein the frames pass through a steam bath and, on a monorail conveyor, through an automatic paint-spraying section and so through an oven which bakes them dry in about 20 minutes. (Fig. 100E.)

It might be thought that such a plant as this would be absolutely inflexible, but this is not so. Generally speaking, about 60,000 frames constitute a reasonable quantity for which to alter the set-up. While this plant is not entirely self-operative, it approaches very near to complete automatism, and it indicates in no uncertain fashion what can be done when technology marches with opportunity. The plant has been in operation, now, for the better part of 30 years, yet men still come from all parts of the world to look at this marvel which has been acclaimed as one of the most complex engineering achievements in the world.

The frame plant is not a freak nor is it the only semi-automatic plant in the A. O. Smith Corporation. They have a plant for making large pipes which works on similar methods. This plant has turned out up to 15 miles of pipe, weighing 3,000 tons, in a single day. It will be appreciated that the mere problem of moving this amount of material from the freight cars to the stock pile, from the stock pile through the mill, and from the finishing line on to the freight cars again needed a most serious study of handling methods. Three enormous hydraulic

The A. O. Smith Corporation also have a pipe-making flow line which might rank as semi-automatic. The following diagram and photographs are a good example of flow production

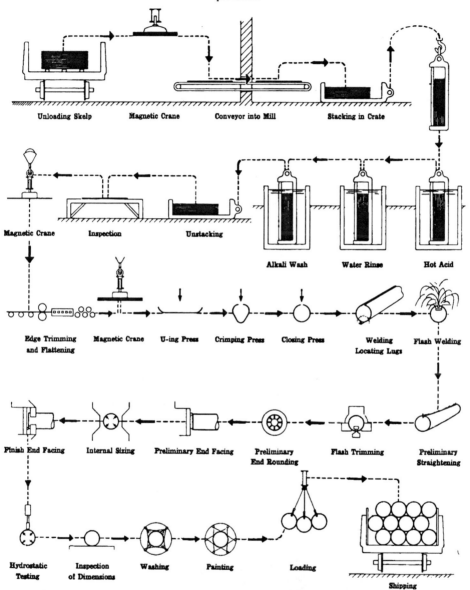

Fig. 101A—Flow line for steel pipes 40 ft. in length and up to 30 in. in diameter, showing the flow process in stages
(Courtesy *Welding and Metal Fabrication*)

Fig. 101B—The first operation in the pipe-making flow line is the pickling of the skelp to free it from dirt and scale

Fig. 101C—The skelp is flattened and edge-trimmed in this machine

Fig. 101D—Three of these great presses are required to form the pipe: a U-ing press, a crimping press and a closing press

Fig. 101E—Flash welding follows, an operation which takes only 30 seconds. Then the pipe is "sized" by expanding it, in a die, by hydraulic pressure

Fig. 101F—Finally, after subsequent minor operations, including flash removal, there is a hydrostatic test on this machine. Then follows inspection, washing, painting and shipment in gondola cars

presses form the flat plates of steel into tubes ranging from $8\frac{5}{8}$ in. to 30 in. in dia. (sometimes larger) by 40 ft. in length. When formed into circular section the pipe edges are flash-welded, the complete 40 ft. length taking only 30 seconds for this operation. After this, each length of pipe is placed in a die of the correct diameter and length, the ends of the pipe are sealed and by hydraulic pressure the pipe is expanded to fit the die, thus providing cold working of the steel and a test of the weld. (Fig. 101.)

F**

The car assembly plant at the Austin Motor Company is another triumph for automatism. Here in a great hall, $1\frac{1}{2}$ furlongs in length, three conveyors set the pace for the whole of the factory and, incidentally, for all the supplying firms outside.

This plant represents one of the major forward steps towards complete automatic control. It has for its objective the reduction of the cycle time by eliminating the waiting periods between operations and of reducing the working capital, locked up in stock in stores and work in progress, to a minimum. At the same time it provides an admirable work-place with nearly ideal conditions for unhurried but steady application to the task in hand. The method adopted, reduced to the simplest terms, consists of marshalling all the components in the order required, delivering them to the right place at the precise moment that they are needed, and providing the proper tools for the workers.

This would be quite a task if only one type of car was in progress, but the plant is capable of dealing with four types of chassis with considerable variations as, for instance, right- and left-hand steering and as many as four different bodies, namely saloon, passenger van, delivery van and pick-up truck; to say nothing of the variations in colour and trim and the addition of heater and/or radio.

Let us first consider what takes place on one of the assembly tracks— say the "Somerset" or A40 line—and then work back to see how it all happens.

This track is laid out for the production of 2,000 vehicles in an 80-hour week. Although, in effect, the track is continuous it is actually in four sections, the first being devoted to chassis assembly, the second to chassis painting, the third to oiling and body mounting and the fourth to final connections.

The assembly commences in the marshalling area of the individual component stores where the slat conveyor, on which are mounted various fixtures, is loaded with such items as propeller shafts, rear springs, silencers, exhaust pipes and so on—down to nuts and bolts.

As the conveyor emerges from this area, the frames are placed on their fixtures by a Telpher drawing from a frame stock which is held in sequence to match the pre-planned output. At the next station the rear springs and shackles are attached to the frame which, proceeding to the next station, receives the rear axle and front suspension delivered by an elevator from a tunnel 20 feet below the floor of the assembly building. These components are attached to the chassis—the propeller shaft, brake mechanism and cable harness being added at succeeding locations.

At another station, the engine assembly elevator drops the power unit into the required position "within less than half a hole" so that the fitters can, with a minimum of manipulation, bolt it into place. Then the clutch control is added and that portion of the steering mechanism carried by the chassis is coupled up.

The car assembly plant at the Austin Motor Company is another triumph for automatism. Here in a great hall, $1\frac{1}{2}$ furlongs in length three conveyors set the pace for the whole of the factory and, incidentally, for all the supplying firms outside.

This plant represents one of the major forward steps towards complete automatic control. It has for its objective the reduction of the cycle time by eliminating the waiting periods between operations and of reducing the working capital, locked up in stock in stores and work in progress, to a minimum. At the same time it provides an admirable work-place with nearly ideal conditions for unhurried but steady application to the task in hand. The method adopted, reduced to the simplest terms, consists of marshalling all the components in the order required, delivering them to the right place at the precise moment that they are needed, and providing the proper tools for the workers.

This would be quite a task if only one type of car was in progress but the plant is capable of dealing with four types of chassis with considerable variations as, for instance, right- and left-hand steering and as many as four different bodies, namely saloon, passenger van, delivery van and pick-up truck; to say nothing of the variations in colour and trim and the addition of heater and/or radio.

Let us first consider what takes place on one of the assembly tracks—say the "Somerset" or A40 line—and then work back to see how it all happens.

This track is laid out for the production of 2,000 vehicles in an 80-hour week. Although, in effect, the track is continuous it is actually in four sections, the first being devoted to chassis assembly, the second to chassis painting, the third to oiling and body mounting and the fourth to final connections.

The assembly commences in the marshalling area of the individual component stores where the slat conveyor, on which are mounted various fixtures, is loaded with such items as propeller shafts, rear springs, silencers, exhaust pipes and so on—down to nuts and bolts.

As the conveyor emerges from this area, the frames are placed on their fixtures by a Telpher drawing from a frame stock which is held in sequence to match the pre-planned output. At the next station the rear springs and shackles are attached to the frame which, proceeding to the next station, receives the rear axle and front suspension delivered by an elevator from a tunnel 20 feet below the floor of the assembly building. These components are attached to the chassis—the propeller shaft, brake mechanism and cable harness being added at succeeding locations.

At another station, the engine assembly elevator drops the power unit into the required position "within less than half a hole" so that the fitters can, with a minimum of manipulation, bolt it into place. Then the clutch control is added and that portion of the steering mechanism carried by the chassis is coupled up.

cards are intended for the Austin "home" factories that produce the main assemblies (power-units, rear axles, front suspensions and bodies) and also for the storage area which forms a reservoir to balance the assemblies which are produced at varying rates in the "home" factories.

Hollerith machines in these departments, actuated by relays on the track, pass each card, in turn, through an electric field which makes a contact, in accordance with the punching of the card, to set in motion the assembly indicated in the pre-selected order. Should the card be blank the units will remain stationary; this means that the output can be varied although the speed of the tracks is constant.

The assemblies are moved by dogs on the chain conveyors, which ride over the units until solenoid operation lowers the chain to effect engagement.

The assemblies when loaded in the correct sequence travel first to the storage area and then, as needed, through a 1,000 ft.-long tunnel to halls under the assembly lines. Here the units are transferred to the particular sidings which serve the assembly line to which they are allotted. Thus the "Somerset" assemblies are switched to the A40 elevator bay, the "Hereford" assemblies to the A70 bay and so forth. The assemblies wait like taxicabs on a rank, until they are "whistled-up" by the customer. The "whistling-up" is accomplished by electrical connections made on the tracks. The elevators hold the unit suspended for a brief period to enable the correct position between assembly and chassis to be established, when the elevator will lower the unit and the slings will automatically disengage.

In the meantime, the individual components (the majority of which come from outside suppliers) are delivered to the bulk stores at the head of the assembly lines. Here sufficient stock is held to take care of any likely interruptions to deliveries. From the bulk stores, the components are moved by fork-lift trucks to the marshalling area through which the assembly conveyor runs. As mentioned, these parts are placed in sets on the conveyor so that they come conveniently to the hands of the assemblers, who do not have to turn round or change stance to pick up the required pieces. This alone is an improvement on old-type assembly lines where components would be arriving from all directions.

It might appear from the foregoing that this method of assembly is somewhat inflexible. This is not so—normal variations can be introduced within 90 to 120 minutes according to what is needed, and even colour changes which involve operations remote from the assembly line can be made in a matter of 8 hours.

This is, of course, only a thumb-nail sketch of one of the most original and interesting developments in flow production. It was achieved by the close co-operation of the planning and engineering staffs of the Austin Motor Company with their contractors, Geo. W. King,

Ltd., who provided all the conveyors, the Donovan Electrical Company who supplied the control gear, C. C. Wakefield and Co. Ltd., who were responsible for the oil dispensing unit, the British Tabulating Machine Co. Ltd., for the punched card operating machines, and the Carrier Engineering Co. Ltd., who, collaborating with Henry W. Peabody (Industrial) Ltd., were responsible for the paint spraying equipment.

From these examples it can be seen that the so-called automatic factory is quite possible. Automatic transfer machines, interoperation transfer devices and semi-automatic assembly lines are already here. Thus most of the technical requirements are available: they are not perfect but they are practicable, and automatic factories, for the mass production of articles based on engineering practice, can come into being just as soon as the industrialist is satisfied that they are economically desirable.

The immediate application of automatic methods to those processes which, by nature, are laborious, unpleasant or detrimental to health, would be logical and desirable. Many plants in the petroleum, chemical, plastics and other such industries are very largely automatic, but, as we have previously noted, these products flow readily. Unfortunately many of the less desirable tasks in the industries based on engineering are difficult to mechanize, but reluctance on the part of workmen to undertake heavy and dirty labour in crude conditions— which reluctance is concomitant with a rising scale of living—will be a challenge which our technicians will, no doubt, accept to the advantage of all concerned.

We have now arrived at a point where we should endeavour to strike a balance between the desirability and the possibility of adopting these advanced techniques. Consideration should also be given to the difficulties that are likely to be met when installing such methods, and to the possible effects that such development may have on our industrial and our social future. The question-and-answer form would appear to be the most convenient way of dealing with these matters.

(1) *What are the advantages of automatism?* Primarily that the machine utilization when these methods are installed is as near 100 per cent as we are ever likely to reach. We have, for more than three generations, paid the closest attention to increasing the efficiency of the cutting tools and now we are turning our attention to the loading and unloading cycle in which there are greater possible economies than in any other operation. Man-handling cannot hope to match the cutting capacity of the modern machine tool; therefore we shall be forced to consider mechanical handling not merely from store to floor and shop to shop but through all stages. Some automatic transfer machines have reduced the number of operators by more than six to one, and Ford say that automation—that is interoperation transfer—shows a saving of 25 to 30 per cent of direct labour even in their, already efficient,

flow production factories. Such figures must not, however, be taken as a net gain. On the other side of the ledger there is an account for more administration, more technicians, more maintenance men, more supervision. Even so, the resultant figure of saving is most impressive. The amount of saving depends, of course, on the state of the factory to which these methods are applied. The economies are not only in labour but in the working capital represented by the smaller stock-in-store and work-in-progress that has to be carried.

(2) *What industries, then, are likely to adopt automatism?* Primarily, the so-called mass production industries; this embraces automobiles, bicycles, sewing machines, vacuum cleaners, washing machines and all the domestic utilities. Moreover, any of the large-quantity products such as portable machines, electrical components, building accessories and such like are a fair field for automatic production.

(3) *Why should these methods be adopted?* Primarily to meet competition, to reduce costs, to provide more goods and services and to bring them within the reach of wider consumer groups. They might also be adopted to offset a scarcity of labour because the work to be done was unattractive owing to competition from other industries; this would particularly apply where the tasks were of a heavy or arduous nature or because the conditions were, of necessity, unpleasant or harmful to health. Then, again, there is the example of the petroleum industry which, because so many variables had to be controlled, was forced to adopt automatically controlled production.

Incidentally, the automatic factory is most likely to come about by a step-by-step process. That is to say that an automatic transfer machine will be adopted for one component and, if successful, the system will be extended to a second and third component. Later the auto-transfer machines may be linked by automation devices and the automatic factory is established. That is what is happening now; tentative beginnings are extended and gain impetus as the method proves itself successful.

(4) *How far are these methods desirable?* The answer to this depends largely on the sort of competition that has to be met, and also on the necessity for combating high labour cost. They can allow for a higher standard of remuneration while at the same time reducing the cost of the product to the purchaser. This is linked with the next hypothetical question.

(5) *How far are these methods possible?* The answer here is: as far as is economically sound. All these matters must be taken on the balance of profitability. There are some things which can only be done by hand operation. Moreover, there is a limit to the specialization, standardization and simplification that purchasers in a free world will adopt. There is, however, an enormous field where the purchaser is not a whit the worse for using a standard article. There was, for instance, the classic case of the brass lavatory sink traps which during the original

simplification campaign in U.S.A. were reduced from 1,114 to 76. This 93 per cent reduction did not, I venture to think, harm anyone even if it were noticed. Nor, I think, would anyone be troubled by the reduction of hot-water storage tanks by 88 per cent or shovels, spades and scoops by 58 per cent. But where the matter of personal convenience or taste is involved, the purchaser is, or should be, in control and it is just there that automatism stops.

(6) *What conditions are required for full automatism?* Automatic operation needs a steady demand of sufficient quantities of standardized articles to justify laying down the necessary plant and tools. This means, in turn, specialization, standardization and simplification of the product. It requires very careful pre-planning, work study, maybe product redesign, cost estimation and replanning in the light of what has been discovered during these exploratory excursions. The whole financial situation would have to be studied against a market research background and it would be very essential that all future possibilities be considered, such as how changes of demand, of technical requirements or of style would react on the machines, fixtures and tools. The decision would be taken on a balance of probabilities but it is improbable that any company would take a plunge into the unknown. It is more likely that the decision would arise out of a known and tested situation. In new propositions a pilot plant might, very probably, be set up to test the market and this would be equipped with normal machine tools.

(7) *What difficulties are likely to arise in adopting automatism?* In the first place, automatic factories of the kind envisaged would be very complicated mechanisms involving a great deal of consideration, a large amount of pre-planning and much intricate plant design. This would tax the resources of our building and machine tool industries and would stretch the capacity of the equipment manufacturers to the utmost. Also automatic—push-button—factories would need large and more skilful maintenance staffs to keep them running and these would have to be drawn from our somewhat meagre reservoir of highly skilled labour. That is why the automatic factory will come relatively slowly.

The problems of maintenance are considerable but not insuperable. It is visualized that maintenance staffs might rise to four times what they are at present but that is only a "guesstimate" and probably on the high side. All maintenance will have to be scheduled and preventive. In other words, "maintenance must be by anticipation, not by default". Tool replacement presents another problem; instruments have been devised to indicate when tools need changing but, until the efficacy of these is beyond all doubt, it would appear that scheduled attention coupled with slower running of the machines to obtain increased tool life will be the answer. The machines are so efficient that a slight reduction of their speed in the interest of longer tool life would, on balance, appear to be an economy.

As to the machines themselves, Professor J. E. Arnold of the Mechanical Engineering Department of the Massachusetts Institute of Technology* says: "Designers must design machines with infinite lives or finite lives that can be predicted accurately". That appears to be a counsel of perfection but it arises from the knowledge that sporadic breakdowns in plant could be cumulative to such an extent that the plant could become inoperative; the real answer probably lies in unit designed machines coupled with a full stock of replacement heads and clamping and transfer mechanisms always available. From the author's experience this should be a feasible answer.

So far as product design is concerned, there must be an alliance between the product designer and the machine-tool and the jig and tool designers. The latter obtains now, the former is a new aspect. Basic redesign may prove necessary, in order that the automatic factory can function at its economic best, but in this field the consumer will have much to say.

It will be necessary to speed up communications in the automatic factory. Some of the transmission of instructions will be achieved automatically by control devices. Nevertheless, there will be a problem in the matter of human communications, which, today, are far from perfect and which will be noticeably wanting when they have to implement a much speeded-up production technique.

(8) *What will be the social effect of automatisation?* In discussing the matter we must be careful to avoid sentimentalism. We must bear in mind that there is a great deal of automaticity in many of our existing industries. Petroleum products, flour milling, beverages, seed products, are all automatic or semi-automatic processes. So also are the production processes of rolled and extruded metals. These all flow easily, being liquid or fluid, actually or in effect. The engineering products and those that are based on the mechanical industries do not flow readily because of the hard, heavy and awkward pieces that need fabrication and because of the accuracy that is necessary for their satisfactory production and functioning.

Let us then forget that there is a tradition involved in the production of these products and let us examine the problem of production with new eyes.

There must, inevitably, be a displacement of labour when these processes are adopted. It is the old story of the hand loom versus the machine loom writ large. We all know that the machine loom, in the long run, gave better service to the consumer and more, not less, work to the operatives. In the ultimate result there is no doubt that these new techniques will increase employment. In the meantime, however, the displacement will mean hardship for those who are dispossessed, and

---

* *Automation and Other Technological Advances. See list of references, page 188, for details.*

anxiety for those who have to learn new tricks. That is a problem that offers no solution, but it can be eased if all those implicated face the problem and play their part. It is not as difficult as would appear at first sight. As previously stated, there are many new jobs in a factory that installs these new machines and devices. The maintenance staff must grow and supervision has to increase. Ford found that 40 per cent more shop floor supervision was required in their Cleveland plant where practically complete automation has been adopted.

Harry Lee Waddell of *Factory Management and Maintenance* recently gave "concrete examples of 50 to 60 per cent increases in total factory production with no change to speak of in the total number of workers employed. What happened in most cases was this: a plant having, say, 700 operators and 300 maintenance workers would end up after a complete change-over to automatic means of production with, perhaps 550 operators and 450 maintenance men." He went on to say that "a man may lose his job as an operator and have to go somewhere else to continue as an operator, but he may possibly find himself up-graded into a maintenance man".

Whilst on this subject, it must be remembered that there are many other causes of redundancy than that of introducing automatic machinery. When low-cost labour in other countries threatens our standard of life, the automatic factory may even be our salvation.

Another offset to redundancy is the large amount of machinery and devices that are required for these push-button factories. A member of the Ford Organization states that his company is prepared to spend from three to three and a half times the annual prospective saving in new machinery. That is for a revenue saving of $1,000 they will spend a capital amount of $3,000 to $3,500. The redundancy problem is therefore rather one of redeployment than of unemployment. Agreed that it is not very pleasant for the individual who is "being pushed around" and that everyone concerned should do all he can to ease his embarrassment.

There will be other changes on the shop floor; for instance, time and motion study as understood today will disappear. They will be absorbed into the work study when the machines are planned and these functions will, so to speak, be in-built with the machine. Moreover, when the machine is in complete control of all operations, normal incentive schemes and, in particular, individual piecework will be ineffective. The incentive will probably be assessed on the net hours that the machine is kept at work and it will, no doubt, be on a group basis.

The question of redundancy has been dealt with at some length because it is an aspect which always bulks so largely when these matters are discussed but, of course, there are many other social consequences which will arise when these methods are widely adopted.

CHAPTER SIXTEEN

HUMAN RELATIONS

Discussion of the automatic factory tends to focus attention on an overriding principle—the last that is offered for consideration—which has nothing to do with the art of production as such, but much to do with a more fundamental aspect of human relations. It is simply that *the system of flow production must benefit everyone: consumers, workers and owners*. Unless this eighteenth principle is satisfied the system cannot reach full stature and, if it does not, the equipment and appurtenances necessary for flow production will not be utilized to the full. They might even, in some instances, become an embarrassment. This principle of "benefit for all" is not based on altruistic ideals—much as these are to be admired—but upon the hard facts of business efficiency.

Benefit to the consumer is essential because it is necessary to the well-being of the flow production factory that there should be a constant and regular demand. This condition can only be achieved by supplying the required articles at attractive prices. This, in effect, means the widening of the consumer market by making the goods available in improved quality or in the same quality at a lower price, or both!

During the past 50 years there has been a growing appreciation of the fact that those who make the goods are also the potential consumers. This was, of course, always recognized in so far as the bare necessities of life were concerned but there was not the same conscious apprehension of the facts in regard to the non-necessities and the luxuries—incidentally the luxuries of one generation are the necessities of the next. Probably Henry Ford did more than anyone to point out that, if the world is to progress, workers must be consumers. It was not so much what he said but what he did that counted. He broke down the idea that the motor car was the prerogative of the well-to-do and established it as a general utility—but he did more than that; he put into practice the idea that profits should be used to increase wages and lower prices. Ford was no sentimentalist but a far-sighted industrialist, who held that "our working class must also become our leisure class if our production is to be balanced by consumption". This is another way of saying that production is the key to the raising of the standard of living—in other words the provision of benefits for the consumer.

For the owners the benefit comes from the price realized for the goods. This must provide a surplus over the cost of the product to cover the replacement of capital as represented by buildings, plant, machinery and equipment. It must also provide means for constant experimentation and development and suitable rewards for those who conceive the projects and operate the plants. In addition, the surplus must give reasonable recompense to the shareholders in proportion to the financial risks they undertake.

As remarked in an earlier chapter, much capital must be regarded as expendable—consumed in the production process or rendered obsolete because of changes in design or processing. Special process plant is naturally more vulnerable to change than standard universal types of machine tools. A sinking fund must be provided to take care of such possibilities and—this is most important—kept in liquid form. Quoting Henry Ford:*

> "A company must do more than keep its plant and equipment in repair. It must continually be changing them to meet changes in design, materials and methods of making—not a single item of equipment can be regarded as permanent. Not even the site can be taken as fixed. We abandoned our Highland Park plant—which was in its day the largest automobile plant in the world—and moved to the River Rouge plant because in the new plant there could be less handling of materials and consequently a saving. We frequently scrap whole divisions of our business—and as a routine affair. And then one has to be prepared against the day when a complete change may be necessary and an entirely new plant constructed to make a new product."

Mr. Ford added a pregnant sentence: "We have gone through all of this".

Discussion regarding the benefit to the workers is a complicated matter, best dealt with by taking—in the first place—the narrow personal viewpoint and secondly the broad issue as to whether mass and flow production is of benefit to mankind in general and to the workers in particular. The term "workers" in itself presents a difficulty. Most people if asked for a spot definition of "workers" would say: Those who work with their hands, who "punch clocks", and who are members of trade unions. This is, however, an old-fashioned and out-of-date conception since more and more of those who would have been manual workers are becoming technicians while a majority of management staffs—being not the owners but the servants of the company for whom they act—are workers. Moreover, if thrifty, it is possible for manual workers to invest in the company they serve, so becoming part owners—albeit with no more voice than other small shareholders. The workers will much more probably be direct or indirect consumers of the goods they produce. In fact, under modern conditions the old landmarks, those clear-cut classifications of workers, owners and consumers are disappearing. Nevertheless, to keep this subject within bounds let us accept, with reservations, the classic definition of owner, worker and consumer with the proviso that management may be either owner, or worker, or both.

---

* *Moving Forward*, by Henry Ford.

In the narrow sense the benefit to workers arising from this new system comes in shorter hours, in better conditions, in lighter tasks and in increased pay packets; for, make no mistake, it was the mass and flow production establishments that led the way in these amenities and improvements; the point being—and this is a very important point indeed—that they could afford it.

Turning now to the broader issue, we know that this is, and rightly so, an age of searching question and not one of blind belief that because things are what they are they are necessarily right. It is wise, therefore, to ask if flow production is good or bad for the community, with special emphasis on that part of it usually referred to as the workers. The answer must be that it is neutral. Flow production is a system—a tool of management—and, just as a plough is a more effective instrument than a spade so is this system better for its specific purpose than the methods that it displaces. As to whether it makes for a better community depends on the uses made of the tool rather than upon the instrument itself. After all, a man can commit a murder with a spade and as we know, only too well, organization can be used to crush the soul of a nation; but neither the spade nor the organization can be condemned because one or the other is put to wrongful uses.

There have been in the past—and there are now—many writers, preachers and others who have the ear of the public, who deplore modern methods and see no hope for mankind unless there is a return to the craftsmanship of the Middle Ages; but that would be "emptying the baby with the bath" with a vengeance. Many of such critics judge modern industry from a viewpoint entirely their own and without first-hand knowledge. They are prejudiced by the history of the earlier stages of the industrial revolution—torn from its context—a history which portrays a horribly harsh world, but a world endeavouring to escape from age-old poverty-stricken conditions.

Not all critics, however, are of this calibre; there are those who really know the conditions and who are aware that there must be a reverse as well as an obverse to any situation. They are aware that the defects of the system are not those which arise from the "assembly belt", so much berated by the nostalgics, but that they are inherent in industrialism as a whole.

The charges brought against mass and flow production fall under two main sections:

(*a*) Complaints alleged on behalf of consumers.

(*b*) The effects felt by the workers.

The consumer is said to suffer by the production of goods of poor quality and also from over-standardization. It cannot be denied that there are plenty of poor-quality goods on the market and some tawdry rubbish but this is not due to the method of production. It is due primarily to a lack of purchasing power and a want of discrimination on the part of the buying public coupled with a determination to take advantage of those conditions on the part of some manufacturers. A public educated to withhold their patronage until they can afford worth-while things would speedily put an end to the offer of indifferent articles. The mass and flow methods can, and do, produce first-class, beautifully and accurately made consumer goods to standards which could never be achieved by hand except in the smallest quantities. The flow production system actually demands accuracy and fine finish to avoid the need for hand adjustment and to ensure that the articles sold will give satisfaction under guarantee.

Two instances may help to put point to this contention. One is that the Ford Motors Organization acquired the Johansson Company—the finest gauge-making business in the world. The other is the recollection by the author of a visit paid by the Rolls-Royce engineers to the Morris Motors engine plant in Coventry to see the method of producing highly accurate cam forms.

The charge that a lot of frivolous and useless goods are made by these systems is also heard. Of course this is true. There always were frivolous and useless goods made as soon as man had satisfied his more pressing wants. They were laboriously made by hand, now they are made by machine processes. Agreed that, if they are not only useless but aesthetically repugnant, it is a grievous waste; but, again, the river cannot rise above its source, although the source can be lifted by educating the public at large, and not merely the few, to a higher appreciation of bijouterie and bibelots. Is this possible? Well, for the answer, you have only to compare the pleasantly dressed, neatly coiffeured, well-shod factory lass of today with her predecessor of 50 years ago to see how far we have come along that road.

As to the charge of over-standardization, there may be, in the present phase, a tendency to the over-standardization of end products. If so, it is due to a clumsy use of the new system since there is vast scope for standardization in those things which do not directly affect the user. There is no reason and no justification for over-standardization in the more personal matters of design, that is to say in those things that affect our senses, particularly those of seeing and feeling. As instance, consider the motor car steering wheel which the owner-driver perceives and handles all the time that he is driving. It is the most intimate contact between man and vehicle and it follows that it should be individual and special to the car. It is a relatively small and not very expensive part, hence it should not be a stock "reach-me-down" component. That would be over-standardization!

There is another form of over-standardization which might be mentioned because it has nothing to do with flow production or belt assembly. It is the standardization of meals served at hotels. From John o' Groats to Land's End the majority of these establishments serve, with little variation, the same meal according to season. They are not forced to do so. The choice of materials is enormous. The preparation is a hand operation. There is no pre-planning or factory schedule to be studied and, apparently, no delivery date which must be served or else. . . . This is no reflection on those hotel and restaurant proprietors who are really doing what they can in extremely difficult circumstances. This tirade is by way of demonstrating that it is not the production system, as such, which is at fault in these matters. It is in the originating thought that the responsibility rests.

The charges as to the effects of the mass and flow production systems on the workers are:

(*a*) The displacement of labour.

(*b*) The monotony due to the division of labour.

(*c*) The frustration of the individual owing to the divorce of labour from the end product.

The displacement of labour, even though it is temporary, is most serious to those who suffer from it, and those who remember the unemployment between the First and Second World Wars may well be fearful of the return of such conditions of technological displacement. These conditions were, however, not due to over-production but to under-consumption, for on every hand there was evidence that more goods would be consumed if they could be purchased. Much has been done since those days to ascertain the root causes of under-consumption and, although no one could prophesy with certainty that the bogey of unemployment has been laid forever, much more is now known of the operative economic forces and correct diagnosis is the first step towards cure.

In this respect it is a consolation to realize that so far we have never been within sight of saturation point in the matter of the needs of the people and that when we do arrive at that position we shall have reached that millennium where everybody's wants are satisfied. This is just another way of saying that the fundamental problem of supply and demand has never been called into question. The problem is one of distribution and that is chiefly a matter of providing purchasing power. In this, by its enlarged output at lower cost, the flow production process is making a fair contribution.

A saying by the late Laurence H. Pomeroy is also comforting. He described the United States as "a place where everybody is furiously working overtime to make labour-saving machinery". Although the Americans have had their setbacks they have been doing just that for a very long time and have not yet caught up with their own needs, let alone those of mankind at large.

The effect of the monotony of factory life is to be deplored but it is liable to be exaggerated. It is no new thing; monotony in labour existed long before mass or flow production was thought of. It existed before the Industrial Revolution and right down the ages. It must be recognized that the man—in films, books or plays—who tightens "nut No. 47" for 44 hours a week might have had no less a monotonous task in mediaeval days, and under far less pleasant conditions than those obtaining in a modern workshop. There has been, and there may always be, a certain amount of drudgery in labour. These new methods have, at any rate, taken the mortifying physical effort out of the drudgery.

Nowadays enlightened management endeavours to relieve the monotony and not merely by such perfunctory methods as "music while you work". They realize that most men, if not women, want a job which is interesting and one, if possible, that will challenge their skill. They realize that those who have the chance of such work are always the keenest, as witness the enthusiasm of men working on new projects. In shops where aircraft, racing motor cycles or sports cars are built a wonderfully enthusiastic spirit is always manifest. Hence appeals to the sporting instincts are made in the beating of previous targets and in competitions between teams of workers. Provided that these are conducted with due discretion, they do help to give point to the work in hand.

Nevertheless, there is nothing quite so interesting as occasional changes of job, and management should address itself to this difficult but not insoluble problem. It is quite possible, for instance, to transfer operators from section to section so that they are able to work at any place on the production lines. This may not, when first mooted, receive the approbation of the supervisory staff, but when they appreciate that such a scheme will provide them with a flexible labour force, capable—in times of crisis—of undertaking virtually any production task, they will be found enthusiastic supporters of this departure from precedent. The desire for change is by no means general among the work-people; some prefer to retain the job they know. They even take a proprietary interest in the particular machine upon which they work. This attitude is more prevalent among the older workers and among women. The younger people are all for change.

Monotony can also be relieved to a very large extent if the operator knows what part he is playing in the whole business. It is extremely difficult to exercise any enthusiasm about what must appear to the worker as a more or less amorphous piece of metal or other material. Displays which show the completed product in such a manner that every man and woman can recognize the part played by the components that he or she has made, or partly made, are invaluable in overcoming this disability. This is particularly applicable in the works of the suppliers of semi-fabricated materials such as castings, forgings, stampings, mouldings and so forth. In this the makers of the end products can assist and it is in their own best interests that they should do so.

Prominently displayed, target figures, output charts and other forms of publicity can be profitably used. Such devices help operators to feel that they are in the picture: that they have a place and responsibility in the scheme of things—that they are not merely performing inconsequent tasks at the bidding of some incomprehensible dictator. There is no doubt that management can, with care and imagination, help to change boredom and monotony into cheerful and willing service.

We are told, quite frequently, that the division of labour and the divorce of the specific task from the end product is the cause of frustration in the individual worker. There is, no doubt, some truth in this contention and management must give it due weight. It is, however, much more likely that the sense of frustration arises not so much from this cause as from the impersonal relationship between management and workers, which is the price we have had to pay for the rapid growth in the size of our industrial undertakings.

Frustration may also spring from deeper dissatisfactions than boredom due to monotony. The persons concerned may be hopelessly miscast for the communal life of the factory or, indeed, for living in any state approximating to urban conditions. He or she may have a deep loathing for the sight, sound and smell of machinery. Such square pegs in round holes will find no satisfaction in any workshop, so the question as to whether mass or flow production causes frustration in them does not arise. Such evident misfits should not be employed in the mechanical industries. They should be directed to work more suited to their temperaments. We are more concerned with those employees who are not naturally antipathetic towards factory life but who may, nevertheless, feel frustrated because their scope is apparently limited to simple repetitive routines. Here again enlightened management can help by providing the remedies mentioned as the antidotes to monotony and by having a visible ladder for promotion, for frustration is so often coupled with the feeling that the person concerned is not "getting anywhere", and is not going to "get anywhere". In this connection it must be remembered that flow production tends to cut down the numbers of manual workers and to build up the skilled mechanic and supervisory grades. Moreover it must not be thought that all flow production tasks are dull or tedious. Much of the work is most interesting and it frequently requires considerable skill and ability.

Flow production establishments have an advantage over others in as much as the employees can, themselves, see the unfolding of a tale to which, if not writing a chapter, they are at least contributing a paragraph. To profit to the full from this happy advantage, arrangements should be made to have operators shown over departments, other than their own, by guides who know and can tell the whole story.

To sum up: flow production is a modern form of mass production, born of a marriage of management and mechanism in which management is the dominant partner. It is governed by relatively simple principles which, however, are not as easy to put into practice as might, from their simplicity, be assumed. This is because flow production is not static but dynamic. It cannot just be adopted as a system and then allowed to look after itself. It is a living, continuously growing function which needs watching from day to day. It needs watching to ensure that, with the development of the product and the expansion of output, there is no break-away from the principles that control its successful operation.

The key to flow production is continuity in every department of the business; continuity in manufacturing operations, continuity in handling, continuity in machining, continuity in assembling, continuity in selling. This continuum provides the background for the system and method that reduces lost time, dissipated effort and waste material to the minimum by high-lighting every activity so that the logic of each and every situation arising is brought home to each and every person in the flow production plant.

On the human side it must also be watched, for—like all tools of management—it can be misused. Flow production, with its obvious sequences and accurate timing, could be the instrument of a slave-driving tyranny, whereas properly employed it will promote discipline in an equitable and gentle, if irresistible, manner, making the daily task lighter for all.

Flow production is, in fact, a logical development that has tremendous advantages and when properly applied is of benefit to the whole community. These methods may not promote any individual art but they can provide a common basis for a comfortable existence, and, when they relieve mankind of the more arduous labours—as ultimately they will—those who labour can, if they desire, follow their bent as individual craftsmen in their extended leisure hours.

LIST OF REFERENCES

SECTION I

PUBLICATIONS BY THE AUTHOR

"Some Notes on British Methods of Continuous Production". *Proceedings Institution of Automobile Engineers*. Feb. 1925.

"Continuous Production Techniques". *The Times Review of Industry*. Aug. 1948.

"Flow-line Production". Paper before British Association at Birmingham, 4 Sep. 1950. Published (abridged) in *Engineering*, 3 Nov. and 24 Nov. 1950.

"The Basic Principles of Mass and Flow Production". *Mechanical Handling*, Apr., May, Jun., Jul., Aug., Oct. 1952 and Jan., Feb., Mar. 1953. *Institution of Production Engineers Journal*. 18-36, Jan. 1953. The advent of automatic transfer machines and mechanisms.

"The Advent of Automatic Transfer Machines and Mechanisms". Paper before Second Scottish Conference of British Institute of Management at Gleneagles, 10-12 Apr. 1953.

OTHER REFERENCES

"Factory Planning". H. E. Taylor. *Proceedings Institution of Production Engineers*, vol. 2, 1922-3.

"Southern Railway All-steel Suburban Electric Stock". L. Lynes & C. S. Shepherd. *Proceedings Institution of Locomotive Engineers*, vol. 38, No. 202.

"Machines and Appliances in Government Offices". H. M. Stationery Office.

"Automation and Other Technological Advances". Manufacturing Series No. 205. American Management Association, 330 West 32nd Street, New York.

Moving Forward. Henry Ford. Doubleday & Co., Inc., New York.

Automation: the Advent of the Automatic Factory. John Dieobld. Van Nostrand, New York; Macmillan, London, 1952.

SECTION II

REFERENCES TO AUTOMATIC TRANSFER MACHINES

American Machinist. 154-155, 4 Aug. 1952. Drum switch sets Snyder transfer machine.

American Machinist. 152-155, 12 Oct. 1953. Ford bet a billion on new tooling . . . automation.

Automobile Engineer. 178-186, May 1950. Cylinder head production: a review of recent developments employed by Vauxhall Motors Ltd.

Automobile Engineer. 255-264, July 1951. Transfer machining: the production of cylinder blocks for Consul and Zephyr engines.

Automobile Engineer. 303-304, Aug. 1951; *Machinery,* 1009-1011, 14 June 1951; *Machine Tool Review.* 87-90, July-Aug. 1951. Centreless grinding: an interesting Scrivener development for transfer machining.

Automobile Engineer. 373-378, Oct. 1951. Cylinder head machining: production methods for Ford Zephyr and Consul engines.

Automobile Engineer. 113-124, March; 163-174, April 1953. Small car production: the manufacture of engines and transmissions for the Austin A30.

Automotive Industries. 38-40, 15 Aug. 1953. Scrap disposal by automation: Fisher Body Plant. J. Geschelin.

Engineer. 529-531, 18 April 1952. A transfer machine for gear boxes. (Morris Motors Ltd.).

Engineers' Digest. 301-306, Sep. 1952. Special purpose machine tools and the unit construction principle. J. C. Z. Martin.

Engineers' Digest. 83-85, 90, March 1953. Recent developments in the Soviet machine tool industry. J. Mannin.

Iron Age. 90-91, 22 Nov. 1951. Planning pays off in transfer machine operation. (Cross Transfer-matic machine for Warner Gear Div., Borg-Warner Corp.)

Iron Age. 117-125, 22 May 1952. Automatic forging presses feature new shell line. (Verson Allsteel Press Co.) J. A. Verson and H. Irwin.

Iron Age. 156-157, 11 Sep. 1952. Transfer equipment stresses flexibility, cuts cost. (Willys-Overland Motors Inc., Toledo, Ohio.) J. E. Snowberger.

Iron Age. 108-110, 2 Oct. 1952. Transfer machines handle 4-ton armour plate weldment. (Massey-Harris Co., Racine, Wis.) J. S. Kis, Jr. and R. M. Olsen.

Iron Age. 142-144, 18 Dec. 1952. Chip engineering vital counterpart to automated machining lines.

Iron Age. 129-132, 12 Feb. 1953. Transfer-type machine tools can be standardized. (Cross Co., Detroit.) W. G. Patton.

Iron Age. 139-140, 19 Feb. 1953. Chip handling: automatic scrap removal helps raise lathe output.

Machine Shop Magazine. 91-98, Sep. 1949. Mechanical handling built into machine tools; automatic transfer machines reduce production costs. (Cross Co., Detroit.)

Machine Tool Review. 108-112, Sep.-Oct. 1952. Archdale machines on Diesel engine production. (L. Gardner & Sons Ltd.) Abridged in *Machinery.* 1237-1239, 12 Dec. 1952.

Machinery. 163-170, 10 Aug. 1950. Renault production methods: extensive utilization of unit heads for transfer and other automatic machines at a French factory.

Machinery. 547-554, 30 Nov. 1950. Production of commercial vehicle engines on transfer-type machines. (Reo Motors Inc., Michigan.) A. W. Zimmer.

Machinery. 70-71, 11 Jan. 1951. Cross Toolometer control unit for automatic transfer machines.

Machinery. 909-910, 31 May 1951. Baush transfer machine for an automatic transmission component.

Machinery. 188-191, 2 Aug. 1951. Longitudinal operations performed on an automatic transfer machine. (General Electric Co., Erie, U.S.A.)

Machinery (New York). 168-173, Sept. 1953. Automation in broaching. A. Lundell.

Machinery. 46-58, 10 Jan. 1952. Machining Morris-Oxford gearboxes on an Archdale transfer machine.

Machinery 699-711, 9 Oct. 1953. Applications of unit type automatic transfer machines: recent developments at the works of Austin Motor, Co. Ltd. Longbridge, Birmingham.

Machinery. 811-813, 23 Oct. 1953. Transfer machines for swivel axles.

Machinist. 419-420, 16 July 1949. Transfer machine produces cycle spokes. (D. Smith Ltd., Wolverhampton.)

Machinist. 688-689, 6 May 1950. Selection of transfer machines for medium-volume production. (Cadillac Motor Car Div., General Motors.) R. LeGrand.

Machinist. 88-89, 20 Jan. 1951. New Buick crankcase line shows many improvements. S. White.

Machinist. 299-304, 3 Mar. 1951. How they handle on the Vauxhall machine lines.

Machinist. 873-882, 16 June; 913-922, 23 June 1951. Transfer machines do the work on Ford's new block line.

Machinist. 1497-1502, 6 Oct. 1951. They have also been working on transfer machines in Russia. L. A. Ferney.

Machinist. 1891-1896, 15 Dec. 1951. Austin build their own suspension link transfer machine to increase productivity.

Machinist. 109-116, 26 Jan. 1952. Easy changeover is a feature of Ford's cylinder head line.

Machinist. 537-544, 12 April 1952. Layout study for an automatic piston factory . . . report by post-graduate students at Harvard Business School.

Machinist. 611-618, 26 April 1952. Austin re-equip with standard unit heads. W. A. Hawkins.

Machinist. 663-678, 3 May 1952; *American Machinist*, 135-150, 17 Mar. 1952. How Ford automates production lines. R. LeGrand.

Machinist. 1062-1064, 12 July 1952. Chain conveyor circulates transfer machine fixtures. (Vauxhall Motors, Luton.) W. A. Hawkins.

Machinist. 133-142, 24 Jan. 1953; *American Machinist.* 109-118, 8 Dec. 1952. Latest improvements in press automation at Ford. M. J. Rowan.

Machinist. 285-289, 21 Feb. 1953. Transfer machines have their transport problems. H. Goebel.

Machinist. 1111-1114, 11 July, 1953. New engine quantities justify transfer machines. (The Perkins story, part 2.) W. A. Hawkins.

Machinist. 1301-1308, 23 Aug. 1952. How Ford extends automaticity to engine handling. M. J. Rowan.

Machinist. 1683-1693, 10 Oct. 1953.   What one engineer found at U.S. Ford's near-automatic engine plant.

Mass Production. 62-73, Sep. 1952.   Transfer machines.

Tool Engineer. 51-68, Feb. 1952.   A text on automation.   (De Soto Division.) G. P. Muir.

Tool Engineer. 53-60, April; 50-56, May 1953.   Automation of machine tools: abstract from paper to 21st Annual Meeting of the American Society of Tool Engineers.   J. Y. Kaplan.

Werkstattstechnik und Maschinenbau. 128-134, April 1952.   Selbsttätige Maschinen-Fliessreihen.   H. Goebel.

INDEX

"Some Notes on British Methods of Continuous Production"

Proceedings of The Institution of Automobile Engineers, The Institution of Automobile Engineers, London, U.K., Proceedings of the Session 1924-1925, Volume XIX, pp. 419-474, 885-890, and Plates XVI to XXXII (Figures 1-26). Copyright Professional Engineering Publishing, London, U.K. Used with permission.

Frank G. Woollard in a 1924 Bullnose Morris Oxford
Prototype Automobile Known as the "Silent Six"
Source: Aston Business School, Birmingham, U.K. Used with permission.

THE

Institution of Automobile Engineers.

PROCEEDINGS

OF THE

SESSION 1924-25.

VOLUME XIX.

The right of Publication and of Translation is reserved.

The Institution as a body is not responsible either for the statements made or for the opinions expressed in the following pages.

PUBLISHED BY THE INSTITUTION,
WATERGATE HOUSE, YORK BUILDINGS, ADELPHI, W.C. 2.

Telephone : Regent 4638.   *Telegrams : Autinst, Westrand, London.*

THE

INSTITUTION OF AUTOMOBILE ENGINEERS.

Founded 1899. | Incorporated 1907.

Past Presidents.

1907-08. Col. R. E. B. Crompton, C.B., M.Inst.C.E.

1908-09. Dugald Clerk, D.Sc., F.R.S., M.Inst.C.E.

1909-10. H. S. Hele-Shaw, D.Sc., F.R.S., M.Inst.C.E.

1910-11. F. W. Lanchester, M.Inst.C.E.

1911-12. L. A. Legros, M.Inst.C.E.

1912-13. T. B. Browne, M.I.Mech.E.

1913-14. J. S. Critchley, M.I.Mech.E.

1914-15. J. S. Critchley, M.I.Mech.E.—Acting President.*

1915-16. L. A. Legros, M.Inst.C.E.—Acting President.*

1916-17. L. A. Legros, M.Inst.C.E.

1917-18. Brig.-Gen. R. K. Bagnall-Wild.

1918-19. A. A. Remington (*Deceased*, 1922).

1919-20. Thos. Clarkson, M.Inst.C.E.

1920-21. Sir Henry Fowler, K.B.E., M.I.Mech.E.

1921-22. George W. Watson, M.I.Mech.E.

1922-23. Lt.-Col. D. J. Smith.

1923-24. H. G. Burford, M.I.Mech.E.

1924-25. W. R. Ormandy, D.Sc.

* Col. Sir Capel Holden, K.C.B., was elected President for the Session 1914-15 and again for the Session 1915-16, but owing to his duties at the War Office could not take up office, and Mr. Critchley remained in office till the re-election of Mr. Legros in 1916.

THE

INSTITUTION OF AUTOMOBILE ENGINEERS.

OFFICERS.

1924-25.

President:

Dr. W. R. ORMANDY ....London.

Vice-Presidents:

L. H. HOUNSFIELD ....London.
Major B. W. SHILSON ....Coventry.
H. KERR THOMAS ....London.
Major C. WHEELER ....London.

Members of Council:

F. A. S. ACRES ....London.
Brig.-Gen. BAGNALL-WILD, C.M.G. ....London.
Major E. G. BEAUMONT ....London.
A. E. BERRIMAN ....Coventry.
H. G. BURFORD ....London.
C. R. CHARLES ....Guildford.
W. CHATER-LEA ....London.
T. CLARKSON ....London.
Col. R. E. CROMPTON, C.B. ....London.
H. H. GREGORY ....London.
A. J. HANCOCK ....Luton.
J. F. HENDERSON ....Glasgow.
W. H. HINGSTON ....London.
W. J. IDEN ....London.
A. T. J. KERSEY ....Manchester.
Dr. F. W. LANCHESTER ....London.
G. H. LANCHESTER ....Birmingham.
MAX R. LAWRENCE ....Dagenham.
L. A. LEGROS ....London.
J. W. MILLS ....Glasgow.
Prof. W. MORGAN ....Bristol.
Lt.-Col. J. S. NAPIER ....Kenilworth.
H. F. L. ORCUTT ....Birmingham.
P. A. POPPE ....Coventry.
T. C. PULLINGER ....Dumfries.
A. J. ROWLEDGE ....Derby.
G. J. SHAVE ....London.
F. R. SIMMS ....London.
Lt.-Col. D. J. SMITH ....London.
H. C. M. STEVENS ....Wolverh'ton.
GEO. W. WATSON ....London.
W. D. WILLIAMSON ....Wigan.
F. G. WOOLLARD ....Coventry.
T. H. WOOLLEN ....London.

Hon. Treasurer:
W. REES JEFFREYS.

Secretary and Treasurer:
BASIL H. JOY, WATERGATE HOUSE, ADELPHI, LONDON, W.C. 2.

Telegraphic Address : " Autinst, Westrand, London.   *Telephone : Regent 4638.*

a 2

THE
INSTITUTION OF AUTOMOBILE ENGINEERS.

LOCAL CENTRE COMMITTEES.

Birmingham Centre Committee.
Chairman: G. H. LANCHESTER.

Hon. Secretary: MAJOR C. W. JORDAN.

MAJOR T. C. AVELING.	W. HOLT.
MAJOR R. V. BROOK.	J. NASMITH.
T. E. B. CHALMERS.	W. B. SHURROCK.
A. V. DAVIDGE.	

Coventry Centre Committee.
Chairman: MAJOR B. W. SHILSON.

Hon. Secretary: P. J. MANNING.

E. GRINHAM.	L. J. SHORTER.
J. L. MILLIGAN.	H. D. TEAGE.
P. A. POPPE.	F. G. WOOLLARD.

North of England Centre Committee.
Chairman: W. D. WILLIAMSON.

Hon. Secretary: R. T. MATTINSON.

H. ALBAN BRAYSHAW.	J. OKILL.
R. A. DOWNS.	W. E. PHILLIPS.
N. JOHNSON.	PROF. G. E. SCHOLES.
A. KENYON.	S. SMITH.
A. T. J. KERSEY.	R. WINN.

Scottish Centre Committee.
Chairman: J. W. MILLS.

Hon. Secretary: G. H. CUTBUSH.

J. F. HENDERSON.	J. D. PARKES.
D. KEACHIE.	J. RICHARDSON.
DR. A. McCANCE.	S. R. RUSHBROOK.
G. E. McCAW.	R. J. SMITH.
G. MACDONALD.	J. WATT.

Wolverhampton Centre Committee.
Chairman: H. C. M. STEVENS.

Hon. Secretary: K. B. MILLER.

E. J. D. BUCKNEY.	H. W. PARSONS.
J. E. GREENWOOD.	J. H. PRATT.
C. B. KAY.	H. STEVENS.

THE

INSTITUTION OF AUTOMOBILE ENGINEERS.

PROCEEDINGS.

FEBRUARY, 1925.

An Ordinary General Meeting was held at The Broadgate Café, Coventry, on Tuesday, 3rd February, 1925, at 7.15 p.m., Mr. J. Budge in the Chair.

The Minutes of the previous Meeting were read, confirmed and signed.

The following paper was then read and discussed:—

"Some Notes on British Methods of Continuous Production," by F. G. WOOLLARD (see page 419).

There were present 92 Members and visitors.

An Ordinary General Meeting was held at the Royal Society of Arts, John Street, Adelphi, London, W.C.2, on Tuesday, 10th February, 1925, at 7 p.m., Dr. W. R. Ormandy in the Chair.

The Minutes of the previous Meeting were read, confirmed and signed.

The following paper was then read and discussed:—

"Some Notes on British Methods of Continuous Production," by F. G. WOOLLARD (see page 419).

There were present 114 Members and visitors.

An Ordinary General Meeting was held at the Engineering and Scientific Club, Queen Street, Wolverhampton, on Wednesday, 11th February, 1925, at 7.30 p.m., Mr. H. Kerr Thomas in the Chair.

The Minutes of the previous Meeting were read, confirmed and signed.

The following paper was then read and discussed:—

"Some Notes on British Methods of Continuous Production," by F. G. WOOLLARD (see page 419).

There were present 23 Members and visitors.

An Ordinary General Meeting was held at the Chamber of Commerce, New Street, Birmingham, on Monday, 16th February, 1925, at 7 p.m., Mr. G. H. Lanchester in the Chair.

The Minutes of the previous Meeting were read, confirmed and signed.

The following paper was then read and discussed:—

"Some Notes on British Methods of Continuous Production," by F. G. WOOLLARD (see page 419).

There were present 83 Members and visitors.

A Joint Meeting with the Royal Aeronautical Society was held at the Royal Society of Arts, John Street, Adelphi, London, W.C.2, on Thursday, 19th February, 1925, at 7 p.m., Mr. H. Kerr Thomas in the Chair.

The Minutes of the previous Meeting were read, confirmed and signed.

The following paper was then read and discussed:—

"Light Aeroplane Engine Developments," by Lt.-Col. L. F. R. FELL (see page 477).

There were present 95 Members and visitors.

An Informal Meeting was held at the Society of Motor Manufacturers and Traders, 83, Pall Mall, London, S.W.1, on Tuesday, 24th February, 1925, at 7 p.m., Dr. W. R. Ormandy in the Chair, when the subject of "Curious Breakdowns" was discussed, followed by an informal lecture by the Chairman.

There were present 40 Members and visitors.

SOME NOTES ON BRITISH METHODS OF CONTINUOUS PRODUCTION.

By FRANK G. WOOLLARD

(MEMBER OF COUNCIL).

FEBRUARY, 1925.

So much has been written about " mass production " in the United States of America that the author considers the time has come for a description of the way in which the problem of manufacturing in large quantities has been handled in this country.

The paper deals with two main themes, firstly, a survey of the economic reasons which themselves demand the practice of continuous production; secondly, a description of methods, machines and operations by means of which the desired end is successfully being obtained.

The author proposes, for the sake of illustration, to draw largely on his experience at Morris Engines (Coventry), Ltd., where are manufactured two sizes of power unit for Morris Motors, Ltd., of Cowley, Oxon., one of 1,550 c.c. and the other of 1,800 c.c. capacity, differing in detail but similar in general design.   A photograph of a sectioned engine is shown in Fig. 1. Plate XVI. to provide a key to the processes described: a brief specification is also given for the same purpose in Appendix I.

Some unusual machines and new methods and organisation will be described, all of which are British developments.   The influence of the American machine-tool maker and the American technical press must, of course, be gratefully acknowledged. but none of the men responsible for the new machines or organisation has, as yet, visited the U.S.A.   This is mentioned to show that. given a similar problem, it can be handled as well in this country as overseas, and, speaking in the broad sense, the development will be on similar lines.   In other words, if the field is sufficiently large to be worth while, it will be dealt with from first principles and something new will be evolved: if that something new be successful, it will probably mark a forward step either in mechanism or in the organisation of Industry.

The author will not attempt to dogmatise as to how far the departure from standard engineering practice and factory organisation has been justified, nor is it for him to decide whether the principles can be applied to industries other than automobile engineering.

When commencing this paper the author had in mind the treatment of the motor car as a whole, but realised that justice could not be done to the subject. Then he decided to confine his attention to the power unit only, but even so, the amount of matter available was so embarrassing that the title has been whittled down to "Some Notes on British Methods of Continuous Production." It will be observed that, although in the first sentence the words "mass production" are used, they do not appear in the title of the paper. The author prefers to call the methods described "continuous production." No authority can be discovered to justify the use of the words "mass production" as applied to engineering manufacture. The term is probably journalese derived from a German military phrase, whereas the processes described hereafter are not aimed at attacking enormous quantities, but are an endeavour to secure continuous flow, so that a relatively small factory may meet the greater overseas plants on fairly level terms.

As the story unfolds, the idea of continuous production should become more apparent and the idea of mass production should retire.

Continuous production is, of course, no new thing. It has been practised for many years in the food, soap, textile, newspaper and other industries. It is, however, comparatively new to the engineering industry, and it presents many novel problems which are not met with in soap boiling, textile manufacturing or chocolate making. The mere physical fact that the materials in process are "hard" definitely marks the metal industry as more difficult in regard to "continuous production" than the industries previously named. The greater accuracy of manufacture is another great line of demarcation between the soft and the hard material industries, but in the automobile industry there is an even wider divergence, due to the fact that many hundreds of different parts have to march together in their processing, and this entirely separates the automobile engineer from the manufacturers already mentioned.

In continuous production the example of the flour miller and the soap boiler must be borne in mind. The ideal of continuous flow must be present from the design and raw material stages up to and even beyond the sales stage. The post-sales stage does not affect the industries previously named, but it is a serious matter for the car manufacturer, for spare-parts requirements affect the flow as to quantity, and, where there are many modifications, the resetting of machines will seriously affect both plant and output. This applies, of course, to the medium-sized British concerns and not to the great American firms, who can set up special departments for machining spare parts.

In following out the idea of "flow," it may be pointed out that practically all staples in bulk flow easily; some are actually liquid, such as beverages, lubricants, etc.; some fluids, as flour, soap and jam, and others, like steel bars and rolled and extruded metals, are semi-solid while being worked and are fairly easily manipulated on the "flow" principle in their cold state: that is, of course, until they begin to take special forms, or to have other parts added to them.

Automobile parts do not spring into view as ideal materials to flow, because of the varying shapes of the semi-raw material, the very divergent character of the operations thereon and the accuracy desired. Owing to these obstacles to the flow principle, it is essential for continuous production that the article to be manufactured be standardised, because, with a sufficiency of similar parts that are rarely altered, the mechanism to provide "flow" can be set up and worked economically. Therefore, it is essential that the article to be manufactured should start right and be not only technically sound, but readily and continuously saleable. It will then stand the test of time with only minor modifications.

Standardisation or the reverse is dependent upon the general policy of a company and upon the sales department, which so greatly helps to shape the policy. If the public are encouraged to look for a change of model year by year, there can be no standardisation and no really large or continuous production.

It is a pertinent comment that, on the one hand, the car which is universally acknowledged to be the finest, and on the other, the car of which production is counted in millions, have not changed their models for many years, though they have, of course, been modified considerably. To make annual radical changes is entirely opposed to the scientific method of altering one unknown factor at a time, and it makes reasonable evolution impossible. The world's finest car has evolved towards technical perfection: the world's greatest-quantity car has evolved towards perfection in administrative and manufacturing economics. Standardisation is essential to both schemes, and no less to the continuous-production methods outlined here because, following the standardised product, come standardised materials, standardised operations, standardised production methods and even standardised limits.

As indicated, changes will take place in the most highly standardised product, but, to make continuous production possible, such changes should only be made at regular intervals and after very considerable experimental work has been done. It is very difficult to forecast the effect of apparently trivial alterations, for in quantities minor matters may become crucial. In other words, the necessity for planning ahead is in proportion to the quantity to be produced. Keeping the car up-to-date without upsetting the continuity of "flow" is one of the greater problems for the engineers of a large-scale production concern, for, unless the product of the factory maintains a certain, and in this country a high quality, the "flow" of orders ceases and continuous production becomes impossible.

In consequence, a great deal of research work and designing must be done which never is seen by the public, for it aims at improvement within very circumscribed limits; hence the design and research staffs have to learn thoroughly the most difficult of all lessons, that "Originality consists in thinking for oneself, not necessarily differently from other people." A free hand is not permissible in large production, for to exist at all it is essential that a large business must be based on sound economic principles.

Standardisation, as the word is commonly understood, and as used in the foregoing paragraphs to imply broadly that parts remain unchanged, is insufficient for continuous production. Standardisation is only one necessary item among a number of others, which are perhaps better described as "regularisation." Rough material, for instance, must not only conform to standardised specifications, both chemical and physical, and be within certain limits of size: it must be regular as regards its surface condition, and uniform in heat-treatment where this is called for. It must also be delivered to time so that there shall be no shortage or glut. Where more than one supplier is employed, it will be necessary to conform to limits of weight, and sometimes, particularly in the case of pistons and connecting-rods, to the distribution of weight. This is all infinitely more essential on large than on small schedules.

Again, in accuracy of work, it is, given the quantities, cheaper to make highly accurate work than otherwise. Operations which do not matter so far as the car functions are concerned, matter greatly when the work-piece has to pass through a series of jigged operations, more especially as sub-division of operations is one of the economising devices of large production. The spare-parts business also obtrudes largely, and it is found necessary to hold even loose fits within close tolerances, e.g., a fit may be 0·007 in. loose yet held to a tolerance of 0·001 in. Cumulative error is the bug-bear of the machine shop, and to avoid this, alone, calls for unusual accuracy, as one of the regularisation devices in a large or continuous-production establishment.

The author is aware that some "mass-produced" articles do not appear to bear out this contention on the matter of accuracy, but, on examination, it will be found that accuracy may be coupled with methods that are foreign to the British idea of what constitutes a "good job." Take the case of pressed-steel parts against drop-forgings, or, for instance, a pressed underpan versus a cast aluminium sump: accuracy may be present in both cases, yet the solid job has an appeal to the engineer, which is wanting in the case of the lighter pressing.

Regularity. then, is the key-note of continuous production:

regularity in sales as to quantity and type; regularity in material as to quantity, quality and time; regularity in processing, workmanship and inspection, and, as in the case from which the author is illustrating these notes, where continuous production also implies working the plant on a basis of 24 hours to the day, regularity has a very special meaning, because a shortage means absolute loss of output, since there can be neither stock nor surplus time from which to make good.

At this point it may be worth while introducing a few remarks on the 24-hour day, which is quite an unusual feature in British machine shops, though advocated by Lord Leverhulme for another class of manufacture. More correctly, it should be described as a working day of $22\frac{1}{2}$ hours, which is made up of three 8-hour shifts, each of which includes half-an-hour for a meal.

The times worked are as in Table I.:—

TABLE I.

Shift.	Hours.	Meal break.	Length of week in hours.	Total hours paid for.
A	6 a.m.—2 p.m.	8.30—9.0	43	47
B	2 p.m.—10 p.m.	5.30—6.0	$37\frac{1}{2}$	47
C	10 p.m.—6 a.m.	2.0 —2.30	45	$61\frac{1}{4}$

The total hours include time paid for as overtime, but during which no actual work is done. This Table excludes Sunday and certain Saturday work, which is only worked if circumstances demand it, and which is real overtime, i.e., over and above the three shifts normally worked.

The mess room plays an important part in the three-shift system, as it is essential that meals should be served with all possible speed, and this part of the business is constantly being overhauled to permit better and quicker service. At the moment of writing, a conveyor service for handling meals is under consideration. At the present time about 750 men have to be accommodated at a time.

Another problem on the domestic side is that of first aid, which can only be met satisfactorily by a nursing service for each shift.

The management endeavour to meet all those minor personal matters, which are pin-pricks, in a liberal spirit; for instance, smoking at all times is permitted, except in danger spots, with quite good results. It was recognised that it was illogical to permit smoking on "overtime" that was worked between 6.0 a.m.

and 8.0 a.m., and then to stop smoking for the rest of the day until 6.0 in the evening.

There is no regular change round for the men working the various shifts, but they can "exchange" with either of their co-workers, provided that they notify their foreman of the arrangement. The foremen do not work the same hours as the operatives, but carry over the shift changes, and so provide the necessary continuity. The management staff goes home when it has finished. The heaviest work naturally falls on the executives and foremen, who of necessity work much longer hours than the operators, so it goes without saying that this system could not be maintained without an enthusiastic and hard-working staff, for whom, in the case under review, no praise is too great.

Payment by results and honouring the unwritten laws between employer and employed, together with reasonably comfortable surroundings, would appear to be the solution of the labour difficulty. The author is not, however, in favour of overmuch welfare work or paternalism ; men are responsible beings, quite able to care for themselves and to find their own amusement. The factory is the means of enabling them to earn a decent living, and they are better citizens if they control their own activities outside the factory. Similarly, men will take quite kindly to new machines and methods if they once realise that they will be dealt with equitably. There is no doubt that the attitude of the employees is considerably influenced by the prosperity of the concern that employs them, but that is probably because they reflect the anxieties or otherwise of the executive staff. Enthusiasm is more than half the battle in dealing with men of any calibre or class, and faith in the concern is the root of enthusiasm.

At first sight it might appear that the overhead charges would be reduced by 66 per cent on the three-shift system, but this is, of course, not true. Supervision must be maintained during the whole of the time that work is in progress. Certain services also are heavier at night, e.g., heating and lighting, and reference to the shift-hours Table will show that overtime and night-shift rates greatly increase the cost of production. Machines and tools suffer much at the hands of two (and much more of three) operators. Scrap is also liable to be higher with three operators, and this and tool breakages are difficult to handle, because it is only human nature to "put it on to George" when "George" is not there to defend his case.

There are, however, many compensations in the three-shift system, mostly in connection with the financial side of the business, such as the increased turnover, the lesser capital tied up in buildings and plant, and the lesser load to carry when trade is restricted. There is also considerable compensation in the fact that the plant can be renewed three times on the three-shift system to once on the single-shift system. This enables a go-ahead factory continually to re-equip with the most advanced machine tools. In this connection it should be noted that many manufacturing concerns have endangered their future by holding on to machinery which should have been scrapped in a previous generation. This attitude is all very well for general engineering shops, where simple tools are used and these are not over-exerted. For the usual run of manufacturing shops it is foolishness; for an automobile shop demanding the highest accuracy it is plain suicide. No operator can produce accurate work on worn tools at full speed; either accuracy or production must suffer. Economy, in other words, is not saving: it is wise expenditure.

Before describing the actual machinery in use at Morris Engines, Ltd., the author would like to review very broadly the subject of how machine shops have grown. Machine shops were, originally, general engineering shops, and, for convenience, similar machine tools were grouped together, and from that there grew up an idea that foremen could best manage shops in which there were similar types of tools. This persisted even when engineering shops were placed on a repetition basis, but, with the advent of the automobile, it became evident that this arrangement involved a great deal of transport, and when, as frequently was the case, every part at each operation was taken to a central view room, the old arrangement became unwieldy. So machines were arranged for the work to flow naturally from stage to stage, and inspectors were placed at intervals in the shop. The foremen became much more versatile, and only certain complicated machines, like gear cutters and automatics, were grouped. Now, when the layout calls for it, even these can be found "in line" with the other plant. The conveyor system is now making itself felt, but this is only feasible on anything like a large scale, on large outputs where a settled manufacturing policy is in force. There is a tendency, in large-scale manufacture, to group all of one operation in one shop, so that the shops rather than the machines are in line, but this does not suit the smaller productions to which this paper refers, and the Morris Engines' methods aim at putting down "continuous machines" to look after a certain output and putting down parallel lines as more production is required.

The Morris Engines Co. took over the Gosford Street works from Hotchkiss et Cie, in January, 1923: it was then a very efficient concern, producing 300 engines per week; by December, 1924, an output of 1,200 engines per week had been achieved. The productive area is now 18,787 sq. yds.; the electric current used is equivalent to 1,520 h.p.; there are 2,200 employees and 768 machines. To illustrate how quantity production cheapens a unit, it may be stated that on an output of 100 per week, it took four men occupying 53 sq. yds. in area, using 2·1 machines and 3·5 h.p. to produce one engine and gear-box. On an output of 1,200 per week, 1·83 men occupying 15·6 sq. yds. area, using 0·64 machines and 1·27 h.p., produced the same articles, the time in both cases being the same. This, it should be said, was brought

about without any noticeable alteration in design. It will, of
course, be asked when the reducing process will stop. The author
doubts whether there is any satisfactory answer to that question.
Obviously, the lowest level of machine-shop costs will be
approached when every machine is fully occupied on one operation, but perfect machine balance can never be obtained, because,
as soon as balance is obtained in one direction, there is an
improvement in either machine or equipment, so that, within
the author's knowledge, which is confined to this country, finality
is a long way off. The nearer approach is made to the best
economic conditions of the plant, the less the reductions. An
efficiency of 100 per cent is never reached. The machine shop is,
of course, only one element; larger operations permit extensions
back towards raw materials, and so produce the vertical trust
position of some of the great companies in the United States
of America.

In order to follow out the description of the routine and, indeed,
of the machines themselves, it is desirable to give a brief description of the factory:—

From the plan, Fig. 2, and aerial view, Fig. 3, Plate XVII, it
will be seen that the works is composed of the five-storey Central
Factory and the four-storey East Wing, which together form an
" L," with the lower limbs facing Gosford Street, and having
the offices at the angle, and the South Factory, which is a ground-
floor north-light building, lying between the arms. This formation was chosen to make the best of what, after all, was an
accidental selection of site, since the works was originally a
machine-gun plant, built for war purposes in the centre of a
congested district.

The cylinder-block machinery, the erection track, the test beds
and despatch, occupy the South Factory, and the parts which have
to meet the cylinder block are machined in the two wings.

The Office block is placed at the corner, so that the members of
the staff are within 112 yards plus a fast passenger-lift journey
of any part of any floor of the factory. Bridges join the East
Wing and Central Factory at the Office-block corner, and an
eight-foot gangway is kept for trucking and for machine removal
on the inside of the " L."

The layout of the factory is purely a domestic matter, introduced here so that the sequence of operations may be followed.
If a fresh location had to be found for the factory, the layout
would alter very materially, but the storey buildings for the minor
parts which flow to a ground-floor building for the heavy parts,
would, subject to local conditions and the exigencies of the business, be maintained. The only disadvantage of the multi-storey
building that the author can see is that the erection takes considerably longer than the single floor, but this objection is out-
weighed by the many conveniences of this type of building.

The layout of the works is arranged around the cylinder block, which, besides being the largest, heaviest and most costly component, may also be regarded as the backbone of the power unit. All other components flow to meet the cylinder block, which does not touch the floor from the time it leaves the foundry until

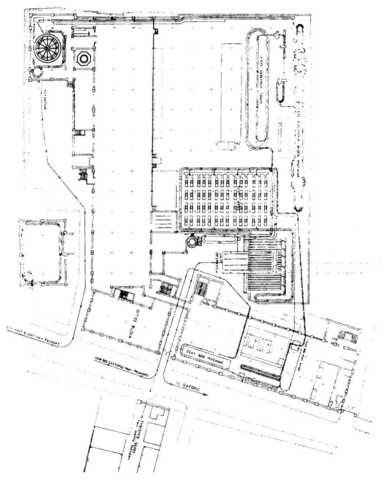

FIG. 2.

it is a finished engine, when it is mounted on a low four-wheeled trolley for convenient handling.

Let us, then, follow the cylinder block from the time it is delivered to the works.

It is unloaded from the tail-board of the lorry by manual labour on to a grid platform, where an elevator of the tray type lifts it to a storage track, which might conveniently be described as a rectangular helix, see Fig. 4, Plate XVII. This forms a self-moving storage bin, which can be extended in height to take any reasonable quantity of cylinder blocks. This storage has been erected above the pickling shop, and the cylinder block gravitates to the pickling tank, virtually filling up the space vacated by the finished engine that has just been despatched. The block enters the pickling shop by means of a true helical roller track of smaller diameter, and is delivered on to a straight piece of track for final fettling and examination for hardness, and thence it is delivered to the pickling bath. The pickling bath, Fig. 5, Plate XVIII (photographed in the course of construction), consists of a lead-lined circular tank 28 ft. outside diameter, 4 ft. 6 in. wide and 3 ft. deep, which contains a dilute mixture of sulphuric and hydrofluoric acid. The block is lifted by pneumatic hoist and taken on a runway to a position over what is commonly called the "roundabout." This is an angle-iron construction, supported in the centre by a vertical revolving shaft, from which radiating arms carry a circular rail 23 ft. 6 in. diameter, from which the blocks are swung on grips made in mild steel and monel metal, two abreast. The journey from the loading to the unloading station, i.e., once round the bath, takes approximately $2\frac{3}{4}$ hours, and this gives sufficient time in which to rid the block of sand and scale. The bath is kept at a moderate temperature by heating pipes, and the fumes are taken off by a fan in the roof of the building.

The total storage capacity held on the spiral, in the tank and on the shop tracks is 850, or, at present output, four days' supply. The advantages gained by this method of storage are as follows:—

A. The provision of a buffer quantity of cylinder blocks between foundry and machine shop.

B. An extensible storage capacity.

C. A great saving of works transport.

D. The cheapest and most compact storage.

E. The saving of ground-floor space on a congested site.

F. Adequate insurance that cylinder blocks shall be used as cast.

G. The provision of better conditions for the operators.

H. Insurance that blocks shall be in the bath long enough to be freed of sand and scale, and

J. Unloading takes less than one-sixth of the time occupied previous to this installation.

After pickling, the block is hosed down with cold water to wash the sand away and then it is transferred by pneumatic hoist into a killing bath and thence deposited on one of four adjacent roller tracks, on which it dries off and is delivered to the cylinder-block machine. These tracks, which are used for sorting the types of cylinder blocks, go right across the shop and form part of the storage space.

The roller-track tiers are stepped at their termini to permit easy access to the blocks, which are lifted off by pneumatic hoist on to the setting fixture on the cylinder-block machine.

This machine is, in many ways, quite unique, but it cannot, perhaps, be described as new without risk of calling forth protest that this feature or the other has been accomplished before, but, as a whole, it is distinctly a departure from normal practice. It is 181 ft. long, 11 ft. 4 in. high and 11 ft. at its greatest width. It weighs upwards of 300 tons, and will shortly be capable of finishing cylinder blocks from the casting to the finished job, including bearing-blocks, crankshaft bearings and all studs, at the rate of one every four minutes, it being understood, of course, that the total time a block takes to pass all operations is 224 minutes. The total weight of metal removed is 40 lb.

There are 53 operation stages employed and 81 electric motors with a combined rating of 267 h.p. It will be noted that the block is to be delivered from the machine complete with studs, bearings, etc., so that the backbone of the power unit will be ready to have all the "loose" parts attached to make it a complete engine, hand-fitting only being required on the assembly line.

To call this piece of plant a machine is, of course, a misnomer: it is an aggregation of simple machines attached to a continuous bed, which bed carries all the services, such as electric power and light, compressed air, also suds where necessary, and a conveyor for swarf. It has a continuous table which carries the fixtures and jigs, and one common control-shaft to time the motion of all the heads. The size of this cylinder-block machine is such that it is impossible to get even a panoramic view of it. The photographs of the separate operations must, therefore, be read in conjunction with the diagrammatic plan, Fig. 6, while Fig. 7, Plate XIX, gives a general view from operation No. 28. Fig. 8, Plate XX, shows a photograph of a model of the old cylinder-block line as it was at the time the new line was building. The new line is capable of providing 100 per cent more blocks than the old, yet the area required for working it is approximately 40 per cent less.

The best means of describing the "machine" will be to run through the major movements—the details being omitted lest the paper should read like a shop operation sheet.

The cylinder is loaded from the track into the setting jig, Fig. 9, Plate XX, and operation No. 1 consists in bringing the block in the jig under the setting fixture: here the block is inspected through sighting holes, and set to the gauges indicated in the photograph, three movements serving to clamp the block firmly in the jig. The pedal A provides the lifting movement to the roller track, enabling the loaded jig to be brought under the fixture. When the roller track drops the fixture sits on the solid

bed. The lever indicated at B locates the jig endwise; the jig
carries a segment which locates the flywheel housing and other
stops are provided. After this setting, which is also the second

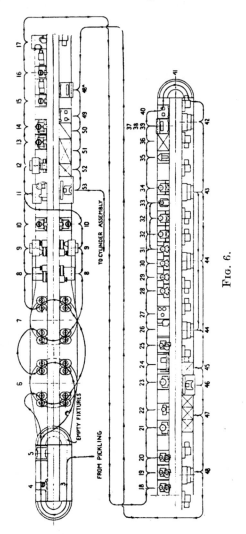

Fig. 6.

stage in the rough-material inspection, the block in the jig travels
round on the roller track to the second-operation head, which
mills the bosses on the engine arms and two "spotting" pads

on the top of the block. Operation No. 3 provides for the drilling and reaming of the arm holes, and from these points all subsequent operations are located.   In operation No. 4 the block, having been lifted from the setting jig by pneumatic hoist, is placed into one of a series of box jigs, on a rotary milling table, where two roughing heads and two finishing heads produce the joint face between the block and the sump, which face is also the bearing-block seating (the bearing-blocks in this engine are not integral with the casting). Operation No. 5, for which the block sits on the previously milled face, held by clamps on the cylinder arms, consists in milling the top face for the cylinder-head joint. These milling tables are shown with their heads in Fig. 10, Plate XIX. The tables are 10 ft. in diameter and revolve once every 112 minutes. Both roughing and finishing cutters for the sump face are 16 in. dia., the single finishing cutter for the head is 19 in. dia., the average depth of cut is 4·5 mm. roughing and 0·75 mm. finishing. The milling cutters are always working on two blocks. Subsequent to this operation are sundry minor ones until rough boring is reached at operation No. 10. The path of the block through this portion of the machine is interesting. The time cycle for the machine, as before remarked, is four minutes. The setting operation is a four-minute operation: the subsequent operations, up to and including rough boring, take eight minutes: after rough boring the four-minute time cycle obtains until the end of the series with two exceptions.

The matching in of the time cycle in the earlier operations was complicated by the fact that on the continuous milling operations the block passes from one side of the machine to the other. The arrows on the diagram of the new machine layout shown in Fig. 6 indicate how this problem was solved. The work-piece from now on slides from jig to jig, the overhead lifting tackle only being used for bridging an operation where two machines are needed to bring an eight-minute time factor to four minutes, such as at final boring, or where a box jig is used, such as in the sump-face milling operation. The sliding is made possible by the introduction of "making-up" plates, which are fitted to the bed of the machine between the jigs, thus making a continuous skid-way.

There is nothing remarkable in the rough boring, but this completes the series of heavy operations, i.e., where large amounts of metal are removed. Then, before reaching the finished boring, there follow a considerable number of light operations. This is necessary to give the block time to cool down—the cut and feeds up to and including rough boring being sufficient to raise the temperature quite appreciably. Operation No. 11 is interesting in the fact that four faces are milled at the same time, two in the horizontal and two in the vertical plane, all at different distances from the datum lines, four separate cutters, each on its individual spindle, being used, Fig. 11, Plate XXI.

Another interesting operation is that of drilling and tapping the block for the head studs, magneto platform and accelerator-pedal seat as a vertical operation, and of the inlet-water-joint face and camshaft-cover face as a horizontal operation requiring twenty-three spindles, four of which are horizontal.

The details given in Table II. are worth noting, because, in spite of the different diameters and pitches, the accuracy attained is such that the threads have been picked up six times in succession on the same block, leaving the holes still within the gauge limits, and this can be repeated at any time. The drilling and tapping has to be controlled within a depth of 1·5 mm. to prevent the possibility of breaking through into the water jacket. The drilling head is in general the same as the tapping head, and so would reverse the spindle motion for withdrawal, but, as this would rub the lands of the drills away quickly, the drills are mechanically

TABLE II.

	No. of holes.	Dia., mm.	Pitch, mm.
Head studs, vertical short reach..................	15	12	1·5
Magneto and accelerator-platform studs, vertical long reach	4	10	1·5
Water-joint studs, horizontal	2	10	1·5
Camshaft-cover, studs, horizontal	2	8	1·0

prevented from revolving on withdrawal. The bottom or sump face of the block also has twenty-three vertically-tapped holes, with two different diameters and pitches, and is equally satisfactory.

The finish-boring operation takes eight minutes, so two machine heads are provided, and the blocks each miss one head alternately, and to enable this to be done the overhead runway is requisitioned, the path being shown in Fig. 6, operation 32.

After finish-boring or reaming, the bores are glazed or burnished by a rolling tool, the four being done at one operation instead of separately, as formerly was the case. This burnishing puts a very fine gloss on the bore, such as would take approximately 5,000 miles of actual car running to obtain. The reaming finish is, of course, very smooth and extremely accurate, for it must not be thought that glazing is a cure for inaccurate work. The value of burnishing may perhaps be judged from Fig. 12, Plate XXI, wherein it will be noticed that the cord left by the machine, which in itself is not measurable by any but research instruments, is almost obliterated.

The water test comes after burnishing, a quick-clamping jig being used, which seals all outlets; the pressure is applied through a siphon tank by compressed air.

Then the block rounds the end of the machine column on a roller track, heading in the direction from which it started. While on the roller track, the bearing-blocks are fitted ready for the next series of operations, namely:—

A. Core drill the bores for the camshaft and magneto shaft— Trepan the magneto boss and rough face;

B. Rough bore the face for the camshaft and magneto shaft— Finish back face of magneto boss;

C. Finish bore for the camshaft and crankshaft—Finish the bore for the magneto shaft and finish front face of magneto boss;

these are all performed by the same types of machine heads, the block being held by a similar pattern of jig. Four heads are used on each operation, although Fig. 13, Plate XXII, only distinctly shows three, the lower vertical head being hidden by the knee of the machine. Each head is driven by a separate motor, and the same feed-box is used in each case, a dummy spindle being inserted where the drive is not required. All the motors are electrically interlocked, so that, in the event of a failure of motor or feed mechanism, the whole group ceases to act. This electrical interlocking is carried out in all cases where damage would be done to the machine or the work by one piece of mechanism "carrying on" while the others had ceased to work.

The series of jigs in this operation are novel inasmuch as the accurate portion of the jig is contained in a moveable member. Figs. 13 and 14, Plate XXII, which show the jig both open and closed, are nearly self-explanatory. It will be seen that it is an open jig with a hinged bush-plate, balanced so that one man can easily raise the heavy plate. The block is pushed in and positioned by means of plugs in the front and rear cylinder bores, and definitely located by the usual dowels in the reamed holes in the arms. Clamping is performed by the handle in front, which operates draw-bolts protruding through the cylinder plugs. The accuracy of the work is determined by very long guide bushes and the fact that the hinged member has two right-angle fitting plates of hardened steel which land on to a rectangular abutment and are locked in that position as the jig closes.

After this series of operations, the block is put into a revolving soda bath mounted on the main column of the machine, the knee of which is broken for the purpose of accommodating this apparatus.

The next operation finds the knee of the machine being used as a fitting bench, for it is here that the bronze-backed white-metalled crankshaft-bearings are fitted to the bearing-blocks. The following operation is that of reaming the bearings, using similar heads and jigs to those just described.

After this, the studs are fitted by a single head of drill pattern, mounted on two slides at right-angles, which covers the block quite easily. A multi-head is not used at this point, as the time factor is sufficient to allow of the accomplishment of the job, and in no case has a complicated head been used when one of a simple type suffices.

The final operation is the paraffin wash to rid the block of all borings and swarf not removed by the previous washing operation. After this, the block goes to the inspection line.

Inspection between operations is of little or no value, and so is being abolished—the machine is timed for a cylinder block every four minutes of its running time, and it is, except for the slight extra power consumed and the tool wastage, as cheap to run the whole machine as to miss certain operations, while the value of the group inspection at the end of the line is very great. It lies chiefly in the fact that there is no stoppage or piling up of the work; the machine relentlessly pushes the work on, and, if there is trouble, it is what the author calls "organised trouble," which is highly visible to the management, and consequently is more quickly remedied than sporadic trouble.

Naturally, the foreman of the machine has to keep a watchful eye on the work and to see that the operators' gauges are in reasonable use.

At this line, which is a roller track, the valves will meet the cylinder block. They are here ground in and held in position until the springs and clip washers are fitted (which is one of the last assembly operations), by an aluminium frame retainer. This line eventually meets the assembly track, which is composed of an oval angle-iron floor track with an elevated roller conveyor forming its major axis.

For assembly, the block first travels down the elevated track, where it collects certain minor components, which can only conveniently be fitted at breast height. At the end of this track longitudinal bearers to make a temporary sub-frame are fitted to the arms of the block. The block is then lifted on to a wheeled stand with "W" shaped ends; the bearers rest in one "V" of the "W" for part of the assembly, and are rolled over on to the other "V" for the remainder, thus enabling the men to work on both top and bottom of the block. As the stand passes certain stations, the components and sub-assemblies are added to the block from a conveyor adjacent to the track from which continuous deliveries are made. Vice stands are provided where necessary.

The engine is rolled over after the sump is fitted, and the valve setting and tappet adjustment is presented at a convenient height. Head nuts and others are driven home by compressed air.

In spite of close limits, it is found that cumulative errors creep in when the tolerances all operate in the same direction. Therefore, certain selective assembly is considered desirable to get the very best results. This is particularly the case with the timing-gear assembly, where there are so many matching parts. Owing to the very close clearances to which they are fitted, selective assembly is also desirable for aluminium pistons. The total variation in weight allowable between the heaviest and lightest piston and connecting-rod assembly is four drams, so that selective assembly becomes necessary in this case. Valves are, of course, kept to their own seats, and camshafts are adjusted for clearance. A history card, giving these and certain test particulars, is made and sent to the Morris assembly plant for future reference.

The finished engine is lifted by an overhead pneumatic hoist and loaded on to one of the four-wheeled steel trolleys which fill a rectangular track around the test bed.

While on this trolley the engine receives its oil charge, and is pushed to the place where the gear-box and clutch assembly meet and are bolted up to the engine.

The power unit is now complete, except for minor details, which have to be added after test.

For testing, the engine is lifted by overhead crane; the empty truck is run from the front of the bed to the rear, where it awaits the tested engine. The engine is placed on the test machine, and the services, namely, the holding-down clamps, the coupling to the dynamotor, the exhaust and inlet and outlet water pipes, the gas and petrol carburettor and the magneto, are coupled up in five minutes. The test machine, Fig. 15, Plate XXIII, has very many novel features; it permits the engine to pass through several phases, giving illuminated signals to enable the testing staff to know the stage which the test has reached, and also gives revolutions and direct horse-power readings.

The first stage is to motor the engine at 350 revs. per minute, a red light glowing to indicate that current is being taken from the power line. When the engine is free, with the motor running at about 750 revs. per minute, a white light gives a clearance signal, when, by simple press-button control, the dynamotor drives the engine from 750 revs. per minute up to a free 1,250 revs. per minute. The horse-power taken by the dynamotor is registered on the negative side of the scale. If two push-buttons are pushed, or the wrong button, the machine stops. When the free stage is reached at 1,250 revs. per minute, the white light again glows.

The engine then drives the electric machine, town gas being the fuel. When the dynamotor delivers power back to the motor generator, which converts the town's alternating current to direct current for testing, a green light glows, and it is the test fore-man's objective to balance green against red lights and so to run his test bed economically. The white light glows again when a pre-determined horse-power has been reached. The fuel is then changed from gas to petrol and the engine is allowed to run in for a period, after which a dummy load is applied by means of a rheostat and resistance frame: an orange light glows whilst this is in operation. This is the actual testing period, and, after "vetting" the engine, the tester sets valves, etc. and leaves the engine until it pulls a definite pre-determined load, which can be raised when alterations to the power-unit efficiency (such as the addition of aluminium pistons) call for it. When maximum power is obtained a blue light glows and the engine is released. Finished engines are lifted and transferred to the trolley at the rear of the bed, whence they are taken to the paint track. The trolley remains with the engine until it is fitted to the chassis at the assembly plant.

Should an engine be rejected from test, it is wheeled to the repair track, which is in front of the test bed, and, before it can be released for delivery, it has to pass through the test bed once again. After painting, the power unit goes into the storage bay, first of all passing on to a loop of track where the final inspection takes place. At the end of this loop an electric hoist lifts the engine in a cage, whence it is run on to a stacking or tiering truck by which any of the 21 engine racks can be selected. These are three tiers high and each tier holds seven engines—441 in all. The trolleys gravitate to the loading deck, but are stopped by an automatic catch which releases only one unit at a time. This catch is operated from a second stacker at the outwards end, which lowers the block to the deck so that it may be picked up by pneumatic hoist and transferred to one of the waiting lorries; these usually carry two tiers of power units, see Fig. 16, Plate XXIV.

The returning lorries discharge the empty trolleys on to the loading deck, whence they are rolled to a chain elevator, which automatically lifts and discharges them on to an elongated "helical" storage track of similar angle-iron construction to the racks and test-bed track. The trolleys gravitate to the floor level, where a stop holds them against release as required by the depletion of the test-bed track due to despatch of finished units.

Having followed the cylinder block through the factory from receipt in stores to despatch as a finished engine, it is desirable to consider how the other components are being handled, and, incidentally, to touch briefly on the main characteristics of other continuous machines. To deal with the small components first, the development that is now taking place consists of the setting up of a raw-material store at the end of each of the long shops in the storey building. From this store the material will be handed out on a feeder conveyor which traverses the length of the shop at the opposite side to the main gangway. The lines of machines are at right-angles to the conveyor, and, incidentally, to the gangway. Material can be taken off the feeder conveyor to the machine line and operations conducted thereon. After each operation, the work is transferred by means of gravity chutes, Fig. 17, Plate XXV, or, if necessary, by other types of conveyor, to the next machine, and so on through the series of operations until it reaches the inspector, who is stationed at the end of the line and who is empowered to stop the whole line if a fault is discovered in the work-piece.

Where a sub-assembly is to be made, two or more lines converge on the assembly bench, it being understood that the small parts or the assembly leave their respective shops in a manner that only hand fitting or final assembly is required. In other words, were it not possible for the part to go straight to the final assembly, it could be passed into stores as a complete spare part. The carrying of the finished minor part or sub-assembly to the final assembly will be effected by mechanical conveyors of types suitable to the function they have to perform. For instance, an escalator has been placed experimentally between two floors of the East Wing, upon which trucks are pushed up or lowered down the incline by means of sprags on a continuous chain, Fig. 18, Plate XXVI. The labourer walks up the incline ahead of or follows down behind the truck, all of which are of the jacking type. This piece of mechanism was installed to cut out the terminal waiting at the lift, exactly as is done by the Tube Railway installations. This system promises an excellent solution of the problem if it is found necessary to persist in hand or power trucking, but schemes are being evolved which may prove even more economical and more regular.

The passage of the finished gear-box to the place where it is attached to the engine will be by power-cum-gravity overhead conveyor. This also forms a storage for finished boxes. The gear-box unit incidentally passes on this conveyor through a silence room, and if not up to standard is rejected and returns to the assemblers. Fig. 19, Plate XXVII, shows the gear-box assembly track, and gives all the necessary information without further reference in the text. Broadly speaking, the gear-box unit follows the procedure of the engine unit. A continuous-operating machine will later be used for the production of the gear-box carcase complete with studs ready for assembly. This machine is still under construction. It differs from the cylinder-block machine in the fact that the movement of the work-piece to each head is automatic, which is achieved by a series of jigs arranged on rails moved and indexed to position by compressed air. Figs. 20 and 21, Plate XXVIII, show this machine, but it is too early to give details of operations. At the present moment standard machinery is producing the carcases, the gears being manufactured in what is known as the North Factory. There is nothing special in the equipment of this factory, nor is there anything unusual in the methods excepting the speed of operation, which, considering that the gears are made of chromium nickel case-hardening steel, is very high. Fellows No. 70 gear cutters are used, and these are packed up as closely as they will go and are bolted together to save space and obtain rigidity.

A third continuous-operating machine probably will be of interest. This is for the production of flywheels, complete with clutch-pins in position. The flywheel is a steel stamping, weighing in the rough 57 lb. and finished 43 lb.

The author would like to diverge a moment here to point out that, in large-scale production, it frequently is more economical to put in the very best work and material rather than run the risk of delays due to irregularity. It was this policy that determined the use of the steel flywheel instead of cast iron, and this, with other examples, should help to stamp out the fallacy that large-scale production necessarily means poor material or indifferent workmanship.

The flywheel machine is also unlike the cylinder-block machine because the movement of the work-piece in its jig is automatic and because the jig travels with the work-piece, whereas in the case of the cylinder block the work-piece goes "bare." This machine has relatively few operations, and, therefore, a brief description can be given to help out the illustrations, Figs. 22, 23 and 24, Plates XXIX, XXX, and XXXI. The machine is of column formation, carrying operating heads that are controlled by cam motion from a central motor. The motor operating the cut is coupled direct with the head. Compressed air is largely used in the operation both of the heads and the work slides. The power, bus-bars, air line, swarf-conveyor, cutting-oil and lighting services are all contained in the machine column. All the heads are mechanically interlocked to stop the machine as a whole if any part fails to function. Press-button control is provided at reasonable distances, so that the operators can stop the machine in case of emergency. The jigs, which are carried on the knee of the machine, are steel castings of frame formation, and are carried on long vee slides. They are arranged for the tools to operate simultaneously on both sides of the wheel. There is a train of seven jigs, one of which is an extra, i.e., it is unloaded and transferred while actual work is being performed in the remaining six. The flywheel stamping is delivered to the end of the machine at the point marked "A" in Fig. 22, Plate XXIX, and is loaded into the extra jig marked "B." The jig, after loading, is brought by a pneumatic appliance in towards the column, under the clamping fixture and on to the jig track: the jig that was in the clamping fixture will have moved a stage forward. Under the clamping head, wedges are driven home at three points pneumatically. The jig is then traversed by means of the compressed-air cylinder at the end of the machine and locked at each station by means of the cylinders shown on the front of the machine heads. The work-piece passes for its first movement under a simple drill head which roughs the centre hole. Then the jig moves to the first roughing head, the chief duty of which is to break the scale on the inside form of the wheels, cutters being employed both from above downwards and from below upwards. The cutting action on these heads is opposed, so that no great strain is imposed on the clamping mechanism. For the next operation the jig travels to similar heads fitted with tools for more advanced processing: the first pair of heads half finishes and the second pair completes the turning of the internal contours. The last head on the track drills the clutch-pin holes from below and reams and chamfers them from above.

The jigs are then carried to an idle station, where the wedges are hammered loose, the jig pulled forward off the track and jacked up, all by compressed-air mechanism. The elevating brings the wheel into contact with a magnet fixed on a swinging arm when the jig is lowered to the bed, leaving the wheel suspended to the magnet. The jig is then grabbed by the lifting tackle on the mono-rail, and returned by gravity to the loading station. The magnet delivers the wheel to the final operation on this side of the machine, and releases it, when the arm is swung into the correct position, by an automatic switch which acts at both of the extreme positions of the travel of the arm.

The flywheel is then placed on a dogged driving plate, and the clutch-pins, six in number, are pushed through the reamed holes into the driving plate, this action being performed by hand. This assembly is tracked under two more heads, the top one being a revolving anvil, and the bottom a combination of ram and driving mechanism; the pins, which are of two diameters, are driven home by a vertical movement of the bottom head, and the wheel is clamped and revolved between the top and the bottom head. Tools, which are carried in horizontal slides, are cam-fed to position, traversing the faces of the rim and forming the periphery concurrently. This operation roughs and finishes the wheel, with the exception of certain highly finished surfaces, to accurate dimensions which require further operations which are performed on the back of the machine by simple vertical heads.

There is some vacant space at the back of the machine, which will probably be used for cleansing the wheel of oil and swarf, also for balancing and inspecting it, thus delivering a completely finished " sub-assembled " component, which can be added to the engine without the use of further tools.

Since the author set out to show that British methods would evolve on, at least, as original lines as those employed by our overseas' cousins, and as the new machines described up to now are the development of the idea of the continuous-operating machine for the larger pieces, it may be useful to glance at two or three machines for handling small components which, solely because of the quantities, became very troublesome and for which standard machines were unobtainable. One of these was the grinding of the gear-box splined main shaft. It was essential to grind the shafts, because highly accurate milling was negatived by subsequent case-hardening, and, in consequence, considerable hand work, involving oil-stoning, had to be performed to obtain shafts up to the requisite standard.

There is an excellent proprietary method of spline grinding, which did not, however, commend itself, simply because of the company's policy not to allow material once delivered to leave the factory, and to employ this process would have meant breaking the rule, which is essential to maintain full control of output. Form-grinding did not appeal, because the requisite experience for maintaining the sharp corners on the emery wheels was not available; hence a new solution had to be found. The problem was solved by milling the form with a pronounced undercut, as shown at (a) Fig. 25, and then grinding the sides of the keys, as at (b), indexing, of course, for the remaining keys, the truing thus becoming a straight movement across the face of the wheels.

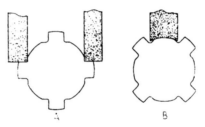

FIG. 25.

The remaining operation of grinding the radius becomes an easy process, the shaping of the wheel being reduced to a simple radius, instead of form trimming.

Another special machine was developed to grind the face and bore of the magneto pinion. This was brought into being to avoid the pitfalls inherent in setting up on two machines. It is essential that the bore should be at right-angles to the face of the gear, which is of cup form. Fig. 26, Plate XXXII, illustrates how, by the use of a duplex slide, this is achieved at one setting; the lower and larger wheel is used for face grinding, the upper wheel for the hole.

Other machines of a special nature to overcome specially difficult tasks have been and are being developed, but these two are sufficient to carry the point made by the author at the beginning of the paper.

Incidentally, it may be mentioned that these machines are now on the open market. This fact goes to prove that the larger producer helps the smaller by taking up problems which, by the very bulk of quantities, clamour for a solution; the lesser manufacturer eventually benefits and avoids the trials attendant upon new ventures.

SUMMARY.

The key-note throughout this paper has been "the flow principle," and several methods of regularisation to obtain that flow have been described. The chief instrument for the regularisation of the machine shop is the mechanical movement of the work-piece under time control.

The novelty in the paper centres around machines built to attain a degree of mechanisation which has not, within the author's knowledge, been achieved before. It is in this new step that the British development has broken away from the American method, which, of course, originated the mechanical handling of "automotive" materials.

The building of the machines, and the organisation of the factory which contains them, have established certain knowledge which will be of great value in future developments. What these may be, the author is not at liberty to discuss, but he can state broadly what the mechanised movement has in its favour.

Mechanised movements of the work-piece are possibly even more of moral than of physical value, notwithstanding the fact that it is the physical help they give that makes the moral value possible. The mechanised movement is a metronome which beats out time for the whole of the works. It does its work quietly and efficiently without argument or any of the old-time bluster which was, erroneously, supposed to be necessary to activity in the factory. If used wisely, it sets a pace which in itself it helps to maintain: it discovers weak spots in the organisation, and shows up inequalities in method which, once visible, good management can quickly remedy. It is beneficial in redressing injustices to the over-worked by urging those who do less than their share.

But this paper was not written to describe the special machines. even though they have the lion's share of the descriptive matter. The machines are only incidental to the whole organisation of the factory, which is again only part of the activity of the entire company.

The author trusts that this account of a British concern. which is achieving success against overseas competition, competition which enjoys a great domestic market, artificially protected, may serve as an inspiration. That it may encourage, not only automobile firms (for they are, for the most part, in the van of applied technology and scientific distribution), but also other industries which have not yet recovered from the aftermath of war. Reorganisation, new methods, fresh outlook and steadfast ideals, coupled with great faith in and love for the work at hand, will perform marvels, if not miracles, in any industry.

In conclusion, the author wishes particularly to express his thanks to Mr. W. R. Morris, the Governing Director of the Morris group of companies, not only for the opportunity of putting these "Continuous Production" theories into practice, but for permission to draw upon the experience for the benefit of the Members of this Institution.

APPENDIX I.

———

SPECIFICATION.

	Morris Cowley Engine.		Morris Oxford Engine.
Bore	69·5 mm.	...	75 mm.
Stroke	102 ,,	...	102 ,,
R.A.C. Rating ..	11·9	...	13·9

CYLINDER.—L-headed mono-bloc, cast with top half of crankcase, each barrel water jacketed to the full depth of the cylinder—detachable head.

CRANKSHAFT.—S26 steel stamping, ground journals and pins, all fitted with bronze-backed white-metal bearings.

CONNECTING-RODS 11·9 ENGINE.—S26 steel stampings. Little end has phosphor-bronze bush arranged for floating gudgeon-pin.

CONNECTING-RODS 13·9 ENGINE.—Has Duralumin rods, and the little end is not bushed.

PISTONS.—Aluminium, fitted with two top rings, the lower one acting as a scraper.

CAMSHAFT.—S14 steel. Integral cams, case-hardened and ground; driven by spiral gear from crankshaft.

VALVES.—Made from K10 steel, operated by mushroom-head tappets.

LUBRICATION.—By plunger pump from camshaft delivering oil under pressure to main bearings and camshaft gear. Big ends and pistons lubricated by dippers fitted to the connecting-rods splashing in troughs.

SUMP.—Of cast aluminium. Filling and level indicator is combined with breather. Front of sump carries starting handle.

COOLING.—By thermo-siphon, fan-assisted.

UNIVERSAL JOINTS.—Totally enclosed. Forks of chromium nickel (S11) steel. bronze ring.

CLUTCH.—Enclosed multi-plate—cork inserts.

GEAR-BOX.—Three speeds and reverse. Chromium nickel case-hardened gears. Spline shaft ground all over.

FLYWHEEL.—Steel stamping.

CARBURETTOR.—Horizontal pattern bolted direct to the cylinder block.

MAGNETO.—Driven by spiral gear—held on plate by strap fixing.

THE DISCUSSION.

(COVENTRY.)

Mr. A. CRAIG, in opening the discussion, said: The most impressive point in the paper to me is that the methods outlined ensure the minimum lock-up of capital in floating stock. If we assume that there is one week's supply of material in the place, and if we take its cost as, roughly, £20 per unit, we have, on an output of 1,200 units per week, a total material value of £24,000. Assuming that an average of £5 has to be added to each unit for labour, we have a week's stock of material and work in progress valued at £30,000 flat cost. A factory which turns its stock over once every ten weeks (which may be regarded as better than general practice) will have a lock-up in respect of material and work in progress of £300,000 taken at flat cost—showing clearly that on a given amount of capital the organisation outlined in the paper will permit of a much greater turnover than ordinary methods of production, which means considerable reduction in percentage of overhead charges, which have so important an effect on the cost. These financial considerations are not less important than efficiency in machining operations and methods of manufacture generally.

Each of the special machine tools is a study in itself, and affords unlimited scope for discussion. The first setting jig for the cylinder block, for instance, shows the care that is necessary to check the initial location of the casting in the jig and permit of the machining of the portions which are used to spot from in the further jigs of the series.

I think that the author, although he has set such a hot pace for other manufacturers in the matter of cost of his product, has put up a performance which has won the respect of all the production engineers in this country. The big American plants are possible by reason of their immense home market, which enables them to contemplate production on a scale we can never think of, and moreover they have an advantage that I do not think is always realised, and that is, very elastic industrial finance. The people with capital in this country are very shy of backing industrial concerns on account of the fact that industrial capital is the first to suffer from labour attacks. I always think that when labour gets more enlightened, it will realise that industrial capital is the last that should be attacked, and if they must interfere with capital, they should turn their attention first to that which is employed in obstructing the passage of goods from the producer to the consumer.

I would suggest to young engineers, when engaged on problems of tool equipment and works organisation generally, that they should bear in mind that the speed at which the parts go through the shops is the most important factor from a financial point of view, and that simultaneous production is essential, so that all parts come through together. Incidentally, the methods indicated by the author practically eliminate the necessity of a progress system in the works, which is always an expensive department, and one that it is extremely difficult to conduct efficiently.

Mr. P. A. POPPE: The author states that a cylinder block is turned out every four minutes. What time does it take to get an engine turned out of the works? If other firms would only work on similar lines to Messrs. Morris, I do not think we should need very many cars from other countries; it is only a question of getting the right spirit. It has been realised by Morris that to sell large quantities, a car must be everybody's car and not a luxury car.

Mr. L. J. SHORTER: I quite agree with the author that it is a mistake for manufacturers to produce a new model every year; new designs should only be brought out when the model at present on sale is obsolete. It is a far better practice to improve in detail.

From the economical point of view, it would be, perhaps, almost impossible for every concern to-day to make cars or units on the same ambitious scale as the Morris Company, but it is purely a question of economics, coupled with the resources of those firms and their prospective sales. It is no use laying out an ambitious programme unless the car produced commands a definite market.

I should like to ask the author how long it would take to change over his plant when a new design is necessary, considering the power unit only: how long the engine test takes, and about what percentage of rejects there are per test. I would also like to ask how plant breakdowns are dealt with, and whether the main crankshaft bearings are bored or broached.

There is nothing in the paper to indicate what laboratory control there is over the various parts. I take it that most of the raw material passes the necessary laboratory tests before delivery.

Major B. W. SHILSON: The paper is specially instructive in so far as it emphasises the absolute necessity of concentrating upon the minimum number of types and of neglecting most of those alterations which are bound to suggest themselves during the progress of the work, and which, though perhaps constituting an improvement in itself, would introduce disadvantages which would far outweigh any advantage which the individual item itself would contribute. Perfection in production is, from the manufacturing point of view, the percentage of the twenty-four hours

(Major B. W. Shilson.)

tor which any one tool is kept actually in operation. It is, therefore, no use to introduce very elaborate and very efficient machines if the output is insufficient to keep them fully occupied and so lock up a lot of capital. At the same time, outlay on plant is necessary to save handling, and so save the physical energy of the worker so that he can not only keep up his output, but also keep up his quality. I am in complete sympathy with the author in his endeavour to do away with the finished stores, which constitute a dead weight, and by occupying that space with production instead of non-production, and also employing that labour more usefully, he should be able to cheapen the work and increase his output. It is very necessary, however, that the organisation as a whole should be keyed up to the same pitch, as such a production as this is only possible by having a very efficient, and, moreover, a very bold, selling programme, so that a definite programme of work can be held to, whether the sales are fluctuating or not. It has to be remembered that an output such as the author's cannot be reached in a day, that it has to be built up gradually, and it depends upon a circle which, in this case, is not a vicious one. By steadily increasing output the sales programme can be steadily worked up, and with increased output cost can be reduced, and each reduction in cost gives the possibility of increased sales.

Mr. R. V. NEWTON: The author advocates an extensive research department; logically, however, research would imply alterations to the design of the car. I have been engaged mainly on the machine-shop side, and it is sometimes a mystery to me where the alterations in design come from. We know that slight alterations are necessary in the evolution of the perfect engine. We also know that radical alteration in design is sometimes necessary such as, for instance, a weak crankcase or weak rear axle which is causing trouble on the finished car, but it seems that small parts are continually being altered without any adequate reason from the point of view of the producer, since when small parts are altered in design they often cause an extensive alteration in tools without any appreciable saving on the production side. With a plant such as that described, such alterations border on the serious. I heard that in 1916 Ford scrapped £20,000 in tools to save 12s. on each car. Doubtless, with their immense production that would be worth while, but it rather leads me to wonder what would happen to the Morris plant if some of the alterations that I have met with in different firms were to be made, although these other firms do not turn out anything like the same quantity of cars. While on this question it seems that there must be, in the lay-out of such a plant, a mean efficiency between the elasticity of the producing plant and the quantity of alterations. For instance, there must be a certain elasticity in the multi-cutter heads to meet alterations. or else there can be no alteration in design until it is radically necessary.

Mr. C. M. WALKER: When visiting the Morris works I was much struck with the speed at which the holes in the cylinder block were tapped, and I should like to ask the author what is the life of the taps and also to have some information about the materials that are used. Is it true that the dies which are used for threading the studs are made at the Morris works? I should also like to know how long these rolling tools used in the cylinder bore retain their accuracy in that operation. I would also like to know how the annealing and carbonising processes are kept within the required limits. There is also the question of testing materials after the case-hardening and other heat-treatment operations. How are they checked afterwards?

Mr. C. BALLARD: In the majority of factories there is a great deal of waste time in transporting various details which go to make up the finished article, from one place to another. Grinding machines, drilling machines, millers, etc., are all grouped in separate departments, and it seems to me that, even in small quantity production, a great deal of saving can be brought about by the assembling of various details into their complete form before transporting them to other parts of the works. The central position of the staff offices at the Morris works must again effect a great saving, as so often the staff is a considerable distance away from a large proportion of the works, and it is this saving of time in apparently unimportant details that is worthy of notice. Can the author tell us how he allows for scrap, so that any particular group of parts shall not get behind? I should also like to know how the spare parts are drawn off the machines for stock, and the quantities which are considered necessary to keep the spare-parts department properly supplied.

Mr. R. W. DAY: I should like to ask the author if the engine which he has described is absolutely standard as regards dimensions? Is it standardised, as far as replacements are concerned, with a similar engine of five years ago when the large production of Morris engines was first contemplated? The author said his drawing office is limited to detail improvements, and that being so it seems to suggest that he has hit upon a successful design for the engine, which certainly has improved out of recognition during the last two or three years. I should also like to know whether the gear-box machinery and the cylinder-block machinery are elastic enough to take up the production, say, of the Morris-Oxford engine—which is only different in that it has a larger bore—or the Morris truck engine? Would it also accommodate the six-cylinder production which was once started? If there is this elasticity, there would be a saving in manufacturing costs; also the production of the smaller and more popular model would not suffer. I should like to know the amount of metal which is left on after boring the cylinders, before rolling to the correct bore.

Mr. S. H. TROUGHTON: I would like to express my appreciation

(Mr. S. H. Troughton.)

of the author's use of the wording "Continuous Production," which not only describes the various methods in an accurate manner, but obviates the use of the word "Mass." I have, myself, for many years used the term "Orderly Production."

I would like to put a question as to spare parts in another form, namely: What steps are taken to ensure continuity when the flow is impeded, say, by an epidemic of trouble in one or two particular items?

Mr. E. B. Lee: I should like to ask the author if the testing of the gear-boxes for noise is by the human ear or by a mechanical device? With regard to the labour on these special machines, is it unskilled, semi-skilled or skilled? If it is skilled, what would happen if there were, say, an epidemic of influenza which knocked practically all the skilled men out?

Do I understand that the testing of the engines is carried out with coal gas or with a mixture of petrol and coal gas?

Mr. Willmott: I should like to hear the author's opinion on the effect of this continuous production on the mentality of the men employed. Is it beneficial or detrimental for an individual to be continually working for periods on the one operation and is any arrangement made for a break? I should also like to ask what arrangements are made in the case of breakages on the multi-spindle machines? If a drill spindle breaks in the part being machined, what means are adopted to prevent scrapping the casting?

Mr. J. Budge: I must congratulate the Morris Company on the manner in which they have shaken up the motor business generally during the last two or three years. I am sure they have been the means of making other firms make much greater strides than they would otherwise have done.

No matter what up-to-date machine tools there may be in a factory or what the rate of production may be, the whole factory is yet dependent to a very great extent upon the supply of outside material, which is very high in price and not made by one firm in quantities. I presume, therefore, that the Morris Company still has to go for castings to three or four outside sources of supply for the same article in order to obtain the quantities, which means that, although the parts are machined in their own factories in great quantities at low cost, yet the castings cannot be produced at the minimum cost in comparison with the machining cost. The quantities of these castings which would be required I know from experience would be very difficult to obtain to-day from one firm only. It is generally known that the actual machining labour costs or piecework prices for the complete car do not amount to much, and if we cut this cost in half the result would not lower the selling price to any extent, yet with the machine tools and methods described in the paper the work perhaps is executed for half the price; but I suppose the real saving is obtained in the time factor and in the saving of overhead charges, which on a limited output greatly increase the manufacturing cost and—in turn—the selling price.

I regard it of the first importance that every firm should have a spares department which is able to supply at once replacement parts and further service, if desired, to their customers. It would be interesting to know the method of providing spares from parts produced by these machines on continuous production, and how the balance of pieces is maintained, say, the proportion for production and the quantity from the whole for replacements and spares.

Mr. Woollard, in replying on the discussion, said: Mr. Craig very ably dealt with two most important matters, namely, the problem of locked up material and machinery and its association with the financial aspect. It is around these problems that the whole of our organisation has been built. The machinery and methods described have not been made to try out theories, or because we are enamoured of wonderful mechanisms, but they have solely one end in view, and that is to guard the financial position by throwing into relief anything that is not economic.

Mr. Pickin, among many other useful comments, said that no company can continue in business unless it is financially successful. I hope I shall not be misunderstood or considered unsympathetic when I say that no firm ought to continue in business unless it is financially successful. A great deal of the discontent among staff and workpeople arises from working for unsuccessful businesses, and in late years there has been too much of this in this country for its good.

In reply to Mr. Poppe, it takes about fourteen days for the new material to be turned into a finished engine; the flywheel-machine time-cycle is four minutes to match the cylinder-block machine. I would like to thank him for what he said about Mr. Morris and the Morris group of companies. Mr. Poppe and myself were collaborators in 1912, working to Mr. Morris' instructions on the first Morris car, Mr. Poppe making a very excellent engine and gear-box, while I was responsible for the design and also partly for the manufacture of the front and rear axles and steering set of that car.

In regard to Mr. Shorter's question as to how long it would take to change over to a new design with this special plant, I think we shall probably avoid an entirely new design. We make a great many changes, but they are not radical changes. We know that working within certain circumscribed limits we can improve the existing engine, and perhaps at the same time cheapen certain parts, which perhaps in the aggregate may amount to new design, but if we do make a complete change, I should estimate twelve months as necessary. In regard to the length of the engine test on the dynamometer, the total running in and gas and petrol test takes roughly about four hours. We deal with plant breakdowns

(Mr. Woollard.)

by carrying a certain number of spare parts, and always have a man on the job ready to deal with anything that goes wrong. In reply to his last question, we are reaming bearings at the present moment, but are considering alternative methods.

Major Shilson and others have raised the point that one breakdown means a stoppage of the whole plant. That is quite true, but whether the plant is one continuous machine or a collection of standard machines, a serious breakdown means stoppage. We have in our standard plant large Ingersoll milling machines, and if we had a very severe breakdown on these we should have to stop the work and repair them, because the spare parts come from America. There are only two or three of these machines in this country, and we cannot get spare parts quickly. It must be remembered that the one thing we aim at under our conditions is to get high visibility, which focusses the attention of the management on repairs, and I believe that in time to come we shall not have any; that is to say, we shall operate by anticipation rather than by default.

Mr. Newton dwelt on the question of alterations. I do not see how they can be entirely avoided; there are always bound to be minor alterations. Even an alteration to limits may give a tremendous amount of trouble; that is why I mentioned standardised limits in the paper, but major alterations, such as really alter the form of the part, are only made when it means a real advance in efficiency, and then we budget a long time ahead. We take a long time to consider an alteration, and make sure that it is really necessary and also right before we alter. We then endeavour to set the date so far ahead that we can make the alteration without too much trouble.

Mr. Walker asked about taps on the multi-tapping fixture. Owing to the fact that formerly the tapping was done on a radial drill, the operator had to work very fast to keep pace, and we had a large number of breakages. To-day, however, we are only tapping at roughly twice hand-tapping speed, and therefore the taps are lasting very much longer. The taps and dies are not made at the Morris works. The length of the life of the rolling tools is about 10,000 blocks, i.e., 40,000 bores. For heat-treatment we use pyrometric control, mostly Cambridge instruments.

Mr. Day asked whether the engine is standardised with the original one. The original Morris car had an engine of 1,000 c.c. capacity. The 1,500-c.c. engine, which is the prototype of the present engine, was brought from America during the war, the design being largely of British origin. The present engine is not interchangeable with either of these models, though it is not very different from the 1,500-c.c. engine. The Morris Oxford engine and the truck engine are different, but, speaking from the production viewpoint, they are practically the same. The new machinery is not elastic for a six-cylinder engine. The present plant is fully occupied, and if any other engine were needed we should have to put up parallel lines of plant.

Mr. Troughton approves the use of my phrase "continuous production." I must say that to my mind "mass" production has a bad name, and I really think that since we in this country cannot carry out "mass" production, we should try and talk about "continuous" production and eradicate the idea of "mass" production from the minds of people. I am sure that the expression is what most sales people would call a sales resistance. Mr. Troughton then asked what would happen if there were an epidemic of trouble. We hope, as before stated, to avoid this by high visibility. When our combination machines are running to form, we shall probably have three foremen (one on each shift). The day foreman will be generally in charge, somewhat like a chief engineer on a boat. There will also be two or three mechanics on each shift responsible for keeping the tools in order. As soon as there is trouble the line will stop, a matter which will force itself on the attention of those responsible, and adjustments will be made and the condition reported to the equipment engineer, who will requisition spares for future use.

Mr. Willmott asked my opinion as to the effect on the men of doing the same job continually, but we do not find in practice that they object to it. There are some of us who might not like it, but most of the workpeople like it; they can earn good money with little responsibility, and it is a mistake to imagine that everyone is anxious for responsibility. At the same time, I believe these methods have certain social implications which we in common with other people will have to face. There is, however, a strong light focussed on this question; much more in the engineering trades than in other manufactures. Go over a linoleum works and see what nasty jobs they have to do there, or a cement or chemical factory, and remember the unpleasantness is additional to the repetitive character of the work. But repetitive work can be made more interesting, and one way of doing this is to give the men a change of scene. By changing men round the machines they are not only given a great interest, but they become more useful men, and that is one way in which this matter will probably be tackled. It must be remembered also that in the present case the machines are in themselves of considerable interest to a great many operators. Machine minders with complicated machines develop a real interest in their work, and that helps them. Again, short hours and high pay are a factor. The Table on page 423, relating to hours of work, shows that the hours are short, that the men get plenty of time off and they have plenty of money to spend. With continuous production high wages are common, because all engaged in it share the savings, including the public, and this keeps the operators interested. They work hard, and we appreciate it, but in working hard they do reap their reward.

In reply to Mr. Lee, the noise test is done by the human ear—

(Mr. Woollard.)

I do not know of any other method that is commercially satisfactory. I should welcome a machine for this purpose, because
the human ear differs in different people, and the results of tests
of this sort sometimes depend on the operator's mental, physical
and moral well-being, all of which are variables. Mr. Lee also
asked what would happen if there were an epidemic of some sort
of illness. That is a problem to which we have no answer—at
any rate we should be no worse off than other people. If, however, a relatively light epidemic has to be met, we replace men
from what we call the "flying squad." This is a gang of men who
are able to do any task in the factory.

As regards the testing of the engines, they are first of all run
in on the dynamometer, then on coal gas, and ultimately on petrol
for the real power test.

As regards casting troubles mentioned by Mr. Budge, the only
way we have been able to get over this difficulty is to have
duplicate sources of supply and trust that the suppliers will not
have common troubles. Mr. Budge hit the right nail on the
head when speaking about the cutting down of overheads; the
great advantage of making work more continuous is that the
mystery is taken out of overheads.

With regard to spares, we budget for them in our weekly production schedule. They are comparatively few, and practice has
improved the accuracy of our estimated requirements.

THE DISCUSSION.

(LONDON.)

Sir HERBERT AUSTIN, in opening the discussion, said: I agree with the author in his objection to the term "mass production." Some of the Press in this country told us immediately after the war that there was no hope for us unless we had mass production, and then, when some of us produced rather more than could be absorbed, these same people told us that this country would not stand mass production, though it might be all very well in the States. At the same time, I do not altogether like "continuous production." I think the principle underlying the paper would be better described if we said "progressive manufacture." In textile manufacture we have continuous production by one particular operation, say weaving or spinning, but that is not what I understand the author to have brought forward in the paper, which is really the idea of building an article from the raw material to the finished state in what he would call a continuous manner, but what I would call progressive manufacture. The spinning of cotton is generally done in one mill, then the material goes to another mill for weaving, then to another for dyeing or bleaching, and to yet another one probably to be printed, and even then it is only the raw material of the man or the firm who is making garments. If, on the other hand, at the end of the spinning loom we were to find a weaving machine, and next to that some means of bleaching the fabric, and next to that again some means for dyeing and then some means for printing, and finally some means for carrying out the numerous operations necessary to make the fabric into the finished garment, then I think the process would carry out the principle underlying this paper, i.e., conversion of the raw material to the finished state. Therefore, I suggest that the term "progressive manufacture" might even be better than "continuous production."

On page 421 the author refers to "continuous flow," which is really necessary if we are to obtain that kind of feeling in the shops that follows from the use of machines such as have been described in the paper. This involves more than the mere assembling of machines; it involves a continuous flow throughout the works in such a manner that everyone concerned must follow the tune or rhythm of the flow of the work. It is not necessary to have enormous quantities, because that kind of atmosphere can be obtained even with moderate quantities. In the United States they have found that line assembly of a car giving an output of

(Sir Herbert Austin.)

approximately 200 cars per day, will produce practically all the big economies that are possible, and that any further quantities off that line only effect small economies. On the same page the author describes the difficulty of allowing for spare parts for repairs during manufacture. In our own works we know from past experience which parts of the car are more liable to break down and require spares, and we simply increase our schedules for these parts to something bigger than the normal output of the day, say 100 per cent of some parts, 110 per cent for others, 115 per cent or 120 per cent, and so on for others, because to run a special plant for spares would be enormously costly and, moreover, the parts so produced would not interchange with the parts produced in the ordinary run of manufacture.

My impression is that the author's cylinder-block machine might prove somewhat inelastic for present conditions of manufacture in this country. I see signs of a change—almost a revolution—in the methods of machining in the near future, judging from the wonderful improvements in grinding surfaces compared with machining them—improvements that we would not, a few years ago, have thought possible—and to-day the grinding of articles in cast-iron, which are very liable to be hard in places and difficult to cut with a tool, gives infinitely better results. The introduction of these big machines will therefore render it difficult to take advantage of improvements such as I have indicated. It will also make it more difficult to put a new model on the market, and even Rolls-Royce, whom the author quotes as one of the chief exponents of standardisation, have been obliged to produce another car entirely different in design from the one they have hitherto been manufacturing. This merely shows that nothing that we design can remain permanent for a very long time, and this has to be taken into consideration.

I agree entirely with what the author says on page 422 as to the necessity of holding up measurements definitely to a fine limit for progressive manufacture, and that is more particularly to assist inspection. To anyone who has had to build an accurate product, the need for inspection is one of the bugbears of the whole business. Even with the most skilful and best paid men, inspection is liable to cost as much as the machining, and the smaller the article the higher the relative cost of inspection.

I hardly agree with the hours which the author has suggested for the three-shift system. We have been arguing for a good many years that a 47 hour week is too short, and certainly if it is necessary to work longer hours to get economic results, the man on the day shift ought to work 47 hours and not less, as in the author's case. Then there is another extremely important point in running a three-shift system. I think that every worker on whichever shift he is working ought to go home with the same amount of money in his pocket if he is to be contented. Whether a man is working a day or night shift, he will want the same amount of wages with which to pay his bills. I suggest that if we agree that each man ought to be paid for 47 hours on a three-shift system, then the first shift should start at 7 a.m. and work until 4 in the afternoon with half hour for a meal, which makes $8\frac{1}{2}$ hours. With a five-day week and $4\frac{1}{2}$ hours for Saturday that makes 47 hours for the day shift. The next shift would come on at 4 in the afternoon and work until 12 o'clock, which, with half hour for a meal, gives $7\frac{1}{2}$ hours. A five-day week in this case gives $37\frac{1}{2}$ hours, but the man would be paid for 47, which, under the Trade Union rates, is equal to time and one-third for the extra hours worked outside the normal working hours after 6 o'clock at night. The next shift would start at 12 o'clock at night and continue until 7 o'clock in the morning, which, with half hour for a meal, gives $6\frac{1}{2}$ hours and $32\frac{1}{2}$ hours for the week. Thus the man who works through the night would work $32\frac{1}{2}$ hours for the week and would get paid for 47 hours, and by that means all the men would be drawing the same amount of pay, whilst the men who were working under the most severe conditions would work the shortest period. The details and success of any three-shift system must, of course, largely depend upon what the Trade Unions will allow, and upon the local train, tram and bus service. I entirely disagree with the author as to allowing smoking in the shops. I do not believe that it is necessary, and I do not think it is an advantage.

The author mentioned the necessity for removing 40 lb. of metal from the cylinder block, which seems to me rather a big amount. No doubt the author has found that in this method of tackling the problem of machining the crankcase, big margins are necessary, but I am looking in the future to a development in the direction of making less chips by casting or forging or at any rate producing our pieces with far less operations necessary in the machining sense. For instance, in the Holley carburettor manufactured in Detroit for the Ford Company, the pistons and other parts are cast in metal moulds, and a great many of these parts are not machined at all, or at all events the amount of machining is very small. I really do think that that is going to be the future method. By attempting to obtain the article we require in the first operation rather than by subsequent machining, we shall effect big economies.

Mr. H. KERR THOMAS: The point I want strongly to emphasise is that the methods which the author has outlined are to a very great extent capable of being applied on a very much smaller scale without the enormous output which the Morris Company has, and such complete lines of machines as the cylinder-block machine would be quite out of the question, because they would involve too much capital expenditure ever to show any return. For instance, a line of tools can be put down to deal with a particular

(Mr. H. Kerr Thomas.)

detail—say, a connecting-rod—but if these machines can only be kept working on the product continuously for three months in the year, then it will not pay. If the machines can be kept running continuously on one detail for six months in the year, I am a little doubtful whether it would pay, but if they can be kept running for nine months in the year, then there is no question about it whatever. That is the only way to manufacture, and when once the processes are going on continuously, without the elaboration of the great machines which the Morris Company have developed, it becomes merely a matter of multiplying the line of machines by n to get any number of units required. Naturally, great care has to be taken that if a line of machines is put down, nothing happens to slow down the operations and get out of time with the following one, because one operation may be too much for one machine and not enough for two, and it is a little difficult sometimes to get them balanced. The whole question of manufacturing in this way turns on standardisation, and with more than one or two models it is hopeless.

On page 422 the author speaks about the importance of getting materials delivered to time. Perhaps the worst point of comparison between this country and America, as far as engineering production goes, is that in this country they have not the faintest notion how to supply raw materials on time, and if some of the raw-material makers in this country went to the United States and took a lesson, it would be to the advantage of all. On page 424 I am glad to see the point touched upon about over-head charges not being decreased as the number of hours is increased, because, with the exception of rent, rates and taxes, practically all other over-heads vary directly with the number of hours worked, so that although three shifts save something, they do not save anything like two-thirds of the over-head charges. I think the author will agree with me also that a machine which is working 24 hours a day or 22 hours a day will depreciate more rapidly than with three times the work at ordinary hours. Apparently, machines need a rest, like human beings. I was interested to see the reference, on page 426, to the multi-storey building. It has always been a matter of astonishment to me how very stereotyped this country has been in having everything on one floor. In America all our engineering buildings were four storeys high, and during the war we even had to finish the assembly of 5-ton lorries on the fourth storey, and I do not think they cost a single cent more than those assembled on the ground floor. They went up and down in a 30-ft. elevator, and the running shed, where the vehicles were taken in for adjustment after being tested, was on the fourth floor.

The author referred to the cooling of cylinders in the cylinder-block machine operation, but he does not appear to use any artificial method of cooling. When I was in the States we used compressed air blowing on the cylinders all the time, and found it a great advantage. I should like to refer to the remarks made by Sir Herbert Austin as to making accurate castings and stampings, and I agree that we have got a long way to go in that respect. Perhaps I may refer to a very large industry in the States, the manufacture of piano players. These require a 3-cylinder vacuum motor, and the whole of the parts of these are made of die-castings without any machining whatever, and they are made to an accuracy of ± 0·001 in. These small die-castings are produced very rapidly in enormous quantities to an almost incredible accuracy, and though the conditions in the automobile industry are very different in that some parts are required to work at a temperature of 2,000° C., yet it would be an enormous advantage if something could be done in that direction.

Mr. RUPERT S. ALLEN: In the case of my own firm we have eight distinct lines, varying from Diesel engines to small pumps, and the fact that in a general way an order takes from 10 to 12 weeks to pass through the shops, means a huge amount of money locked up as floating capital, which, if we were doing production in large numbers of a single commodity, could be spent on machine tools to better advantage. Obviously, we cannot afford to spend large sums of money on single machine tools, but so far as possible machine tools are arranged in line, so as to follow out the continuous production idea. It would be interesting to learn exactly how long it takes to get an engine through the author's factory from beginning to end; he mentions 220 hours as the machining period, which would represent about two weeks' work. The Ford Co. claims that the car which is driven away by the customer on Thursday night is iron ore on the previous Monday morning.

I associate myself with the remarks of Sir Herbert Austin and the author in their desire for a new expression for " mass production." Personally, I think " continuous production " has just hit the nail on the head, for continuity is our aim. I do not think there is question or doubt that an Englishman, given the opportunity, is not as good as any man. It is the want of courage in the individual and the want of encouragement on the part of his fellow countrymen that causes backwardness. The three qualifications that are essential in an engineer are vision, courage and pertinacity; vision to see, courage to tackle and obstinacy to overcome all difficulties.

The author rightly points out that wise expenditure before is better than extravagant expenditure afterwards, because if it is not spent in the first place it is spent in increased costs of production. I believe Henry Ford spent no less than £50,000 in developing a single machine which is now saving him £3,000 a day. Such figures and facts bring home to us the necessity for wise judgment in laying out our money. I am greatly interested

(Mr. Rupert S. Allen.)

in the remarks of the author on the lay-out of machine shops. So many shops to-day are still arranged in that mistaken method of grouping machine tools, but there is nothing which adds more to the cost of production than such an arrangement. I have felt it in our own shops for some time, and have often suggested that the best way to bring the situation to a head would be to stop all means of transport for one day. We should have such hopeless confusion that we should at once appreciate how incorrectly our shops are arranged, for a part instead of moving continuously forward is jockeyed from pillar to post backwards and forwards according to the operation involved.

The author states that the cylinder casting, on arrival from the foundry, is moved from the lorry by hand labour; it seems to me that here is an opportunity for the use of an electro-magnet. I should also like to ask the author whether he has any regrets for having permitted smoking in the shops. I am open to be convinced, but I think it has disadvantages, though I was reading the other day of a works' manager who claimed that his output had been increased 25 per cent by its introduction. In our works we forbid it.

My last question relates to limits. Does the author use the bi-lateral or the uni-lateral system? We, like other firms, are being pressed to adopt the uni-lateral, but, against great opposition, I have retained the bi-lateral, not because it is right, but because of the complication of a change at the present time. We have to consider old customers, for if a customer wants a bearing after 20 years—that is the life of many of our machines— he must have it to the original limits. I think we introduced our present system of limit gauges in 1900, and although the tolerances do not correspond exactly with any B.E.S.A. table, we are altering the actual limits, surreptitiously, to conform to their nearest, but on the bi-lateral system.

Mr. E. CHATTERTON (representing the London Graduates): The question of continuous production, as opposed to the idea of mass production, has been raised several times this evening. I do not suggest that the term "mass production" can be justified on any grounds at all, but I am going to question whether the term "continuous production" can be justified either. "Continuous production" is quite a good and sound idea as long as it is confined to an engine, or a connecting-rod, or any one unit, but it is when we come to consider a car as a whole, consisting of many hundreds of different units, that the idea of continuous flow would appear to be almost impossible. The mere fact that there is to be a continuous flow of engines means that there cannot be a continuous flow of, say, flywheels, and it seems to me that there can only be a continuous flow of the component which takes the longest time to machine. The cylinder-block machine described in the paper is an extremely interesting example. Let us assume that the cylinder block is the component which occupies the largest amount of machining time. Another special machine is illustrated in the paper for the flywheels. The number of flywheels required is exactly the same as the number of cylinder blocks, or approximately so, and if the cylinder-block machine is kept working at its full output the flywheel machine cannot be kept working in a like manner, and if that principle is applied to the whole of the components of a car I think the idea of continuous flow does not quite fit in. I should like to ask the author how the change over between the shifts is effected in the three-shift system. It seems to me there must be some difficulty in assessing the work done by any one man. Either there will be batches of unfinished work lying about the shop idle during two of the three shifts, or a most elaborate system will have to be instituted to discover the work that any one man has done during his shift. There is one other matter upon which I should like to ask for a little more information. The author states that payment by results is employed. The fundamental principle is, I suppose, that the worker should be paid a sum which represents his value to the organisation, and some means has to be employed to assess the value of each employee. Usually a man's value is assessed by the amount of work he turns out in a given time. There are many people, however, who consider that this is not sufficient, and that there are other items which should be taken into account when determining a man's value, such as his loyalty and length of service with the firm, and there is at least one motor-car firm in this country which does assess a man's actual value to the company in this way. I should like to ask the author what method of payment by results is adopted at the Morris works, because the system employed in such an organisation must affect the cost of production to quite a large extent.

Mr. N. V. PAGE: Will the author give us some further information as to how the rolling of the cylinder is done?

Mr. PICKEN: As machine tool makers we sometimes think that production does not receive, amongst the higher executives of engineering concerns, the consideration to which it is entitled. There is perhaps a tendency to take a greater interest in the efficiency of the article produced rather than in the methods by which it is produced, and the designer does not always realise the effect of his design on the cost of production. Will the author tell us what methods are employed in the Morris organisation to co-ordinate design with methods of production?

Major E. G. BEAUMONT: Sir Herbert Austin disagrees with the author on the question of smoking in the works, but I believe that permission freely given is the surest way of effecting reasonable limitation. I should like to ask the author how he secures not, continuous production, but continuous satisfaction on the part of the workers engaged in a process of this kind. We know that some-

(Major E. G. Beaumont.)

times, despite high organisation in machinery methods, a Trade Union will step in and upset the finest scheme. There is also the question of national characteristics, what will content men in this kind of work. Will they go on year in and year out as teeth in this big machine? Money apparently does not satisfy a man all the time, and the question of occupation is of very great importance. Sometimes it may be possible to secure a change in occupation and give that mental rest which will enable the human machine to keep going, but unless that is borne in mind and provided for, it seems to me that this intensive production by continuous methods may bring about a reaction in the future.

Mr. L. A. HARRINGTON: I should like to ask the author as to the arrangements for replacing cutters and others tools on the cylinder-block machine which must be changed at times for sharpening. As there appears to be no accumulation of cylinder blocks between each operation, as is usual where separate machines are employed for each operation, surely the whole of this large machine must be held up when the output from any one operation ceases.

Mr. R. PENTONY: Will the author give us a little further information about viewing? For instance, there is a cylinder block coming off the machine every four minutes. Is any attempt made within that four minutes to view the whole of the block, or is a percentage of the blocks taken away for more extensive viewing afterwards?

Dr. W. R. ORMANDY: Major Beaumont raised an interesting point with regard to the monotony of working on such a plant as this, and Henry Ford in his book says that 99 per cent of the men do not want a change, and he almost infers that 99 per cent of his employees have no mental life and are perfectly satisfied with monotony as long as they are well paid. It is, indeed, very much a question whether the whole subject of the monotony of work is not over-stressed. I think the majority of working men prefer a job which is easily within their capacity so long as they earn an amount of money which they consider reasonable having regard to the work they do, and in all probability the spirits which are dissatisfied with their work are the men who could be picked out either as ne'er-do-wells or as prospective foremen. The most interesting part of the paper is the conclusion, in which the author expresses the hope that this new departure may afford a lesson to manufacturers in other realms of life. We have got to deplore the fact not that the workman, not that the foremen, and not that our technologists and scientists are incapable of doing what is done elsewhere; we have to deplore more than anything else the absolute lack of foresight and lack of imagination on the part of those who control the means, the money, wherewith such new enterprises can be carried out. Yet in Germany the Badische Anilin und Sodafabrik have spent some £100,000 in twelve years on a series of experiments to test the possibility of making methyl alcohol out of water gas. They have solved the problem, and now they have plants producing 6,000 tons of methyl alcohol a year at about £12 per ton. It is very largely used for making organic dyes, and we in this country are trying to compete with Germany when buying methyl alcohol at about £65 a ton made from wood. Are we going to find firms in this country who will put chemists to work for twelve years on a problem the solution of which will lead to the formation of an industry which will pay 100 or 200 per cent per annum? I do not know; there may be such firms, but for the most part they remain unknown.

Mr. WOOLLARD, in replying on the discussion, said: Sir Herbert Austin has suggested the term "progressive manufacture" instead of "continuous production." I do not quarrel with whatever he calls it so long as we get rid of the words "mass production." I see that one of the technical journals, in taking me to task, has suggested yet another phrase, namely, "flow production." It may be that this expression would have some advertising value and be an improvement on "continuous production." Sir Herbert Austin also spoke of spares: luckily our spares are not very numerous. This point was mentioned many times at Coventry, so I made a few notes on the matter, and I find that for some 70,000 cars we have supplied under 500 sets of gears and less than 300 crankshafts: this figure includes spares for the American-built engines that were bought during the war, and some of the replacements were necessary as the result of misuse or smashes, so that in spares we have no very difficult problems. Of course, we have a certain amount of scrap in the works, but this is under 1 per cent. We add the spares and scrap together, and include them in the weekly issues.

The lack of elasticity in the special machine which has been mentioned is not so great as may be thought, and we have figured that we can afford to dispense with it in four years, if necessary.

Inspection was also mentioned by Sir Herbert Austin, and though I learn that some of the American factories have found this a real bugbear, we have not as yet found it so, but on high production it might easily so become. Our inspection staff is about 7 per cent of the total personnel. We do, however, find that inspection methods are, on the whole, very much behind production methods: elaborate machines giving very high production are installed, and then largely negatived by slow and laborious inspection. That will have to go, and our ideas on this, as in continuous production, are to throw light on places where the work flows through a bottleneck, and inspection is liable to be one of these points.

The three-shift system is not at all general in this country, and I believe the same applies to the U.S.A. I have known many

(Mr. Woollard.)

companies who have tried it, but they have nearly always abandoned it after two or three months; even I do not necessarily recommend it as a whole-time policy, but it is very useful as an "expansion chamber." Sir Herbert Austin's suggestion as to hours is a very useful one. We adopted the present hours, not because they are best, but to meet transport facilities. Many of our people come from Rugby, Leamington and Birmingham, and, I believe, there are men who come in from Wolverhampton. This must, of course, have consideration.

With regard to the permission to smoke at all times, I can only say that there have been no ill effects on the output but rather the contrary, and I consider that where a little allowance can be made for personal habits, it is better to be lenient in such matters.

The reason we take 40 lb. of metal off the cylinder block is because we find that in that way and in no other can we get good cylinder blocks. The reason why we take 15 lb. off the flywheels is because the stampers cannot get any nearer. We have our eye on these wastes, however, and I agree with Sir Herbert Austin that, however unavoidable they may be at the moment, we must never cease to attack that problem. •

Mr. Kerr Thomas emphasised the fact that similar methods to those described can be used for small outputs. With that I am in complete agreement: it is all a matter of thought, hard work and the balancing of costs with returns. Some companies, on products of a smaller size, have already shown that good results can be obtained in this way. But it must not be imagined that I suggest special machines as the essential method of attacking the continuous production problem. This is a matter that each company must solve for itself. Just as a system cannot be taken wholly from the Business Exhibition and put piecemeal into a works, neither can one of these machines be swallowed piecemeal: the economy of the works and the product must call for it.

With regard to delivery of materials to time, of course, we, in common with others, have had a great deal of trouble, but the larger our output the easier this becomes.

I am pleased to hear that Mr. Kerr Thomas is a champion of the multi-storey building. I find that for the relatively light parts of the automobile, the multi-storey building has many advantages over the single floor.

The cooling of cylinder blocks by compressed air is not actually in being at the moment for the reason that the machine line is not complete, but plant is being installed for this purpose.

Answering Mr. Rupert Allen, it takes rather less than fourteen days to get an engine out from the time the raw materials are received. There are not more than 2,500 cylinder blocks on the ground at any time, and the financial advantages of this method need not be elaborated. The Ford Co. in the United

States of course hold an unbeatable record in turnover from raw material to the finished product, but on this side I believe we have the record.

Electro-magnets for handling the cylinder blocks are receiving our attention, but I do not think they would be much good for unloading cylinder blocks from the lorries, because these are packed upon end, and I think in any case would have to, be man-handled. Mr. Allen asked if I had any regrets at having introduced smoking: I have no regrets whatever in allowing smoking all day in the works, except in danger spots, but that does not in effect mean that there is too much smoking. On the other hand, it does mean definitely that there is practically no lounging in out of the way places where visibility is not high.

So far as our gauging is concerned, it is based largely on the unilateral system. We do not hold to any one system or standard in this or other matters; if it pays to change over from one recognised system to another, we make our own standards, and that, I think, always follows on large production, which is a law to itself, but I would like to emphasise that we should not depart from a recommendation of the British Engineering Standards Association unless there were very cogent reasons for so doing, and this, I submit, is very different from departing from standard for no reason at all other than the whim of the designer.

Mr. Chatterton's remarks about balancing the smaller with the larger components do not apply, because the larger components require a larger number of operations, and so there are more pieces in process at one time. The flywheel machine is in fact timed to four minutes, the same as the cylinder-block machine. This also applies to connecting-rods, pistons and so on through the whole unit. Four minutes is the standard time-cycle to-day, but it may be altered as required. With our sub-divided and simplified operations, there is no difficulty in changing shift. In practice the operators adjust little difficulties between themselves. By our system we can pay fairly high wages, and it is to the men's advantage to make sure that the job goes right, thus we get the team play spirit, which all manufacturers should try to instil. As for payment by results, that is in the melting pot. There is no doubt that continuous production is showing us so many new viewpoints that we may have to make future modifications, but the present system is based on straight piece-work.

Mr. Page asked about the rolling of the cylinder blocks. This is done by a tool in appearance not unlike a boiler-tube expander, except that it does not expand. The enlargement by rolling is very little: on the average 1/200 to 1/300 mm., or about one thousandth of an inch. The limit for finishing a cylinder bore is 0·000 to 0·002 inch.

Mr. Picken asked about co-ordination in design: everything of that nature is done in committee. I do not believe in committees

(Mr. Woollard.)

for getting work done, but I do believe in them for discussion, and if any alteration is due it is raised at a meeting, which all the officials concerned attend, so the equipment officer has a chance to state a case before the design has gone too far.

On the general question of keeping the men contented raised by Major Beaumont, I believe that the operator whose mentality desires variation can be dealt with by a change of occupation: this does not, of course, apply to the entirely untractable type. After all, machines are quite interesting to the average man, and quite often, more often than imagined, the men do not want a change of occupation from one operation to another. We even find that men who have been promoted to a charge-hand's position will ask to be put back again, although the promotion carries with it advantages in the way of holidays with pay, etc., besides being a step on the ladder of promotion. It must also be recognised that in a factory we are dealing with the average worker, a number of whom simply come to work just to get a living, and who are not interested in work of any sort for any other reason. These will have certain outside interests, and if they earn sufficient money to indulge their hobby, whatever it may be, they will work and be happy. We seem to hear a great deal more about monotony in engineering works than we do in other industries, perhaps because engineers are a much more humane body of people.

Answering Mr. Harrington's criticisms about changing cutters, the work is, of course, held up when cutters are changed, but there is the same hold-up in a normal machine line, only it is hidden. In our case, if a member of the staff comes into the works and finds 300 tons of machine lying idle for any considerable period, he wants to know why, whereas with an ordinary machine line he would not necessarily know that it was standing.

With regard to viewing mentioned by Mr. Pentony, all the important parts receive 100 per cent inspection, and we get this into the four-minute time-cycle. For instance, the cylinder blocks are dealt with by more than one viewer, and so, although it takes more than four minutes to inspect a block, we still have them passed at the rate of fifteen per hour. No one inspector has, of course, more than a four-minute operation.

COMMUNICATIONS.

Mr. H. G. HARDING wrote: The few points that have impressed me for years in connection with standardisation of parts and the large output of those parts are:—

(1) Simple original design of parts, although such parts may be unorthodox, as long as they are strong, do their job properly, and appeal to the public from all view-points, is truthfully what has proved the rule. A complicated part, as a rule, must have a complicated pattern and complicated dies, jigs, tools, etc., whereas if such parts are plain, strong, but, at the same time, not heavy, they can be turned out in larger numbers in a given time with cheaper machinery, or at least be the means of quickly paying for expensive machinery.

(2) The aim of a large standardised output of parts should be to turn over capital many more times in a given time, which amounts to a given profit every time the capital is turned over, which in turn places a company quickly on a firm basis to finance their research departments to such an extent as to place them in a position to explore such avenues which might lead to failure or success.

(3) The service of such a company can become universal, and its parts supplied at every corner of the earth and at low prices, which is an advertisement in itself.

(4) Service depôts are set up by such companies who do things on a large enough scale, and such depôts are equipped with tools that are the means of helping the management to get the repairs through quickly and to standard; any addition or improvement to the car can be fitted, because the design lends itself to the extra fitting, and all working parts that are likely to require renewal are small and designed to sell cheaply, and can be renewed together, making the mechanism almost as good as new, at the same time enabling the repair to be done cheaply, which Insurance Companies are quick to recognise.

Major F. STRICKLAND wrote: I think we have to thank the author for showing that, given the demand for an article of the nature of a motor car in large enough quantities to justify continuous production, English engineers can tackle the job with complete efficiency. I have never had any doubt that this is the case, and the question of quantity production is not technical but commercial, that is to say, the question of whether it is worth while adopting such methods is a commercial matter. It might be put another way by saying that, granted that a capitalist is prepared to produce an article by such methods, the question as to whether he puts his works in England or elsewhere is a purely

(Major F. Strickland.)

commercial question depending on which will give him the largest market.

The author points out that continuous production is already in operation in certain English soft industries such as textiles, soap and food. He might, perhaps, have mentioned some other article a little more akin to motor parts and which can hardly be described as "soft." Needles, for instance, are produced in quantities larger than motor cars are at present in any country. I do not know the tolerance allowed on needles nominally the same size, but I think it must be very small, and they are produced at a very low price. Ammunition, again, is produced in very large quantities from fairly hard materials. During the war we had some small-arms ammunition made across the Atlantic, but I never heard that it was either cheaper or better than our own.

Military rifles, again, are an instance of continuous production in which very accurate work is required in material a great deal harder than soap. I do not know the tolerance allowed on the depth of the grooves in a rifle, but the grooves themselves are only a few thousandths of an inch deep, so I presume the tolerance must be some fraction of a thousandth. It is interesting to note that the needful accuracy in this case is got without grinding. I think we shall all agree with the author's remarks as to standardisation in principle. The difficulty is to carry them out. If a car can be designed that will still sell without modification in fifteen years, it is, of course, easy to standardise, but I venture to think that many of the cars contemporary with the original model T Ford would not sell now however cheaply they were produced, and if it is found that a certain design will not sell, surely the only thing to do is to produce something that will. Again, here, the commercial question arises as to whether in any particular case it is better to stick to standardisation and cheap production, or to keep improving with a view of getting a higher price. This, however, all emphasises the author's point that alterations should only be made after long consideration.

THE DISCUSSION.

Mr. H. KERR THOMAS, in opening the discussion, said: The whole basis of the work which the author has described is standardisation, and it is quite impossible to apply anything approaching these methods without standardisation, which for some reason is a very weak point with us in England. For instance, the Dunlop wheel works at Coventry has a very large output for cars of the 12 h.p. class, of which there are great numbers all approximately of the same weight and more or less of the same size, and all using the same tyres, yet the whole output of that factory is handicapped because those cars do not all use the same wheels, or rather because, though the wheels are identical, the number and size of the bolts which secure them to to the hubs differ. I saw two wheels for similar cars, both of which had three attaching bolts, but they were on different centres, while my own car has five bolts instead of three, and so on. Surely, if cars are going to use the same size of tyres there is no logical reason why the dimensions of the wheel should not be similar.

The author states that the engines are tested, when they are run under their own power, by town gas. I would like to know whether that is from motives of economy or convenience, and also whether the carburettors are specially adjusted for town gas, and if so, how are they adjusted afterwards?

Mr. H. C. M. STEVENS: Will the author tell us what tolerances are allowed in the reamering operation on the cylinder bore, and whether the rolling affects the size of the bore to any considerable extent? With regard to the final inspection, I should like to know what is done in the case of small parts, which are more susceptible to variations from such operations as hardening than they are from ordinary machining operations. Our experience is that the centreless grinder is rather liable to affect the scleroscope reading of the parts, due to the generation of heat on the wheel. Has the author had any trouble on that account, and are the results obtained uniform?

Mr. BASIL JOY: The author, on page 435, says that he uses selective assembly in certain parts, but with a huge production like that at the Morris engine works, does it not sometimes happen that with selective assembly there is a proportion of parts left over that do not match?

Mr. J. E. GREENWOOD: I should like to ask why the author adopts this rolling system for cylinders. I think a more accurate and better finish would be obtained by grinding. It may be that

(Mr. J. E. Greenwood.)

there is no time for grinding, and that this rolling process is very much quicker and keeps the machines in tune to the 4-minute output. With regard to the output of engines at various stages of the test, can the author give us some figures regarding the horse-power at various speeds and mean effective pressures?

Mr. LAVENDER: I should like to ask the author if he uses any means for taking out the strain due to the machining of the pistons. If it is an annealing process, is the leaving of the pistons in the rough soft condition likely to result, after running a certain time, in piston slap?

Mr. T. P. JONES: The author tells us that the cylinder-block machine is not stopped for scrap, but the work goes right through to the end. That being so, how does he deal with castings which have hard spots in them? Is the metal made to a specification to suit their own requirements, or is it made of ordinary cylinder metal?

Mr. WOOLLARD, in replying on the discussion, said: I quite agree with Mr. Kerr Thomas that "continuous production" is based on standardisation, and it is to be regretted that standardisation has not gone a great deal farther than it has done.

We run our preliminary tests on town gas for the sake of economy, and switch over to petrol for the final test, so as to coincide with actual conditions. Town gas is used, I should imagine, for about 60 per cent of the test period. At the moment we are using two carburettors, but a combined instrument is shortly being adopted.

In reply to Mr. Stevens, the reaming tolerance in the cylinder bore is roughly 0·000 to 0·002 in. The burnishing operation increases the size of the bore on an average by 0·001 in. The burnishing tool revolves at 500 revs. per minute, and has to pass once up and once down.

Inspection of case-hardened parts takes place before and after case-hardening, and in order to ensure that the processes are correct we make a breaking test out of a percentage of parts.

The gudgeon-pins are passed through the Cincinati grinder five times under a flood of coolant. We have had no trouble with the softening of the pins.

In regard to the question of selective assembly, we do get a proportion of parts that do not match because, as all production engineers know, the operator tends to work on the high side of his gauges in order that he shall not scrap work, but as soon as the stock rises we arrange that the operators work to a slightly lower limit, still within the tolerance, and the stock decreases to normal. We run our pistons at very close clearances, which necessitates selective assembly, and I imagine that about 1,000 would probably be about the stock ahead of the job. At present we are using 4,800 pistons a week, and there are spares to take into account, so that the stock mentioned is not much more than a figure of speech.

Mr. Greenwood asked why we roll the cylinder bores, and I would like to point out that we have no feeling about any particular method or operation at all. Frankly, we have adopted rolling because it is quicker than grinding, and, moreover, we could not afford to give up the floor space that would be required by that process. Also, I submit that grinding leaves a surface which is much too sharp, whereas rolling leaves a finely polished surface, such as has to be achieved after grinding by running-in. I have noticed that some makers, who grind the bores, afterwards finish their cylinders by lapping. We do nothing of that sort. I really think that when everything is taken into consideration, rolling is the better job, but it is not an easy task. It took us a long time to learn about it. Many firms have taken it up and dropped it because there is quite a lot of technique behind a rolling job. Mr. Greenwood also asked about the power output of engines. An average curve, taken from new engines well run-in, can be seen in the catalogue.

Mr. Lavender asked about the treatment of pistons. We raise the pistons to just above the running temperature of the engine to prevent growth, but not sufficiently high to affect the hardness. The pistons do not slap, because certain mechanical features prevent this phenomenon.

Mr. Jones asked about cylinder metal. We, of course, work to specification, and with a long run the foundry has reduced troubles to a minimum, but even so we occasionally get hard spots. If this affects the cutters, the blocks are pulled off the line and sent to inspection, the operators standing until the next batch of cylinders come through.

THE DISCUSSION.

(BIRMINGHAM.)

Mr. C. R. ENGELBACH, in opening the discussion, said: There is one difficulty in the technique of continuous production, and that is the question of intermediate hardening operations. That is a fence which we all come up against immediately, as little hardening shops cannot be placed all over the factory, and at some stage or other the flow has to be broken and the parts taken away to the hardening shop and brought back again into line. This is a difficulty which I know has troubled the author, but I have no doubt that, eventually, he will solve it.

The question of scrap on the cylinder-block machine is another difficulty. The author is probably much luckier than we are, but in our own works faulty cylinder castings present a great problem. The author stated that with his particular method the cylinders are machined from start to finish and any scrap was only detected at the end. This is, of course, quite a satisfactory method if there is only a small percentage of scrap, but when I state that one day last week we had 25 per cent of cylinders scrapped, it will be seen that if such an occurrence took place in the Morris works manufacture would become disorganised.

The fundamental difference between the cylinder-block machine and the gear-box machine is that the cylinder block travels along and is fitted into definite locations, whereas in the gear-box machine the gear-boxes travel along in fixtures. The difficulty I see is that in the gear-box machine a large number of similar jigs have to be made which have to index at the same point. In every good tool-room a single jig can be manufactured to practically absolute dimensions, but to make half a dozen of the same type that will be exactly uniform is an exceedingly difficult matter.

The cylinder heads must also raise another difficulty, as the multiple drill for the stud holes, etc. must be exactly similar to the multiple drill which drills the stud holes in the cylinders.

The only other question that I wish to ask is whether the cradles, or structure, of the pickling tank are made of wood or some non-corrosive metal, otherwise I am afraid they will not last very long.

Mr. J. NASMITH: I have a very great admiration for Mr. Ford and Mr. Morris, because they are both men who know their own minds and can gauge accurately the demands of the public. I agree with the author that the greatest enemy to production is the constant change of models. It is reported of Mr. Ford that he was once asked why he did not make a better car, and he replied that he did not want to make a better car but a cheaper one. I also agree as to the necessity for having the material very carefully inspected before it is issued to the shops. Material that is inaccurate and will not fit into jigs causes delay and confusion and a strict inspection of raw material is most essential.

I particularly wish to call attention to the author's remarks on page 424, where he mentions the necessity for employing up-to-date machine tools. The Morris people have carried this out, and their success has been phenomenal, and it is interesting to note that they have been to the trouble of designing their own and have taken a good many risks in so doing. It is usual to find nowadays that machines have to be developed in the makers' works to a very high degree of perfection, and makers have to give most exacting guarantees of production, whereas in the old days it was the maker of the tool who had to get his orders from a few sketches and the user who had to take most of the risk. I would like to ask the author if (supposing he had another works to lay down) he would introduce the very elaborate machines, or rather assemblage of machines, that he has described. These huge machines must surely render the question of replacement of plant a very difficult one.

Mr. T. E. B. CHALMERS: Standardisation, as defined by the author, is undoubtedly one of the keys to the problem of continuous production, and I feel that much more could be done in works where continuous production is not possible towards the standardisation of the small component parts.

The author truly says: "It is very difficult to forecast the effect of apparently trivial alterations." Sir Henry Fowler, in his Presidential Address in 1920, said: "I well remember a recognised leader of engine design in the United States suggesting to me that he should re-design a piece of engine mechanism to get over a production difficulty, who, after a few minutes discussion, admitted that it would entail a complete re-design of the engine itself."

"Regularisation" and continuity of production, in the broad sense, are essential to the welfare of every automobile manufacturer. If there is one thing which scares a customer it is "the broken promise." The delay in supply of raw material, with production held up in consequence, difficulties of machining due to design, elastic viewing, parts tooled up before having been thoroughly tried out, etc., all add their speck of grit to the otherwise smoothly revolving wheels of business.

A reputation for fair dealing; a psychological study of the employees as individuals as well as in the mass; ready recognition that an employee is a responsible person; an eye to his creature comforts during extremes of weather conditions; good ventilation; even temperatures, both in offices and works; distribution of light so that eye strain is eliminated; exclusion of draughts as far as possible; the quick disposal of scrap and refuse, and all that the

(Mr. T. E. B. Chalmers.)

above implies, are matters which no employer with a full appreciation of the possibilities of the future can conscientiously ignore.
Apart from this, I agree with the author that "over much welfare
work or paternalism" is apt to defeat its own object.

Taking the case of the pressed steel underpan versus a cast
aluminium sump, as presented by the author—has the physical
solidity of the aluminium job a *real* appeal to the engineer of
to-day? Is the appeal, as such, not rather a reflection of our
solid British characteristics?

Major R. V. Brook: I think we all agree that the success of
the Morris Company is very largely due to their having produced
what they thought was a good thing and then sticking to it.
They have not chopped and changed about as certain firms have
done in the past, and, in consequence, they have been able to
improve methods of production. The electric testing plant is
particularly interesting, and I should like to have some figures
as to how the balancing operations come out, i.e., whether the
units generated nearly balance the units consumed for running
the engines in. Up till now the Froude water brake seems to
have held sway rather more than the electric dynamometer, but
I have always been in favour of the latter, because it gives
accurate readings of power consumption and the readings of the
load can be altered very rapidly and readily, but the problem has
been to know what to do with the power generated. Mr. Engelbach asked for information as to the metal used in the construction
of the grips in the pickling tank for holding the cylinders whilst
passing through the solution. These are made of Monel metal,
and I believe the Morris Company have found that grips of that
metal, although they cost four times as much, last eighteen times
longer than steel grips. Monel metal is a natural alloy of copper
and nickel, and it is being very largely used now. Finally, I
should like to ask the author whether the cylinder blocks are tested
for porosity either before or after passing through the pickling
tank and before being machined in any way, also whether aluminium parts other than the pistons are normalised before or
during any of the machining operations.

Major C. W. Jordan: To my mind, the first secret of the
author's success is that he has got a managing director who knows
his own mind. Continuous production and heavy purchases of
special tools are quite impossible if the design of the car is to
be subject to frequent alterations, and most of our manufacturers
fail because they make too many models and change them too
often. In all my experience in different branches of engineering,
it has only been by strict standardisation that we have been able
to produce cheaply and quickly and in large quantities. One
difficulty then was the regularity not only of supply, but of quality
of the raw material. We very soon found that our constant flow
was seriously interfered with because our material did not fit or
was not up to standard or the castings were bad. Will the

author tell us how with his very big machine he gets over these very serious interruptions to flow? I should also like to know how, after the part has left the cylinder-block machine, he ensures a proper sequence of the other operations so that the assembly of the engines with their multifarious parts goes on without interruption. The difficulty is not with the big things, but how to arrange the small parts so that they fit into the right place at the right time and in the right quantity. I think the author is wise in throwing his works open to inspection by visitors, because although the visitors may get some information, it is hardly likely that the author will not be able to turn to some practical use any suggestions made by visitors, even though they might at first sight appear impracticable.

Mr. T. C. AVELING: There is no doubt that continuous production tends to a high level of morality on the part of the producer, since it can only be obtained by paying a very high price or giving a very big order for the material required. Money is in fact saved by spending and increasing expenses in the cost of materials. It leads also to extreme accuracy, because without accuracy continuous production cannot be achieved. Will the author tell me what is the percentage increase in over-head charges due to the three shifts per day, and when does the week begin and when does it end?

Mr. WOOLLARD, in replying on the discussion, said: With reference to the remarks by Mr. Engelbach, the intermediate hardening operations are certainly a very great trouble. We have been trying to solve that problem for eighteen months without success, but we are hoping to find the answer in the not too distant future.

With regard to scrapped cylinder blocks, sometimes we have a bad run, and then we find our scrap may amount to 7 per cent, but usually it is under 5 per cent, and I submit that for 5 per cent it is not worth while withdrawing the blocks from the machine, unless, of course, they are hard and spoil the cutters, or, if by machining fully, we should destroy the evidence of the iron-founder's mistakes.

With regard to the two types of machine described, I agree with Mr. Engelbach that the fixed location is preferable to the travelling fixture.

So far as the drilling of the cylinder-head studs is concerned, we have no trouble in matching up jig with jig. We are not drilling the cylinder heads on a continuous machine line yet, but on a multi-spindle drill, and we find no difficulty in matching the studs in the blocks. The structural work for the pickling tank is covered with bitumastic paint, and there is a fan which draws off the fumes.

Mr. Nasmyth asked whether, if I had another works to lay down, I should adopt the same type of machines. I think I should, given that the conditions were the same. Of course, they would

(Mr. Woollard.)

not be exactly the same machines, because, in developing these machines, as is the case with all pioneers, we find better ways of carrying out our ideas, so that the next machines would embody the improvements suggested by experience. Continuous machining shows up the weaknesses in organisation, because if the operator has no material he cannot work, and if he has no tools to cut with he cannot cut. The continuous operation focusses the attention of the whole of the management on what is wrong, and then it does not take long to clear the trouble.

With regard to electric power testing mentioned by Major Brook. we believe from our observation of the incomplete installation. that we shall run the test beds very economically, and that it will only cost a little on account of the power required from the supply station for balancing. I do not think we shall ever generate current to go back into the factory network.

The cylinder blocks are not tested for porosity immediately after pickling. because from experience we find that the number we should throw out would be very small. Therefore, we carry the block to the finished boring before we do any water testing. With the small amount of scrap I have indicated, it is not a very serious matter to lose the value of the machining up to this point.

The aluminium pistons in both engines, and the Duralumin connecting-rods (used only in the Morris-Oxford engine) are heat-treated. but other aluminium parts are used as from the foundry.

Major Jordan asked whether we had overcome the difficulty of material supplies. Broadly speaking, we have three sources of supply, and if one fails we make up with the others. The fact that we have had our contractors working for us for a considerable period has helped to clear away many of the difficulties. We also have an inspection staff which operates very quickly, so that the manufacturers are advised immediately of any defect or default. The whole of that question is one of the education of the suppliers. So far as finished parts are concerned, we stock a buffer quantity, about fourteen days' supply. We buy locally as much as possible, so that we can keep in immediate touch with our suppliers.

Major Aveling asked about the percentage difference of oncost due to the three shifts. I have not yet solved that question myself: I am working on it at the moment. It is a difficult question. because there are so many things to take into account. It is perfectly obvious that whatever is saved is rather counterbalanced by the tremendous amount of money that is paid away in overtime rates. The week starts at 10 p.m. on Sunday and ends at noon on the Saturday, and thus two hours on Sunday night are worked.

Then there is the point about taking people round the works. One of the great advantages of that is that the works are seen through the visitors' eyes, and that is extremely valuable and educative.

THE

INSTITUTION OF AUTOMOBILE ENGINEERS.

SCOTTISH CENTRE.

The Sixth Ordinary General Meeting of the Session of the Scottish Centre was held at the Royal Technical College, Glasgow, on Monday, 16th March, 1925, at 7.30 p.m., Mr. J. W. Mills in the Chair.

The Minutes of the previous Meeting were read, confirmed and signed.

The following paper was then read and discussed:—

" Some Notes on British Methods of Continuous Production,"
by F. G. WOOLLARD (see page 419).

There were present 310 Members and visitors.

THE DISCUSSION.

Mr. D. KEACHIE, in opening the discussion, said: What appeals to me very much is the fact that each casting must be machined in its order of arrival. There is no such thing as putting away, say, 200 castings in the store, and after two years finding that they are faulty and should have been returned to the makers. By this system any defect comes to light at once. It is an inevitable drawback to such a huge machine as that which the author has devised for machining cylinder blocks that it must tend to keep back new design, but this is not so serious in view of the fact that he expects it to pay for itself in four years. The whole question is one of nice compromise between the desire to embody improvements and the necessity for production, and, if we alter the design too frequently, someone—probably the customer—must pay for it. When we remember that a complete set of jigs may cost anything up to £30,000, it is easy to appreciate what a large output is required if the customer is not to pay the greater part of the cost.

With regard to the vexed question of smoking in the factory, I think it is a problem that each factory must face for itself. Another point which the author rightly stressed is regularity—regularity of output and regularity of sales. The one re-acts upon the other, and it is certain that regularity in output means economy in production, and so helps sales quite apart from punctuality in delivery dates. I was rather struck by the amount of metal—40 lb.—which is allowed for removal in the cylinder-block machine. It really does look as if more could be done by the introduction of die-castings. Is it too much of an ideal to hope that some day we may have a cylinder-block casting in which the only operation required on receipt from the foundry is the boring of the holes, the other parts being all die-cast?

The author has naturally confined his remarks to the motor industry, but the principles involved are capable of a much wider application, and I hope that engineers in other branches of industry will take the points which he has raised seriously to heart, and even although they cannot adopt them in their entirety, it may lead their thoughts towards the improvement of their own production. In conclusion, I must express my appreciation of the stress which the author has laid upon the need for maintaining high quality both in workmanship and material. The trade of this country has been built up by good quality, and though we have lost much of that trade to-day, it will come back to us again through quality.

Mr. G. E. McCaw: The author has brought before us, not only the continuous flow principle, but the multiple-tool principle—the mechanised movements of the work-piece, and the work carried through by a series of what might simply be called multiple-tool operations. This principle came into favour some five or six years ago, but I think that in many industries it has lately been found beneficial to depart from the multiple-tool operation and come back to the single-tool operation, particularly where the part under consideration may be subject to change in design. I would therefore like to ask the author whether, if he was starting again without being confined within a specified area, as he was in the works at Coventry, he would proceed on the same lines as those on which he has developed in the present factory, or whether he would simplify his operations, bringing in more movement between the operations and allow a greater elasticity for alteration in design.

Mr. Hirst: Could the author give us any indication as to what is his tool-room oncost on the basis of direct wages? I believe it must be very heavy.

Mr. J. Craig: The machine tools in the author's factory are driven by alternating current, whereas the testing plant which we made used direct current. I should like to ask the author the purpose in the factory for which direct current is applied.

Mr. J. D. Parkes: I could not help feeling as I went through the author's shops that the machines are incidental to the organisation; it is the brain behind that has achieved the results that have been obtained. The machines, though interesting, are not essentials. I would like to ask the author what his attitude and that of his production staff is towards those who wish to introduce alterations in the design, and how far his system of production is absolutely rigid. Is it, for instance, possible at certain stated intervals, after a certain number of units have been produced, to introduce modifications and improvements which in production have been found necessary, because I believe that the Morris group of companies expend a great deal of money on real research as distinct from the development of methods of production?

Mr. G. McDonald: One point that should not be lost sight of is that it is not only the people actually employed in the Morris works that benefit by their operations, but there are the people who make the tools, the castings, the forgings, the tyres and so on, so that a firm such as the Morris Co. is of very great value to the country as a whole.

Mr. J. B. Mavor: The author has mentioned payment by results, but does not the regularity of the metronome do away with the necessity for that method of payment? Yet the men must be satisfied, or the results cannot be satisfactory. I shall be very much interested to hear how this matter has been treated. On a recent visit to a works where some of the smaller units were

(Mr. J. B. Mavor.)

getting into a state approaching that at which the author has arrived with his larger units, this point was raised by the manager; he said: "We know the time it will take a man to do the work, and he does not have to work any harder. Are we going to pay piece-work prices for a quantity of work controlled entirely by the capacity of the machine, or pay at a predetermined time rate?" I think that is the problem that will emerge as the organisation goes forward.

Mr. GRAY: I should like to ask the author what class of steel he uses for his cutters, and if he has had any experience of Stellite steel.

Mr. MALLET: I think it would be a great help to us engineers if the author would tell us not only of his successes, but also of some of his failures, and how he overcame them.

Mr. WOOLLARD, in replying on the discussion, said: I would like to point out to Mr. Keachie that the design is not fixed because of the cylinder-block machine, but rather because, with an output of 200 a day and upwards, it would be quite impossible to make any general change in design in under twelve months. In lesser degrees changes are always taking place; we have to keep improving or we should lose our position in the race. Mr. Keachie objected to the removal of 40 lb. of metal from the cylinders, but this is essential in the present state of the foundryman's craft. Die-castings in iron are limited at present to small pieces. We, of course, use a number of die-castings in light alloys, and we have used die-cast aluminium sumps, which are quite large parts, but die-cast cylinder blocks will not be a practical possibility for many a long day.

Answering Mr. Hirst, I regret that I am unable to give the proportion of tool-room oncost to direct wages, but the figure relative to the total engine cost is by no means heavy; I should describe it as normal.

With reference to Mr. Craig's remarks, the direct current that is developed on the testing machines under power is used to balance the running-in. We run-in our engines for a considerable period before we put them on to power.

Answering Mr. McCaw, I would say that, given the same problem in every respect, we should probably proceed in the same manner, but the same problem may not repeat itself, and our knowledge has grown so that the next machine line will be a development from this, and if there is time would probably be 100 per cent special, but, if the time element were an important factor, we should probably link up machines of a standard type; the machines are only incidental to the whole problem.

Answering Mr. Parkes, I may say that we do spend a considerable amount in research, but we always endeavour to bend the existing conditions to accomplish that to which our research has been directed. We do make modifications, sometimes drastic modifications, and we usually choose a holiday period for the change-over date.

Mr. McDonald stressed one point which I was pleased to hear, and that was the advantages of continuous production to the operators. I believe we have our workpeople entirely with us; we have always dealt fairly with them, and on their part they have taken to these new machines without any trouble whatever.

Mr. Mavor mentioned the question of payment by results. I agree that with continuous operation the methods of payment may have to go into the melting pot, but I have no idea of what will replace those methods. Piece-work has the advantage of rewarding the individual worker and keeping him keen, but there are simpler methods and methods which are cheaper to administer. It is, however, essential to exercise caution in regard to methods of payment.

We have not used Stellite steel long enough yet to be able to tell Mr. Gray definitely whether we shall standardise on this material.

Answering Mr. Mallett, I shall be only too pleased to come to Glasgow again to tell you of our future developments, when I shall be able to hold the balance between that which is not and that which is worth while.

COMMUNICATION.

Mr. J. D. MORGAN wrote: It is characteristic of the author that in dealing with a problem of machines he gives proper recognition to human and economic factors. Continuous production is to him not merely a matter of machines. It is also a matter of men, and the co-ordination of men and machines within economic limits. It must be inferred from the author's statements that the success of the continuous production method described by him includes the prosperity of both owners and men, as well as the satisfactory operation of plant. The facts set out in the paper show quite definitely that a combination of proper machines with efficient management brings both benefits to the owners and improvement in the conditions of life for the operatives. Those who advocate the restriction of mechanical aids as a means of ameliorating social conditions would do well to read the paper. That the machine should have developed into an agent of justice between man and man (see par. 5 of the author's summary), is a fact of deep significance.

I am not quite sure that the central idea of "continuous production" has been quite definitely expressed by the author. If my reading of the paper is correct, the fact that differentiates "continuous production" from that of any ordinary factory where there is undoubtedly "continuous activity," is that the various processes carried out by machines are mechanically co-ordinated. It is, I imagine, in the "mechanical co-ordination" that the solution of the author's problem lies.

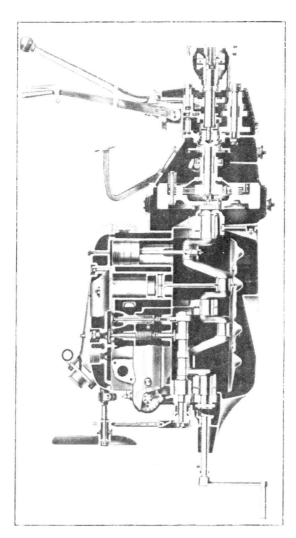

FIG. 1.

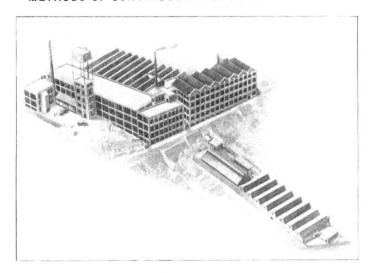

Fig. 3.

Fig. 4.

FIG. 5.

FIG. 7.

FIG. 10.

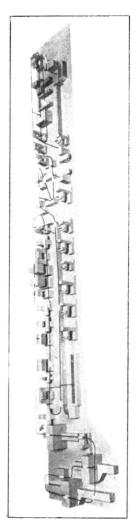

Fig. 8.

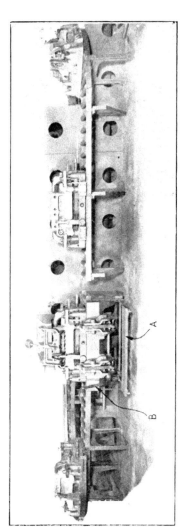

Fig. 9.

Fig. 11.

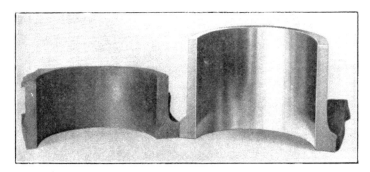

Fig. 12.

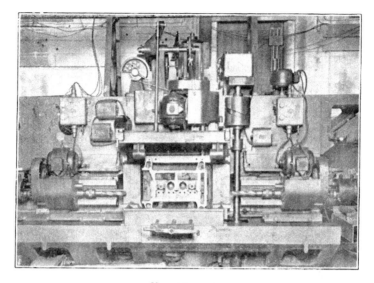

FIG. 13.

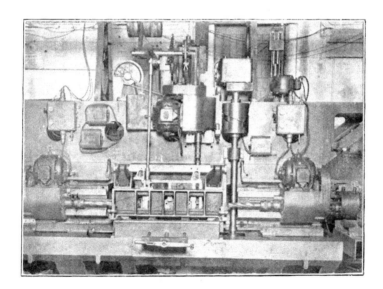

FIG. 14.

Fig. 15.

FIG. 16.

Fig. 17.

Fig. 18.

Plate XXVII

METHODS OF CONTINUOUS PRODUCTION

Fig. 19.

FIG. 21.

FIG. 20.

FIG. 22.

Fig. 23.

FIG. 24.

Fig. 26.

ne United States
00003BD/211-240/P

9 780972 259187